WRITERS IN REVOLT:

AN ANTHOLOGY

WRITERS IN

AN ANTHOLOGY   edited by

published by

EVOLT:

RICHARD SEAVER, TERRY SOUTHERN
and **ALEXANDER TROCCHI**

FREDERICK FELL INC.   NEW YORK

N.B. The sources of the present volume are varied, and the editors have obviously made no artificial effort to alter spelling or punctuation for the sake of conformity. Such discrepancies as occur, the editors trust, are limited to those stylistic variations peculiar to the individual authors or translators.

ACKNOWLEDGMENTS AND PERMISSIONS

The editors wish to express their special thanks to Stephen Levine for his help in the preparation of this volume, and their indebtedness to the following authors, translators, publishers or agents for permission to reprint copyrighted work:

ANTONIN ARTAUD: "No More Masterpieces" from *Evergreen Review* #5 copyright © 1957, by permission of *Librairie Gallimard*, Paris, France.

CHARLES BAUDELAIRE: *The Intimate Journals of Charles Baudelaire*, translated by Christopher Isherwood. First published by the Blackamore Press, 1930. First American publication by Beacon Press, Boston. Reprinted by permission of the translator.

SAMUEL BECKETT: "The End" copyright © 1957 by Grove Press, Inc. Reprinted by permission of *Les Editions de Minuit*, Paris, and the author.

LOUIS-FERDINAND CELINE: *Journey to the End of the Night* copyright 1934 by Louis-Ferdinand Celine. Reprinted by permission of New Directions, Publishers.

EVAN S. CONNELL, JR.: "The Fisherman from Chihuahua," from *The Anatomy Lesson and Other Stories* copyright 1957 by Evan S. Connell, Jr. Reprinted by permission of The Viking Press, Inc.

EDWARD DAHLBERG: *The Sorrows of Priapus* copyright © 1957 by New Directions, Publishers, and reprinted with their permission.

LAWRENCE DURRELL: "On Henry Miller" originally appeared in *Horizon* Magazine, edited by Cyril Connolly, London, 1949. Reprinted by permission of the author.

CHARLES FOSTER: "The Troubled Makers" first appeared in *Evergreen Review* #4 copyright 1957. Reprinted by permission of the author.

WILLIAM GADDIS: *The Recognitions* copyright 1952, 1955 by William Gaddis. Reprinted by permission of the author and Russell & Volkening, Inc.

JEAN GENET: *Our Lady of the Flowers* copyright © 1951 by *Librairie Gallimard*. Reprinted by permission of Grove Press, Inc. and the author's agent, Rosica Colin.

ALLEN GINSBERG: *Howl* copyright 1956 © 1959 by Allen Ginsberg. Reprinted by permission of City Lights Books.

HERMAN HESSE: *Steppenwolf* copyright 1929, copyright renewed © 1957 by Holt, Rinehart and Winston, Inc. Reprinted by permission of Holt, Rinehart and Winston, Inc.

EUGENE IONESCO: "The Avant-Garde Theatre" from *Notes et Contrenotes* copyright © 1962 by *Librairie Gallimard*. Reprinted by permission of Grove Press, Inc.

CURZIO MALAPARTE: *The Skin* reprinted by permission of Franz J. Horch Associates on behalf of Vallecchi Editore, Milano.

H. L. MENCKEN: "The National Letters" reprinted from *Prejudices:* Second Series copyright 1920 by Alfred A. Knopf, Inc.; "The Anglo Saxon" reprinted from *A Mencken Chrestomathy* copyright 1949 by Alfred A. Knopf, Inc.; "Libido for the Ugly" reprinted from *A Mencken Chrestomathy* copyright 1927, 1949 by Alfred A. Knopf, Inc. Reprinted by permission of Alfred A. Knopf, Inc.

HENRY MILLER: *Tropic of Cancer* copyright © 1961 by Grove Press, Inc. and reprinted by their permission.

CHAPMAN MORTIMER: *Young Man Waiting* published by The Cresset Press, London, and reprinted by their permission.

IRIS MURDOCH: "The Sickness of the Language" from *Sartre*, published by the Yale University Press and reprinted with their permission.

SADE: The selections from *La Philosophie dans le boudoir* and *Pensée* from *Marquis de Sade*, translated by Paul Dinnage, copyright © 1953 by Grove Press, Inc. Reprinted by permission of Grove Press, Inc. and Rosica Colin.

HUBERT SELBY, JR.: "Tra-la-la" copyright 1960 by Hubert Selby, Jr. First published in *The Provincetown Review* #3. Reprinted by permission of the author's agent, Sterling Lord.

JEAN-PAUL SARTRE: *Baudelaire* copyright 1950 by New Directions. Reprinted by permission of New Directions, Publishers. *Saint Genet* copyright 1952 by Librairie Gallimard, Paris. Reprinted by permission of the translator, Bernard Frechtman, and the American publisher, George Braziller, Inc.

E. S. SELDON: "On *Naked Lunch*" first appeared in *Evergreen Review* #22, copyright 1957. Reprinted by permission of the author.

AUSTRYN WAINHOUSE: "Of the Clandestinite" originally appeared in the quarterly review *Merlin*, Vol. 2, No. 2, 1953, and is here reprinted in a revised version by permission of the author.

TO SEYMOUR LITVINOFF

If there is still one hellish, truly accursed thing in our time, it is our artistic dallying with forms, instead of being like victims burnt at the stake, signaling through the flames.

—ARTAUD

CONTENTS

INTRODUCTION ix

ALLEN GINSBERG 1
"Howl" (Parts I & II) 2

SADE 10
From *La Philosophie dans le boudoir* 12
From *Pensée* 21
"Of the Clandestinite" by Austryn Wainhouse 24

BAUDELAIRE 45
From *Baudelaire* by Jean-Paul Sartre 45
From *The Intimate Journals of Charles Baudelaire* 50

DOSTOEVSKI 57
From *Notes from the Underground* 57

HERMAN HESSE 71
From *Steppenwolf* 73

ARTAUD 84
"No More Masterpieces" 84

CELINE 92
From *Journey to the End of the Night* 93

MALAPARTE 102
From *The Skin* 103

HENRY MILLER 128
"On Henry Miller" by Lawrence Durrell 130
From *Tropic of Cancer* 146

IRIS MURDOCH 154
From *Sartre:* "The Sickness of the Language" 154

GENET   166
  From *Saint Genet* by Jean-Paul Sartre   166
  From *Our Lady of the Flowers*   182

CHAPMAN MORTIMER   205
  From *Young Men Waiting*   207

WILLIAM GADDIS   225
  From *The Recognitions*   226

EVAN S. CONNELL, JR.   250
  "The Fisherman from Chihuahua"   251

CHARLES FOSTER   261
  "The Troubled Makers"   261

EDWARD DAHLBERG   277
  From *The Sorrows of Priapus*   277

H. L. MENCKEN   286
  Three Pertinent Essays
    From "The National Letters"   286
    "The Anglo Saxon"   293
    "Libido for the Ugly"   301

HUBERT SELBY JR.   305
  "Tra-la-la"   307

WILLIAM BURROUGHS   323
  On *Naked Lunch* by E. S. Seldon   323
  From *Naked Lunch*   328

IONESCO   338
  "The Avant-Garde Theatre"   338

SAMUEL BECKETT   348
  "The End"   350

TOWARD THE ETHICS OF A GOLDEN AGE

In existentialist thought, the death-of-God concern is not with the wisdom of abandoning the god-idea but the acknowledgment that the role of this idea is no longer one of dynamic force in Western cultures. Rain prayers have given way to the pragmatics of the cloud-seeding plane; in our own society, more recent developments have lent this conventional form of realism a new dimension and an everyday relevence. As a nation we would seem to be finally committed to an era of *absolute* realism, of a character Machiavelli did not foresee. If there were such a thing as collective thought, one might say that we plunged into this commitment without thinking; but, in the summer of 1957, when the first sputnik went up, plunge we did. This becomes apparent when one considers, for example, what the Russian reaction would have been had America sent aloft the first space vehicle. The event would have been ridiculed as the ultimate in "decadent absurdity"—a conspicuous waste of money, which could have been better spent (to put it mildly) in discovering the cure for cancer or in feeding the starving of Asia. Is there any doubt we would have ended up chagrined by the whole affair and investigating it? Thus our reaction to the Russian success was equally paranoiac; we took it as another in an endless series of insulting challenges. Moreover, as a nation of poker players, we treated it as a *bluff*—but, of course, there are no bluffs in chess, only gambits.

Up until that moment, the critical contest, as we saw it, was not technical but moral, and we were quite secure in the lead we presumed to hold. A moral contest is a comfortable one because each side can use its own home-grown elastic yardstick; the purpose of the Russian gambit was to change the game. And now we are up against

it, because the righteous emotion which served us in such good stead
in the old days, whether feigned or genuinely primeval, cannot put
a man on the planet of Venus, nor can any amount of Dirksenesque
rhetoric conceal another one being there. Like the girls in *True Story,*
we have now "come to realize" this in a deep though as yet ineffable
way. And its realization foreshadows the formal emergence of a strong
cult of realism, necessary to compete in this new game—a realism
which will in turn permeate everything in the culture. A new kind
of realism, a realism of methodology, or *pure* pragmatics, the threshold
of an existentialist system of inquiry where goals, or the values behind them, are as yet undefined. It is a realism which is already with
us in everyday life, in an altogether recognizable form: with the
secretary who goes to bed with her boss, because, "well, why not?"
Or doesn't because, "well, why should I?" It is seen in the particulars
of the price-fixing arrangements between rival corporations, and in
the contradictions on editorial pages; it exists in every case in the
unparalleled profusion of murder, rape, mayhem, suicide, insanity,
divorce, drug addiction and fraud taking place in our culture—or, in
short, wherever a man and an act are seen to discard tradition, to
smash an idol, to grope with blind urgency for something of value.

When alien cultures are, or presume themselves to be, in dangerous conflict, each tends to assess its own well-being in terms of the
apparent strength of the other. The strength of cultures is, by tradition, measured in terms of resources and technology, and, more criti-
cally, in terms of unity: unity of purpose, of direction and of determi-
nation. But unity, of course, is not a voluntary matter, any more
than is snake worship or Catholicism; it is not a cause but an effect;
and to expect unity where there is no unifying force is to be seriously
misled. The present clamor for unity in our own culture, or as some
wag put it, "togetherness," is nothing more than the panicked recognition of its total absence. And what is even more ironic is the fact
that wherever this togetherness has had any success at all in our
present society it has been viciously self-defeating—because, due to
its abortive unnaturalness, it can only occur in the form of clans, cults
and gangs . . . those fraternal and religious groups which, having
no access to a higher, more comprehensive allegiance, are themselves
the direct and initial source of discord, and of discrimination in the
worst sense of the word. And it is, of course, only in relating to Russia
—*in trying to draw our ideals and morality from Russia,* or from our
own dead past—that we can consider unity to be vital. *Were* it vital,
we should be lost. That which is impossible, however, is not vital;

nor is that which violates the life force of one's environment even desirable. One simply adapts.

To understand the absence of unity in our own culture, and its lack of immediate prospect, we have only to examine the nature of the principal dynamic force at sway. In considering a dynamic force in any particular culture, it is usually clear what is intended: that is, a force of influence which determines motivation and behavior to the extent that it is broadly felt or evident in the society. It is implicit that at the heart of such a force would be a body of knowledge, belief and prophecy, in varying proportions. In the strict sense, then, the term is synonymous with the word "religion." For example, cathedrals—the construction of which at one time represented the greatest expense of goods and man-hours devoted to a single enterprise—are no longer built; nuclear reactors, on the other hand, are built, as are mental institutions and museums of art, and on a scale as grand as that of any temple. So that one does not properly say that religion is dead, but rather that the objects of dedication, of worship or of religious concern have changed.

On those terms one must ask what is the principal force to which our own culture is dedicated, the mainspring source from which we attempt to draw our ethics and our sense of values? Certainly it is not Marxism, any more than it is Christianity; nor is it Science, which does not pretend to deal in abstract values. The answer, rather, is *psychology.* All phenomona which fall outside the realm of science are now explained psychoanalytically—including both art and traditional religion. All definitions which are not purely physical are psychological definitions. The ethics of behavior, that is to say, the correctness of human relationships—some of the most personal nature, as between parents and children—are prescribed by psychology. We are attempting, in short, to formulate our notion of values from our knowledge and study of the human mind. We have come to think of this as a natural and understandable thing to do; it involves ramifications, however, which are not accounted for in any existing philosophy. Consider, for example, the attitude toward the criminal—for it is here we get the sharpest reflection of the value judgments in currency, because a society's criminal is, by act and definition, antisociety. What then does the notion of understanding the criminal and the criminal act imply? This concept, by now taken for granted in almost every civilized country in the Western world, and which appears wholly uncomplicated, is unique in the history of organized societies. Its implication, in terms of any previously operative philosophy or cultural structure prior to this century, is shattering, for its ultimate meaning is that there is no such thing as crime; it destroys the *idea* of crime. Certainly there are societies where crime itself is unknown, and throughout history there has existed in many forms the concept of forgiving the criminal; but the notion of understanding the criminal is unique—it is, by all previous standards, the strongest possible contradiction in terms. We have rid ourselves of the precept of *right* and *wrong*.

Meanwhile, our total orientation remains strongly contingent on the vis-à-vis Russia attitude we have assumed, and it is this constant half conscious comparison which has given our condition of apparent aimlessness the sharp focus it has in our mind's eye and which otherwise it could not have. For in this perspective it is understandably disheartening to see the opponent moving with evident unity of purpose and direction while one's own energies are either querulously dissipated or thrown to the winds. That the opponent's motivations and goals are recognized as spurious is no consolation, but in fact only makes his smug security and resolve all the more irritating. And here we touch the crucial difference between the Marxist and Freudian agencies—which is one of law. The Marxist heritage did include a strong body of law; whether these laws are absurd or not is of no concern, the point is that in this social philosophy there does exist a definite *juris corpus* (*"Each according to . . ."* etc.) and these laws may be amended until they are completely reversed without disturbing the basic fact that at any given time they constitute what is necessary for the emotional security of a culture, even as it is for children, namely, a basic set of tenets to work from—for otherwise there is no anchor, no focus, no possibility of common values.

Freud, as is well known, left no such legacy. "We have only scratched the surface," he was fond of saying, *"we have only begun to learn."* For a culture whose orientation—or its memory of, or aspiration to, an orientation—was something as concrete as the Ten Commandments, and whose opponent now has its own laws framed in that very format, to accept such amorphous honesty as words-to-live-by takes some getting used to, even when there is no alternative. Thus are we at an impossible disadvantage in those areas where we submit to value comparisons, either on Russian terms or on terms of our own past. It is evident that we are searching for a new system of values; and to find it we must swim with the tide.

Ethical climate and trends are nowhere more apparent than in art, or more exactly, in a culture's encouragement or denial of an art's particular forms. It is to be noted that among prevalent art forms those in highest regard on a broad scale are precisely the ones which most directly relate to principles embraced by our body of psychiatric knowledge and belief: abstract expressionist painting, method acting, modern dance, free-form sculpture, improvisational music and the mind-flow technique of prose writing. All of these espouse the purest line of self-expression possible; for this is at once the requisite and *summum bonum* of each—and it is also, of course, the keystone of the psychological heritage.

The success of these forms—that is to say, the popular insistence upon them—points up the inherent lawlessness of our situation. The decline of figurative or representational painting is an example: figurative painting is unacceptable now because it always appears to make a statement—and all statements must presently be regarded as either untrue or offensively trite . . . and in both cases easily explained psychoanalytically. The most one could hope for in a figurative painting is patent ambiguity; but ambiguity is not what is required, it is statement, or the illusion of statement which the participant demands of art—though no longer the kind of statement that can be verbalized or agreed about, for then it is not art, but mere glorification or pamphleteering. A basic agreement between two people in the interpretation of a work of art must now result in their ultimate rejection of it for the reason that any consideration of the work beyond the most elementary point becomes a psychoanalytic consideration in which they place themselves above the work, and from this vantage proceed to explain the art right out of it. Abstract expressionist painting does not allow for this, because it is quite openly the child of psychology, whose behavior (pure self-expression) meets the parents' warm approbation. Abstract finger painting of disturbed children is carefully explained by child psychologists, as is the painting of the insane by psychiatrists; as yet, however, we, as laymen, do not presume to so treat the work of adult artists whose paintings hang in the great museums—though, to be sure, we may have a few incisive remarks to make about "the obvious death-wish Whistler felt toward his mother," "Da Vinci's blatant homosexuality," and the like.

The statement, that is to say, the illusion of statement, in abstract expressionist painting is not ambiguous but flexible, seen and felt differently by each person. It is the art then, like all that which is now in prominence, of "the unstated statement."

Contemporary music, or such of it as is genuinely creative—as that, for example, involving the improvisational techniques put forward by the late Charles Parker, and which now dominate the entire art—also adheres to this national insistence on nonstatement. Such music, in fact, has been generally defined as "variations on a theme which remains unstated." Interpretations are made from this music, meanings are gleaned, messages received—and while to each individual listener they are *definite,* they are of themselves *unlimited.* It is by reason of this same insistence on unlimited flexibility that the work of composers like Bach and Mozart remains current.

In the medium involving the use of language itself, that is to say, literature, the identical requirements obtain; thus we see in ascendence champions of the deceptive non-statement, Beckett and Ionesco; a resurgence of poetry, which, by form, is more tolerant of nonstatement that is prose; and sudden advanced critical interest in the deceptively oblique novels of Henry Green. It is significant, too, that where statement *is* made, simple and direct, it is invariably iconoclastic—as in the work of Sartre, Celine, Malaparte, Genet and Henry Miller. For it would appear that the irreverent statement is the only statement presently permitted.

The implication is not that nonstatement, or ambiguity, is an end, or of value per se; it is rather the logical effect of assaulting established canons, now deemed suspect, if not totally inadequate. In an era of total search—or total research—such art as is genuinely creative is totally unfettered. The exploratory nature of art should be welcomed, for it may reveal an answer. But while we have grown conditioned to accepting implicitly, and welcoming, each new advance or discovery in medicine or science—or now in space research—limiting our reservations, if any, not to the scientist's methods or even his ends, but at most to the applications, the writer still struggles for the freedom to use his tools—language—without restriction. Both language and subject remained threatened by forces whose avowed purpose is to protect those unable to judge or think for themselves. "I assume that the law exists for the protection of the public," Allen Tate remarked at the Provincetown trial of "Tralala," "not of psychopaths or the criminally insane." Sadly, his assumption belies the facts. In France, a publisher is condemned in court because the protagonist of a work of fiction bearing his imprint advocates a policy deemed insidious by the Government. In the United States, Henry Miller's work is pilloried by local vigilantes because, obviously, he accomplished too well his stated objective "of recording all that which is omitted from books," i.e. of using his artistic freedom unrestrictively.

No, the millennium is not upon us. But if ever the artist is to be truly free, his public must shed its apathy, its own ambivalence. It is precisely this ambivalence which has current importance because it is contrary to the individual self-reliance which does, and must, come more into its own if we are to contribute in our own lifetime to the development along lines of our heritage, and to which there is, in any case, no foreseeable alternative. Distrust of personal taste in instances where it violates an imaginary majority opinion is the greatest single deterrent to this development.

Throughout the whole body of psychoanalytic knowledge nothing is considered more dangerous or despicable than the double standard; it is known, of course, in its clinical extreme, as schizophrenia. Because of stigma, no less than because of knowledge itself, we are now consciously tending away from double standards. What is required, then, is the deliberate avoidance of lip service to assumed values, and adherence instead to deeply personal impulse, as well as the active response to the most private value inclinations. For it is in this way alone that the great hollow symbols by which cultures pretend to live are given face and substance, the dead lips color, warmth and, perhaps, in the end, something meaningful to say.

That is the message the selections in this volume contain.

ALLEN GINSBERG

Romantic agony in literature may be compared with the manic-depressive syndrome in psychology, with ecstasy as its counterpart. It flourishes where conventional religion is dead, as in the worlds of Sade, Lautréamont, Huysmans, Rimbaud, Baudelaire, where the possibility of comparable sensation (to the "religious experience") must be sought elsewhere. The reasoning beneath it would seem to be the same as that which equates sin and penitence—that is, that ecstasy is attainable only when one's range of being and awareness is so extended as to include, at its other end, agony. In philosophic terms, this proclaims both the heartiest acceptance as well as the most severe denial of life, either as it is or as it is seen to be. The development and status of romantic agony in American literature may be inferred from the work of at least three of our most widely acceptable writers of the past—Whitman, Wolfe and Sandberg—and one of our most influential writers of the present, Henry Miller. Except in the latter instance, however, the American species of romantic agony has not been a full-blooded one; it has generally had the *nae* edited right out of it, either before or after leaving the author's hand. What we find now in the literature of the Beat is a reassertion of these established and favored principles, in their extended or European form, to include both the bitter and the sweet. Allen Ginsberg's *Howl* represents the classic achievement within this framework. What is new about it is new in the sense that today is newer than yesterday; and this newness is the result of a natural, or wise, fidelity to current and personal methods of expression, and to actual and personal values—rather than being merely a projection of *literary* methods and *assumed* values. It is this freshness, bestowed by a legitimate fidelity, that serves to distinguish such work from that of the past in the same tradition; and it is the inclusiveness of it which, when otherwise successful, gives it credence, and thus ascendency, over previous American writing in a similar vein.

from *HOWL*

for Carl Solomon

I

I saw the best minds of my generation destroyed by madness, starving
hysterical naked,
dragging themselves through the negro streets at dawn looking for an
angry fix,
angelheaded hipsters burning for the ancient heavenly connection to
the starry dynamo in the machinery of night,
who poverty and tatters and hollow-eyed and high sat up smoking in
the supernatural darkness of cold-water flats floating across the
tops of cities contemplating jazz,
who bared their brains to Heaven under the El and saw Mohammedan
angels staggering on tenement roofs illuminated,
who passed through universities with radiant cool eyes hallucinating
Arkansas and Blake-light tragedy among the scholars of war,
who were expelled from the academies for crazy & publishing obscene
odes on the windows of the skull,
who cowered in unshaven rooms in underwear, burning their money
in wastebaskets and listening to the Terror through the wall,
who got busted in their public beards returning through Laredo with a
belt of marijuana for New York,
who ate fire in paint hotels or drank turpentine in Paradise Alley, death,
or purgatoried their torsos night after night
with dreams, with drugs, with waking nightmares, alcohol and cock
and endless balls,

2

incomparable blind streets of shuddering cloud and lightning in the
mind leaping toward poles of Canada & Paterson, illuminating all
the motionless world of Time between,

Peyote solidities of halls, backyard green tree cemetery dawns, wine
drunkenness over the rooftops, storefront boroughs of teahead joy-
ride neon blinking traffic light, sun and moon and tree vibrations
in the roaring winter dusks of Brooklyn, ashcan rantings and kind
king light of mind,

who chained themselves to subways for the endless ride from Battery
to holy Bronx on benzedrine until the noise of wheels and children
brought them down shuddering mouth-wracked and battered bleak
of brain all drained of brilliance in the drear light of Zoo,

who sank all night in submarine light of Bickford's floated out and sat
through the stale beer afternoon in desolate Fugazzi's, listening
to the crack of doom on the hydrogen jukebox,

who talked continuously seventy hours from park to pad to bar to
Bellevue to museum to the Brooklyn Bridge,

a lost battalion of platonic conversationalists jumping down the stoops
off the fire escapes off windowsills off Empire State out of the
moon,

yacketayakking screaming vomiting whispering facts and memories and
anecdotes and eyeball kicks and shocks of hospitals and jails and
wars,

whole intellects disgorged in total recall for seven days and nights with
brilliant eyes, meat for the Synagogue cast on the pavement,

who vanished into nowhere Zen New Jersey leaving a trail of ambiguous picture postcards of Atlantic City Hall,

suffering Eastern sweats and Tangerian bone-grindings and migraines
of China under junk-withdrawal in Newark's bleak furnished room,

who wandered around and around at midnight in the railroad yard
wondering where to go, and went, leaving no broken hearts,

who lit cigarettes in boxcars boxcars boxcars racketing through snow
toward lonesome farms in grandfather night,

who studied Plotinus Poe St. John of the Cross telepathy and bop
kaballa because the cosmos instinctively vibrated at their feet in
Kansas,

who loned it through the streets of Idaho seeking visionary indian
angels who were visionary indian angels,

who thought they were only mad when Baltimore gleamed in supernatural ecstasy,

who jumped in limousines with the Chinaman of Oklahoma on the
impulse of winter midnight streetlight smalltown rain,

who lounged hungry and lonesome through Houston seeking jazz or
sex or soup, and followed the brilliant Spaniard to converse about
America and Eternity, a hopeless task, and so took ship to Africa,

who disappeared into the volcanoes of Mexico leaving behind nothing
but the shadow of dungarees and the lava and ash of poetry
scattered in fireplace Chicago,

who reappeared on the West Coast investigating the F.B.I. in beards
and shorts with big pacifist eyes sexy in their dark skin passing
out incomprehensible leaflets,

who burned cigarette holes in their arms protesting the narcotic tobacco
haze of Capitalism,

who distributed Supercommunist pamphlets in Union Square weeping
and undressing while the sirens of Los Alamos wailed them down,
and wailed down Wall, and the Staten Island ferry also wailed,

who broke down crying in white gymnasiums naked and trembling before the machinery of other skeletons,

who bit detectives in the neck and shrieked with delight in policecars
for committing no crime but their own wild cooking pederasty and
intoxication,

who howled on their knees in the subway and were dragged off the
roof waving genitals and manuscripts,

who let themselves be fucked in the ass by saintly motorcyclists, and
screamed with joy,

who blew and were blown by those human seraphim, the sailors,
caresses of Atlantic and Caribbean love,

who balled in the morning in the evenings in rosegardens and the grass
of public parks and cemeteries scattering their semen freely to
whomever come who may,

who hiccupped endlessly trying to giggle but wound up with a sob
behind a partition in a Turkish Bath when the blonde & naked
angel came to pierce them with a sword,

who lost their loveboys to the three old shrews of fate the one eyed
shrew of the heterosexual dollar the one eyed shrew that winks out
of the womb and the one eyed shrew that does nothing but sit on
her ass and snip the intellectual golden threads of the craftsman's
loom,

who copulated ecstatic and insatiate with a bottle of beer a sweetheart
a package of cigarettes a candle and fell off the bed, and continued along the floor and down the hall and ended fainting on the

wall with a vision of ultimate cunt and come eluding the last gyzym of consciousness,

who sweetened the snatches of a million girls trembling in the sunset, and were red eyed in the morning but prepared to sweeten the snatch of the sunrise, flashing buttocks under barns and naked in the lake,

who went out whoring through Colorado in myriad stolen night-cars, N.C., secret hero of these poems, cocksman and Adonis of Denver —joy to the memory of his innumerable lays of girls in empty lots & diner backyards, moviehouses' rickety rows, on mountaintops in caves or with gaunt waitresses in familiar roadside lonely petticoat upliftings & especially secret gas-station solipsisms of johns, & hometown alleys too,

who faded out in vast sordid movies, were shifted in dreams, woke on a sudden Manhattan, and picked themselves up out of basements hungover with heartless Tokay and horrors of Third Avenue iron dreams & stumbled to unemployment offices,

who walked all night with their shoes full of blood on the snowbank docks waiting for a door in the East River to open to a room full of steamheat and opium,

who created great suicidal dramas on the apartment cliff-banks of the Hudson under the wartime blue floodlight of the moon & their heads shall be crowned with laurel in oblivion,

who ate the lamb stew of the imagination or digested the crab at the muddy bottom of the rivers of Bowery,

who wept at the romance of the streets with their pushcarts full of onions and bad music,

who sat in boxes breathing in the darkness under the bridge, and rose up to build harpsichords in their lofts,

who coughed on the sixth floor of Harlem crowned with flame under the tubercular sky surrounded by orange crates of theology,

who scribbled all night rocking and rolling over lofty incantations which in the yellow morning were stanzas of gibberish,

who cooked rotten animals lung heart feet tail borsht & tortillas dreaming of the pure vegetable kingdom,

who plunged themselves under meat trucks looking for an egg,

who threw their watches off the roof to cast their ballot for Eternity outside of Time, & alarm clocks fell on their heads every day for the next decade,

who cut their wrists three times successively unsuccessfully, gave up

and were forced to open antique stores where they thought they
were growing old and cried,

who were burned alive in their innocent flannel suits on Madison
Avenue amid blasts of leaden verse & the tanked-up clatter of the
iron regiments of fashion & the nitroglycerine shrieks of the fairies
of advertising & the mustard gas of sinister intelligent editors, or
were run down by the drunken taxicabs of Absolute Reality,

who jumped off the Brooklyn Bridge this actually happened and
walked away unknown and forgotten into the ghostly daze of
Chinatown soup alleyways & firetrucks, not even one free beer,

who sang out of their windows in despair, fell out of the subway
window, jumped in the filthy Passaic, leaped on negroes, cried
all over the street, danced on broken wineglasses barefoot smashed
phonograph records of nostalgic European 1930's German jazz
finished the whiskey and threw up groaning into the bloody toilet,
moans in their ears and the blast of collossal steamwhistles,

who barreled down the highways of the past journeying to each other's
hotrod-Golgotha jail-solitude watch or Birmingham jazz incarnation,

who drove crosscountry seventytwo hours to find out if I had a vision
or you had a vision or he had a vision to find out Eternity,

who journeyed to Denver, who died in Denver, who came back to
Denver & waited in vain, who watched over Denver & brooded &
loned in Denver and finally went away to find out the Time, &
now Denver is lonesome for her heroes,

who fell on their knees in hopeless cathedrals praying for each other's
salvation and light and breasts, until the soul illuminated its hair
for a second,

who crashed through their minds in jail waiting for impossible criminals
with golden heads and the charm of reality in their hearts who
sang sweet blues to Alcatraz,

who retired to Mexico to cultivate a habit, or Rocky Mount to tender
Buddha or Tangiers to boys or Southern Pacific to the black
locomotive or Harvard to Narcissus to Woodlawn to the daisy-
chain or grave,

who demanded sanity trials accusing the radio of hypnotism & were
left with their insanity & their hands & a hung jury,

who threw potato salad at CCNY lecturers on Dadaism and subsequently presented themselves on the granite steps of the madhouse
with shaven heads and harlequin speech of suicide, demanding
instantaneous lobotomy,

and who were given instead the concrete void of insulin metrasol
electricity hydrotherapy psychotherapy occupational therapy pingpong & amnesia,

who in humorless protest overturned only one symbolic pingpong
table, resting briefly in catatonia,

returning years later truly bald except for a wig of blood, and tears
and fingers, to the visible madman doom of the wards of the
madtowns of the East,

Pilgrim State's Rockland's and Greystone's foetid halls, bickering with
the echoes of the soul, rocking and rolling in the midnight solitude-
bench dolmen-realms of love, dream of life a nightmare, bodies
turned to stone as heavy as the moon,

with mother finally . . . . . . , and the last fantastic book flung out of
the tenement window, and the last door closed at 4 AM and the
last telephone slammed at the wall in reply and the last furnished
room emptied down to the last piece of mental furniture, a yellow
paper rose twisted on a wire hanger in the closet, and even that
imaginary, nothing but a hopeful little bit of hallucination—

ah, Carl, while you are not safe I am not safe, and now you're really
in the total animal soup of time—

and who therefore ran through the icy streets obsessed with a sudden
flash of the alchemy of the use of the ellipse the catalog the meter
& the vibrating plane,

who dreamt and made incarnate gaps in Time & Space through images
juxtaposed, and trapped the archangel of the soul between 2 visual
images and joined the elemental verbs and set the noun and dash
of consciousness together jumping with sensation of Pater Omni-
potens Aeterna Deus

to recreate the syntax and measure of poor human prose and stand before you speechless and intelligent and shaking with shame, rejected yet confessing out the soul to conform to the rhythm of
thought in his naked and endless head,

the madman bum and angel beat in Time, unknown, yet putting down
here what might be left to say in time come after death,

and rose reincarnate in the ghostly clothes of jazz in the goldhorn
shadow of the band and blew the suffering of America's naked
mind for love into an eli eli lamma lamma sabacthani saxophone
cry that shivered the cities down to the last radio

with the absolute heart of the poem of life butchered out of their own
bodies good to eat a thousand years.

II

What sphinx of cement and aluminum bashed open their skulls and
ate up their brains and imagination?

Moloch! Solitude! Filth! Ugliness! Ashcans and unobtainable dollars!
Children screaming under the stairways! Boys sobbing in armies!
Old men weeping in the parks!

Moloch! Moloch! Nightmare of Moloch! Moloch the loveless! Mental
Moloch! Moloch the heavy judger of men!

Moloch the incomprehensible prison! Moloch the crossbone soulless
jailhouse and Congress of sorrows! Moloch whose buildings are
judgment! Moloch the vast stone of war! Moloch the stunned
governments!

Moloch whose mind is pure machinery! Moloch whose blood is running money! Moloch whose fingers are ten armies! Moloch whose
breast is a cannibal dynamo! Moloch whose ear is a smoking
tomb!

Moloch whose eyes are a thousand blind windows! Moloch whose
skyscrapers stand in the long streets like endless Jehovahs! Moloch
whose factories dream and croak in the fog! Moloch whose smoke-
stacks and antennae crown the cities!

Moloch whose love is endless oil and stone! Moloch whose soul is
electricity and banks! Moloch whose poverty is the specter of
genius! Moloch whose fate is a cloud of sexless hydrogen! Moloch
whose name is the Mind!

Moloch in whom I sit lonely! Moloch in whom I dream Angels! Crazy
in Moloch! Cocksucker in Moloch! Lacklove and manless in
Moloch!

Moloch who entered my soul early! Moloch in whom I am a consciousness without a body! Moloch who frightened me out of my
natural ecstasy! Moloch whom I abandon! Wake up in Moloch!
Light streaming out of the sky!

Moloch! Moloch! Robot apartments! invisible suburbs! skeleton treas-
uries! blind capitals! demonic industries! spectral nation! in-
vincible madhouses! granite cocks! monstrous bombs!

They broke their backs lifting Moloch to Heaven! Pavements, trees,
radios, tons! lifting the city to Heaven which exists and is everywhere about us!

Visions! omens! hallucinations! miracles! ectasies! gone down the
American river!

Dreams! adorations! illuminations! religions! the whole boatload of
    sensitive bullshit!
Breakthroughs! over the river! flips and crucifixions! gone down the
    flood! Highs! Epiphanies! Despairs! Ten years' animal screams
    and suicides! Minds! New loves! Mad generation! down on the
    rocks of Time!
Real holy laughter in the river! They saw it all! the wild eyes! the
    holy yells! They bade farewell! They jumped off the roof! to
    solitude! waving! carrying flowers! Down to the river! into the
    street!

SADE

Sade has survived even his myths: to adulate the divine Marquis or to assault the monstrous libertine—expropriating his name and saddling it for all time with the onerous epithets, "sadism," "sadistic" —only moves him farther from us, into the shadow realm. To extol him, after a century of virtual oblivion, as prophet and genius, moves us no nearer the small, bright kernel of truth than does his total excommunication by the fearful self-righteous.

His excesses in no way distinguished him; many others of his time and station indulged themselves as freely, and paid no like penalty. For them eroticism was an end in itself, a convulsive grasp, in a dying world, for superiority and self-affirmation; for Sade too it was a means of self-fulfillment, but a means only, the scaffolding for that ideal universe elaborated in each of his works. "It is by this deliberate act," notes Simone de Beauvoir, "that Sade attains a real originality." And in transposing the reality of his acts into the realm of the imaginary—for him the imaginary was much more important than reality—he created and bequeathed a brutal, inspired, exasperating, often incoherent, often compelling record, a world of superhuman lusts, ambitions, urges, subjugations. Abhorring abstractions, and the abstract morality in which man takes refuge and in the name of which he condemns, justifies, commits with impunity and in good conscience the most heinous crimes, Sade chose cruelty and crime. And if it is difficult, or impossible, to accept his solutions, it is similarly impossible to deny the validity of his attacks on hypocrisy, indifference, mediocrity, and the "flights from reality" to which man has always succumbed, to varying degrees, as if consciously denying his own existence.

10

Sade has yet to be rehabilitated; society is far from ready to seek him out and readmit him on his own terms. But the day will perhaps come, if freedom is ever more than an abused, empty expletive, when the vestment of monster will be lifted, and we shall be able to judge him, equitably and unemotionally, as a man and a writer. For surely it is apparent, under the current siege of revivals of ever more potently forbidden fruit of the creative past, that the search for Sade has, indeed, already begun.

from *LA PHILOSOPHIE DANS LE BOUDOIR*

Christian morality, far too vague on the subject of man's relation to his fellows, proposes axioms so full of sophistry that we cannot admit them; for if one wishes to erect principles one must take care not to base them on sophistries. This absurd morality tells us to love our neighbor as ourselves. Nothing indeed could be more sublime, if only falsity did not often have the appearance of beauty. There is no question of loving one's neighbor as oneself, for that is against all the laws of Nature, and Nature should be the sole guide of our life; it is only a question of loving our fellow men as brothers, as friends given to us by Nature and with whom we will be able to live far better in a republican state, when distances between us are abolished and ties made closer.

Let humanity, fraternity, benevolence so prescribe our mutual duties, and let each one individually fulfill them with the amount of energy with which Nature has endowed him, without blaming and above all without punishing the phlegmatic or the melancholy who do not feel the same delight as others in these tender bonds; for, let us agree, it would be a palpable absurdity to wish to prescribe universal laws; it would be like the ludicrous procedure of a general who dressed all his soldiers in uniforms of the same size; it is a fearful injustice to expect men of different temperament to bow to the same laws; what suits one man does not suit all.

I agree that one could not make as many laws as there are men;

12

lish laws which will force woman to yield to the ardors of him who desires her; violence itself being one of the results of this right, we can legally employ it. Has not Nature proved to us that we have this right, by allotting us the strength necessary to force them to our desires?

In vain may women protest modesty or attachment to other men in their defense; these chimerical reasons count for nothing; we have already seen that modesty is an artificial and despicable emotion. Neither has love, which might be called *madness of the soul,* any right to justify their fidelity: it satisfies only two individuals, the beloved and the lover, and cannot therefore increase the happiness of others; but women were given to us for the general happiness, not for an egotistical and privileged enjoyment. All men, then, have an equal right to the enjoyment of all women; and there is no man, according to Nature's laws, who can institute a unique and personal claim to any woman. The law which will oblige them to prostitute themselves in the brothels I have spoken of, which will force them if they evade it, is therefore the most equitable of laws and one against which no legitimate excuse can be urged.

A man who wishes to enjoy any woman or girl may thus, if you pass just laws, summon her to appear in one of the houses I have described; and there, safeguarded by the matrons of this temple of Venus, she will be offered in complete meekness and submission to satisfy all the caprices he wishes to indulge with her, however strange and irregular they may be, for there is none that is not inspired by Nature, none that she can refuse. It would only remain then to fix the age; but I claim that this cannot be done without hampering the freedom of whoever desires a girl of such and such an age.

Whoever has the right to eat the fruit off a tree may assuredly pluck it either ripe or green according to his taste. But it will be objected that at this age the interference of a man will have a decisively bad effect on the health of the child. That consideration is meaningless: once you have accorded me the right to enjoyment, this right is independent of the effects of the enjoyment; from that mo-

---

to force her; I repeat that it is not a question of property but of enjoyment; I have no right to the ownership of the fountain that lies in my path, but I certainly have the right to make use of it; I have the right to enjoy the limpid water offered up to my thirst; in the same way I have no actual claim to the possession of such and such a woman, but I have an incontestable one to the enjoyment of her; and I have the right to force her to this enjoyment if she refuses me for any motive whatsoever.

ment on, it makes no difference whether the act of enjoyment is beneficial or harmful to the object submitting to it. Have I not already proved that it would be legal to force a woman, and that as soon as she kindles a desire to enjoy her, she must submit to being enjoyed without any egotistical considerations?

It is the same with her health. The moment that the enjoyment of him who desires and has the right to take possession is spoiled or weakened by such considerations, the question of age must be forgotten; for we are not concerned with the sensations of the object condemned by Nature and the law to assuage momentarily another's desires; we are only concerned in this analysis with what pleases the one who desires. We shall redress the balance.

Yes, it shall be redressed, it undoubtedly must be; these women that we have served so cruelly must certainly be recompensed; and this is going to form the reply to the second question I asked.

If we admit, as we have just done, that all women should submit to our desires, surely we should also allow them fully to satisfy their own; our laws should in this respect look favorably upon their ardent natures; and it is absurd that we have assigned both their honor and their virtue to the unnatural strength they must use to resist the inclinations with which they have been far more profusely endowed than we. This social injustice is even more glaring since we agree both to weaken them by our seduction and then to punish them when they yield to all our efforts to make them fall. The whole absurdity of our morals, it seems to me, is contained in that atrocious injustice, and the revelation of that alone should be enough to make us realize the absolute necessity of changing it for a purer morality.

I claim that women, who have far more violent desires than we for the pleasures of lust, should be able to express them as much as they wish, free from the bonds of marriage, from all the false prejudices of modesty, completely returned to the state of Nature. I want the law to permit them to enjoy as many men as they like; I want the enjoyment of both sexes and all parts of their bodies to be allowed to them as to men; and under the ruling that they suffer themselves to be enjoyed by whoever wants them, they must also be allowed the freedom to enjoy whoever they think is capable of satisfying them.

We will, then, have brothels destined for the concupiscence of women; and like those for men, they will be under the protection of the government; there, all the individuals of either sex that they might desire will be supplied, and the more they frequent these houses the more they will be respected. Nothing is so barbarous and ridiculous as the fact that we have identified woman's virtue and honor with the resistance she employs against the desires she has received from Nature and which burn continually in those who have the barbarity to condemn her for submitting to them. From the most tender age,[2] therefore, a young girl who is free from a father's care, having no need to save herself for marriage—completely abolished by the wise laws I advocate, free from the prejudice that has enslaved her sex, will be able to surrender herself to all that her temperament commands, in places devoted to this subject; there she will be received with respect, satisfied in profusion, and on her return to society she can speak as publicly of the pleasure she has tasted as today she speaks of a ball or an excursion. Fair sex, you will be free; you will enjoy, as men do, all the pleasures that are your duty to Nature; you will stop at nothing. Must one half of humanity chain the diviner half? Oh, break the chains, Nature commands it; know no other curb but your preferences, no other laws but your desires, no other morality but Nature's; no longer languish beneath those savage prejudices that wither your charms, fetter the divine impulses of your hearts,[3] you are as free as we are, and the career of Venus' battles is open to you as to us; no longer fear absurd reproaches; pedantry and superstition are overthrown; we will never again see you blush at your charming excesses; crowned with myrtle and roses, our esteem for you will be the greater as you give these excesses yet wider scope.

Our foregoing analysis obviously makes it unnecessary to discuss adultery; let us glance at it, nevertheless, however meaningless it becomes after the laws I have established. How ridiculous it was to consider it a crime under our former institutions! If there was one thing in the world particularly absurd it was the eternal duration of the marriage bond; one had surely only to observe or experience the

[2] Babylonian females did not wait till the age of seven to bring their first fruits to the temple of Venus. The first stirring of desire that a girl feels is the moment that Nature means her to prostitute herself, and with no other consideration in mind, she should obey Nature's voice; she outrages her laws if she resists them.

[3] Women do not realize how much their sensualities embellish them. Compare two women of about the same age and beauty, one of whom lives in celibacy and the other in libertinism; you will see how the latter takes the prize for brilliance and bloom; any transgression against Nature is more aging than an excess of pleasures; and everyone knows that confinements make a woman more beautiful.

weight of these chains to cease to consider any alleviating action a crime; and Nature, as we have remarked, having endowed women with a more passionate temperament and greater sensibility than the other sex, the marriage bond was undoubtedly more stifling for them.

Ardent women, on fire with the flames of love, recompense yourselves now without fear; realize that there cannot be any harm in following Nature's impulses, that she did not create you for one man but for the delight of all. Let nothing restrain you. Imitate the Greek republicans; their legislators never dreamed of making adultery a crime, and they nearly all authorized women's excesses. Thomas More in his Utopia proves that it is advantageous to a woman to give herself up to debauchery, and this great man's ideas were not always mere fantasy.[4]

Among the Tartars, the more a woman prostituted herself the more she was honored; she showed the marks of her immodesty openly on her neck; and a woman with none of these decorations was considered worthless. In Pegu, wives and daughters are lent by the family to passing travelers; they are hired out at so much a day like horses or carriages! Volumes could be written to prove that sexual indulgence was never considered criminal among any of the wiser nations. Every philosopher realizes that we have only the Christian impostors to thank for making it a crime. The priests had a good reason for forbidding us indulgence; this command, by keeping the knowledge and absolution of these secret sins for them alone, gave them unbelievable power over women and opened the way to a life of unlimited lust. We know how they profited by it and how they would still if they had not irretrievably lost their credit.

Is incest more dangerous? Undoubtedly not; it extends the family ties and consequently makes the citizen's love of his country more active; it is commanded us by Nature's first laws; we feel the necessity of it; and it makes the enjoyment of objects that belong to us seem yet more delicious. The earliest institutions favored incest; it is found in primitive societies; it has been consecrated by all religions, and favored by all laws. If we survey the whole world we see that incest has been established everywhere. The Negroes of the Pepper Coast and the Gaboon pimp for their wives to their own children; the eldest son of Judah had to marry his father's wife; the peoples of Chile

---

[4] He also suggested that betrothed couples should see each other naked before marrying. How many marriages would not take place if this law were enforced! It will be admitted that otherwise it is a case of what we call buying a pig in a poke.

sleep with sisters or daughters indifferently and marry mother and daughter at the same time. To put it briefly, I dare affirm that incest should be the rule under any government based on fraternity. How could reasonable men go to the absurd lengths of thinking that the enjoyment of mother, sister, or daughter could ever be a crime? I ask you, is it not abominably prejudiced to make a man a criminal if he enhances his appreciation of the object closest to him by ties of Nature! It is like saying that we are forbidden to love too much just those individuals whom Nature teaches us to love the most, and that the more she inclines us towards an object, the more she also bids us keep our distance. These contradictions are absurd; only races debased by superstition could believe in them or adopt them. Since the communal state of women that I propose would necessarily involve incest, there is little more to say about this supposed crime that is so obviously a fallacy; and we will pass to rape, which seems at first sight to be the most clearly injurious of all forms of libertinism because of its apparent outrage. It is nevertheless certain that rape, so rare and hard to prove, does less harm than robbery, for the latter appropriates the property, while the former only spoils it. And how could you answer a violator if he objected that in fact he had done but slight harm, since he had only made a certain alteration in an object which would soon have been made in any case through marriage or desire?

It now remains to discuss man's duties towards himself. Since the philosopher only adopts such duties inasmuch as they minister to his pleasure or self-preservation, it is useless to recommend their adoption or to impose penalties if they are not observed.

The only crime of this type that a man could commit would be suicide. I shall not amuse myself here by pointing out the imbecility of people who make that action into a crime; I shall send anyone with doubts on the matter to Rousseau's famous letter. Almost all the governments of the ancient world authorized suicide on political or religious grounds. The Athenians disclosed to the Areopagus their reasons for killing themselves; then they stabbed themselves. All the Greek republics tolerated suicide; it was a part of the scheme of the ancient legislators; people killed themselves in public and made a formal ceremony of death.

The republic of Rome encouraged suicide; the famous sacrifices for the motherland were simply suicides. When Rome was taken by the Gauls, the most illustrious senators vowed themselves to death;

by adopting the same attitude we shall acquire the same virtues. A soldier killed himself, during the campaign of '92, for sheer grief at not being able to follow his comrades at Jemappes. If we are constantly measured against these proud republicans, we shall soon surpass their virtues: the government makes the man. The age-long habit of despotism has sapped our courage completely; our ways have become depraved; but we are being born again; soon it will be seen what sublime actions the French genius and character are capable of when they are free; let us maintain, at the cost of our fortunes and our lives, that liberty that has already cost us so many victims, let us not regret one of them if we reach our goal: they gave themselves to it voluntarily; let us not allow that blood to have been spilt in vain; but let us unite . . . unite, or we will lose the fruit of all our labors; let us now try to make fine laws after the victories we have won; our first legislators, still enslaved to the despot we have laid low, have given us laws worthy of the tyrant whom they still flatter: let us refashion their work and remember that we are working for republicans now; let our laws be as mild as the people they govern.

In disclosing here, as I have done, the nullity, the indifference of an infinite number of actions that our ancestors, misled by a false religion, believed to be criminal, I am reducing our task to a very simple one. Let us make few laws, but good ones—it is not a question of multiplying restraints but of making those we do employ quite indestructible—let the laws that we promulgate have no other object than the peace and happiness of the citizen. . . .

from *PENSÉE*

To man, God is precisely what colors are to a man born blind, impossible for him to imagine. The reply you get to that is that those colors exist all the same, and that if the blind man does not imagine them it is due to his lack of a sense, not due to the thing's non-existence; and similarly, that if man does not comprehend God it is due to his lack of some sense, not due to that being's uncertainty of existence.

Now here is the crux of the sophism, for the names, the properties of, and the differences between, colors are merely matters of convention that derive from the necessity our senses place us in to differentiate among them, while the question of their existence is frivolous, that is to say, it is highly frivolous of us to dispute whether a ribbon dyed brown is really brown: nothing is real in all that but our conventions. And so with God, who is presented to our imaginations precisely as color is to the brains of blind men, that is, as something one is told about but which nothing proves the reality of, and consequently may very well not be at all—just as, when you present a ribbon to a blind person assuring him it is brown, you not only give him no idea of it but you tell him, moreover, nothing he cannot deny, regardless of all you might argue or be capable of arguing to convince him. Similarly, when you speak to man about God, not only do you give him no idea of it but you bring to his imagination, moreover, only something he is capable of denying, combatting or destroying, while you are left without the smallest real argument with which to persuade him.

God, then, no more exists for man than colors do for men born blind; and man is, then, as right to maintain there is no God as the blind man is to hold that there are no colors, for colors are not real things but simply matters of convention and all matters of convention acquire reality in men's minds only insofar as they affect their senses and are capable of being understood by them. Thus, a thing may very well be real in the eyes of all men equipped with their five senses and yet become doubtful or even nonexistent to him who lacks the sense necessary for its conception, while the thing that is utterly incomprehensible, utterly impossible for the senses to perceive, becomes nonexistent—as nonexistent as color becomes to the blind man. Consequently, if color is nonexistent to the blind man because he lacks the necessary sense for assuming it, then God is nonexistent to man because none of his senses is capable of perceiving it and this God has, then, not even a coventional existence like color but in itself no reality whatever. A society of blind men, lacking the guidance of other men, would similarly have conventional names to express things without reality; with reference to this fine chimera that we qualify with the name of God, we are that society of blind men: we have imagined a thing we believed necessary but which has no existence other than our own need to create it.

Measured by this same yardstick, all principles of human morality would similarly be reduced to nothing, for all duties, being simply conventions, are similarly chimerical. Man said such and such a thing will be virtue because it is useful to me, such and such another will be vice because it harms me: these are the futile conventions of blind men's society whose laws have no intrinsic reality. The true way to judge our weakness relative to Nature's sublime mysteries is to judge by the weakness of beings who have one sense fewer than we. Their errors with respect to us are our errors with respect to Nature: the blind man sets up his conventions according to his needs and the mediocrity of his faculties, while ordinary men have similarly made their laws in accordance with their little knowledge, their little views, and their little needs. But there is nothing real in all that, nothing that could not be either misunderstood by a society inferior to ours in faculties, or formally denied by one that surpassed our own by its possession of more delicate organs or additional senses.

How hateful our laws, our virtues, our vices, our divinities would be in the eyes of a society possessing two or three more senses than we and a sensitivity double our own—for such a society would be more perfect and closer to Nature. Consequently the most perfect being we could conceive would be the one who would depart most radically from our conventions and would consider them most hateful —as we consider those of a society inferior to us. When we follow this chain of reasoning and arrive at Nature herself, we shall easily understand that everything we say, everything we order and assume, is as far from the perfection of her views and as inferior to her as are the laws of a society of blind men in relation to our own.

Without the senses, no ideas, *nihil est (in) intellectu, quod non prius fuerit in sensu* is, in a word, the great foundation and the great truth the preceding argument establishes, and it is fantastic that M. Nicole attempted in his logic to destroy this proven axiom of all philosophy. There come into our minds, he claims, other ideas than those acquired through the senses, and one of these great ideas which can occur to us, apart from the senses, is *I think, therefore I am.*

This idea, the author says, has no sound, no color, no odor and thus is not the product of the senses—is it possible so to bury oneself in the dust of the school as to reason with this degree of falseness? Certainly this idea, *I think, therefore I am,* is not of the species "this table is whole"—because the sense of touch proves it to my mind. It is not, I grant, due to the operation of any one particular sense but is the result of them all—and really so, for if a creature without senses could exist, it would be totally impossible for it to formulate this thought, *I think, therefore I am.* Consequently this thought is the result of the operation of all our senses, although not of any one in particular, and therefore it cannot destroy the great, infallible reasoning as to the impossibility of our acquiring ideas apart from our senses. Religion, I grant you, does not agree, but religion is the thing in the world one should consult least on the subject of philosophy, because it is religion that most obscures all principles and most shamefully bows man down under the ridiculous yoke of faith, destroyer of all truths.

Translated by Paul Dinnage

OF THE CLANDESTINITE   by Austryn Wainhouse

> If it be a civilized society you want, the intellect must be free to deal as it pleases with whatever comes its way, it must be free to choose its own terms, phrases, and images, and to play with all things what tricks it will.
> —CLIVE BELL, *Civilizatation*

1

. . . The intellect must be free. There are more or less free intellects? If you wish. In your terms (and phrases and images) Sade's was one of the very freest; but according to Sade, *free* is an absolute quality, one is not more free or less free, one is either free or one isn't: with him all frivolity ceases, freedom undergoes a transformation and its expression becomes serious.

2

As if to bring the conversation back down to earth (to earth: to this booth in the depths of a rue de Tournon café where I work) the person who has been listening to me with difficulty, his eyes wandering in search of a distance in which to lose his gaze, his mind fixed on something indistinct within, asks me, honestly: "Why are you interested in Sade?" By now he knows, knows that there is no "honest" answer to this question, and I can tell him that this is simply, but also par excellence, the interest you may have, you should have, in anyone whose situation appears to be in its most significant aspects similar to your own.

He understood that situation better than anyone else.

"For our generation," I go on, "it is clear. None of us can pretend to confusion. Unless we are willing to falsify our lives and accept living and participating in a false world—and can you believe in the existence of anything this false?"

"Can you not believe in it and not accept madness?

"Where madness defines madness it is a sign of health and a virtue to be 'mad.' Unless we are willing to identify ourselves with this nonexistence, there is nothing else to do but live the important, the essential, part of our lives underground. Clandestinely. This does not mean indifference, or detachment, or irresponsibility; to the contrary. The law being what it is, and so long as it remains what it is, we are outlaws. Our sufferings and satisfactions are secret, so are our ambitions. Don't worry, this situation—this extreme situation—won't last forever. Nowadays our civilizations are mortal. The day this one dies you and I shall at last have something to do, and something to be; until then, in order to preserve the *yes* in you, continue to say *no*. In the name of that *yes*.

"I read Sade in that perspective."

3

This "monster author"[1]—one of
those perverse writers whose corruption is so dangerous, so
active, that their single aim is, by having their appalling doctrines printed, to immortalize the sum of their crimes after
their own lives are at an end; they themselves can do no
more, but their accursed writings will incite others to crime,
and they carry this sweet idea with them to their graves: it
consoles them for the obligation, enjoined by death, to give
over the doing of evil (*Justine*).

[1] "It has been said that as a child his countenance was so charming ladies would stop and stare at him. He had an oval face, blue eyes, curly fair hair. His movements were of a perfect grace, and his harmonious voice contained accents which used to touch women's hearts." Apollinaire.

—is about to appear in paperbacks. Sade's writings, rigorously and for sound reason suppressed under the Directory, the Empire, the Regency, the several Republics, has served as fuel to the bonfires common sense has lit for one hundred and fifty years. This summer, on the quays, in the kiosks, tourists will find moderately priced English-language versions of *Justine* and *La Philosophie dans le boudoir*.[2] Perfectly suited for the *auto-da-fé*, seeming even to aspire to nothing else—"*Mais pourquoi suis-je aussi affreux, et pourquoi le crime est-il si charmant? Il m'immortalise, il faut le faire régner dans le monde*"[3]—actually burned in effigy at Aix-en-Provence, Sade and his incomparable fictions, sunk, buried in darkness and interdiction, have, rather than perished, subsisted as a kind of infernal legend, sacred. . . . And now these treasures are about to be discovered. The prospect is troubling: Sade a popular novelist! Is it really a service this dauntless young publisher is rendering, who with his scorn for censorship, his defiance of confiscation, his intrepidity before the *brigade mondaine* and the magistrates, issues pocket editions of Sade? Sade suddenly become available! No, I'll not feign to be out of sympathy with the arguments of those who, for motives of their own and which have nothing to do with public health, maintain that it would be better for the one totally condemned writer to remain out of sight.

Donatien Alphonse-Françoise, first the Marquis and later the Comte de Sade, was born in 1740 in the Hotel de Condé and in 1814 died at Charenton, in an insane asylum. The last article in his will is as follows:

[2] These translations have been mistaken for eighteenth-century performances. 'Pieralessandro Casavini' is the pseudonym of the American political thinker living in exile in Paris.

[3] L.-A. Pitou, *Analyse de mes malheurs et de mes persécutions depuis vingt-six ans.* "During the eighteen months I spent at Sainte-Pélagie in 1802 and 1803, while awaiting my *lettres de grâce*, I was in the same corridor occupied by the famous Marquis de Sade, author of the most execrable works human perversity has ever invented. That wretch was so infected by the leprosy of the most inconceivable crime that the authorities had found him unfit for the scaffold; lower even than a beast, he had been ranked among the maniacs: justice, wishing neither to have its archives besmirched by this creature's name, nor to have the executioner's blade provide him the celebrity whereof he was so avid, had relegated him to a corner of the prison, the while giving everyone else detained there leave to rid it of this burden."

Finally, I expressly forbid that my body be opened under any pretext at all. With the greatest earnestness I do insist that it be kept forty-eight hours in the room where I die, placed in a wooden bier not to be nailed shut before the expiration of the period stipulated above; at the end of which the said bier will be sealed; during this interval there will be sent word to the Sieur Le Normand, woodseller, boulevard de l'Egalité, Number 101, at Versailles, to beg him to come, in person, with a cart and to get my body to be transported, under his escort and in the said cart, to the woods on my estate at Malmaison, commune of Mancé, by Epernon, where I wish that it be put without any kind of ceremony, in the first copse to be found to the right in the said woods when they are entered from the side of the old château. . . . The pit . . . will be dug by my tenant at Malmaison, under Monsieur Le Normand's supervision, who will not leave my body until after having placed it in the said pit; he may, if he so wishes, be accompanied on this occasion by those of my relatives or friends who, foregoing all display, will be kind enough to give me this last testimony of their attachment. Once covered over, acorns will be strewn above the pit, so that later, the terrain of the said pit garnished again and the copse wooded as before, the traces of my burial place may disappear from the face of the earth as I flatter myself the memory of me will vanish out of the minds of men, there being excepted those few who have in goodness loved me till the end, and of whom I bear a most gentle remembrance to my grave.

Done at Charenton-Saint-Maurice in a state of reason and health, this 13th of January eighteen hundred six.

(The Marquis' body however was not buried at Malmaison, but in the Charenton asylum cemetery; a few years later, some of the graves were opened, his among them. A Dr. Ramon, resident physician at Charenton, was present at the operation and was able to salvage Sade's skull; he studied it "from the phrenological and magnetic viewpoints." What did this examination reveal? "Superior development of the cranial dome (theosophy, benevolence); no exaggerated protuberances in the temporal zones (no ferocity); no exaggerated protuberances behind or above the ears (no aggressiveness); cerebellum of moderate dimensions, no exaggerated space between one mastoid apophysis and the other (no excess in physical love). In short, while nothing about Sade's person as he moved about, solemn and dignified in his bearing, almost patriarchal, suggested anything of the author of *Justine* and *Juliette*, the inspection of his head would lead me to deny that he could be rightly charged with having produced such works; his skull was in all its features similar to that of a Father of the Church."[4])

4

The picture is not simple. Of Sade's life we know mainly *what happened to him;* but each of these experiences, again and again surprising a veritable innocence, left an indelible mark. His, originally, was a passive, reflective nature, candid at first, with a willingness to believe, a strong susceptibility to influence; he acquired his form from the outside, and sought it from there; for him it was above all his relationship to others that counted. His "philosophy," in the eighteenth century, was materialist; had he been born a hundred years later, he would have been an existentialist: existence precedes an essence that is elaborated, wrought, over a life which eventually *is* what during that life a man has *done.* Sade's itinerary was a constant becoming. He sensed it. He is a pure example of an historical personality.

His epistolary novel, *Aline et Valcour,* is autobiographical; this passage from it doubtless refers to his own earlier years:

> Through my mother allied to all that was great in the realm, through my father connected with all that was distinguished in the province of Languedoc, born in Paris, in the midst of luxury and abundance, as soon as I reached the age of reason I decided that Nature and Fortune had joined hands to shower their gifts upon me; I thought so because others were stupid enough to tell me so, and this ridiculous notion made me conceited, despotic, and ill-tempered; it seemed to me that nothing could by rights stand in my path, that the whole world was there to yield to me, to flatter my caprices, and that I had merely to form them in order that everyone fly to satisfy them.

And yet the little Marquis would not appear to have been anything like an unruly or even difficult child. He was the irreproachable

[4] Marquis de Sade, *Cahiers personnels (1803–1804)*, Paris: 1953. *Appendice II: Notes sur Monsieur de Sade, par L.-J. Ramon.*

pupil of his uncle, the Abbé de Sade d'Ebreuil, to whose care he was entrusted at the age of five or six; he remained in the Vaucluse until he was ten, then was sent back to Paris and entered at the Collège Louis-le-Grand, where his teachers were Jesuits. At fourteen he was withdrawn from school; late in 1755, after completing twenty months of training, he was commissioned *sous-lieutenant* in the King's Infantry; at sixteen, with the rank of *cornette,* he went off to war against Prussia. "The campaigns began," Valcour says, "and I can honestly assert that I played my part in them well. That native impetuosity of character, that fiery spirit I'd received from Nature only fortified in me the ferocious virtue called bravery—a virtue very mistakenly beheld as the only one necessary to our state." But from the camp at Obertistein the soldier, now twenty years old, wrote to his father:

> You ask for an account of my life, of my doings. I shall give you a detailed one, and sincere. I am taxed with being fond of sleeping; it's true that I do rather have this fault: I retire early and rise very late. I often ride out to examine the enemy's position and ours. After considering them, I submit my opinions, favorable and unfavorable; I say what I think, and am praised or blamed in proportion to the little or no common sense my reports contain. Sometimes I pay courtesy calls. . . . I do so without excess of ceremony; I don't like them. If it weren't for M. de Poyanne I'd surely go through this campaign without ever once setting foot in headquarters. This isn't wise behavior, I'm aware of it; to succeed, one must put oneself out a bit at court; but I dislike doing it. . . . Be polite, honest, dignified without arrogance, helpful without obsequiousness; enjoy yourself whenever you can, whenever it does no harm to yourself or to anybody else; live to the full, have a good time without going beyond your means or causing yourself upsets; have few friends, perhaps none, for a truly sincere friend is something that does not exist, and they will all sacrifice you twenty thousand times over if it's in the slightest way to their advantage; evenness of temper and constancy, so as to be able to get on well with everyone, without however laying yourself bare to anyone, for you have only to put yourself at somebody's mercy in order to regret it the next instant; speak well, speak highly of people who, often without cause,

have spoken very ill of you and behind your back. . . .
Those are my virtues, they are the ones I aspire to. If I may
congratulate myself upon having a friend, I think I have one
in the Regiment; but even of that one I'm not entirely sure.
. . . There's the whole of my confession; I open up my heart
to you; not as though to an often dreaded and unloved
father, but as though to the sincerest friend, to the warmest
one I believe I have in the world. Cease looking for grounds
for pretending to hate me, give me back your devotion,
never deprive me of it again. . . .

The father—"He was a severe and rather somber man, a *grand
seigneur*, distant to the point of iciness, compassed in his manners
and speech, pompous with his servants and his family as well, very
jealous of his rights, rigid, unbending, but in his spending uncautious
to the point of prodigality. He squandered his fortune with com-
punction and decency, apparently never having been tempted by a
folly"[5]—was in serious financial straits; the son was frequenting
actresses, gambling. The Seven Years' War ends in 1763; Sade, a
captain, comes out of the army to devote himself to dissipation, mind-
less of the future and neglectful of his courtier's duties. Not once
has he resisted authority; without liking "things as they are" because
mistrustful of them (dare one rely upon "things" whose certitude,
whose reality is guaranteed by nothing more solid than "opinion"?),
disinclined to take any responsibility for them, limiting his participa-
tion in them, the place he covets is mediocrity; toward society—that
is, the members of his class—the attitude he has devised is con-
ciliatory; his concern is to avoid collisions, and to pursue his pleasures
smoothly is the extent of his announced ambition; amiable, correct,
with his failings of course—but they are after all the failings of the
age, and serve almost as credentials—the Marquis de Sade looks to
be anybody and no one; an anonymous *"agréable."*

And he is accommodating when the Comte, to get this son "who
has not one good quality" off his hands and into those of a wife—
but the right wife—negotiates his marriage to Mlle. de Montreuil. To
be sure, Sade had made it known that he did not wish to marry
except for love; and he had been in love, with a Mlle. de Lauris,
still his fiancée two weeks before he obediently became the husband

---

[5] Paul Bourdin, ed., *Correspondance inédite du Marquis de Sade de
ses proches et de ses familiers avec une introduction, des annales et des
notes,* Paris: 1929.

of the girl his father had chosen for him. That was May 17, 1763. On October 29, 1763, he was arrested and jailed for excesses committed in a brothel where he had been a regular visitor since the month of June.

At this stage everything changes. From here on he is permanently in trouble: successive detentions, after the Rose Keller affair, at Saumur, the fortress of Pierre-Encise near Lyon, the Conciergerie, the debtors' prison at Fort-l'Evêque, the Château de Miolans. . . . Hunted by gendarmes, continually in flight when not behind bars, banished from the company of his peers, more and more extravagant, always in debt, simultaneously a victim of others and of himself, Sade says—after fifteen years of this—that he has tried every means to reform himself but is persuaded none has a chance of success: "*J'ai toujours été plus malheureux que coupable.*" One of his correspondents, Mlle. de Rousset (in a letter of October 21, 1780, which reaches Sade in the Château de Vincennes), concurs: "*Enfin, mon cher ami, il est des individus si baroquement organisés qu'ils inspirent plus de pitié que de colère.*"

Amidst silence, in solitude, words take on weight, decisiveness; everything starts anew for a man locked up with his meditations.

Writing about Goethe, a man who stood so well with his times —he and Sade were contemporaries—Ortega reminds us that:

> Life is, in itself and forever, shipwreck. To be shipwrecked is not to drown. The poor human being, feeling himself sinking into the abyss, moves his arms to keep afloat. This movement of the arms which is his reaction against his own destruction, is culture—a swimming stroke. When culture is no more than this, it fulfills its function and the human being rises above his own abyss. But ten centuries of cultural continuity brings with it—among many advantages —the great disadvantage that man believes himself safe, loses the feeling of shipwreck, and his culture proceeds to burden itself with parasitic and lymphatic matter. Some discontinuity must therefore intervene, in order that man may renew his feeling of peril, the substance of his life. All his life-saving equipment must fail, he must find nothing to cling to. Then his arms will once again move redeemingly.
>
> Consciousness of shipwreck, being the truth of life, constitutes salvation. Hence I no longer believe in any ideas except the ideas of shipwrecked men. We must call the

classics before a court of shipwrecked men to answer certain peremptory questions with reference to real life.

A little further on:

> At this point I propose that you imagine a Goethe without Weimar—a Goethe thoroughly immersed in the life of the Germany of that epoch, a Germany all ferment, all rising sap, all open pores; a wandering, weather-beaten Goethe, with his material basis (economic and social) *insecure*, without a neat set of boxes filled with duly filed engravings, about which he perhaps never says anything interesting. In other words, the opposite of a Goethe enclosed at the age of twenty in the sterile flask of Weimar and magically desiccated into a *Geheimrat*. Life is our reaction to the basic insecurity which constitutes its substance. Hence it is an extremely serious matter for a man to find himself too much surrounded by apparent securities. A consciousness of security kills life. Herein lies the cause of the regularly recurring degeneration of aristocracies. What a delight to humanity an insecure Goethe would have been, a Goethe distressed by his surroundings, forced to realize his fabulous inner potentialities!

Two years later (1782), Sade tells Mlle. de Rousset that "*Si ma situation a des épines, il faut avouer cependant qu'elle suggère souvent des pensées d'un genre de philosophie bien plaisante.*"

While outside the Revolution is preparing, Sade, "shut up like a wild animal behind 19 doors of iron," interrogates himself; and is already halfway to freedom.

> . . . you supposed you were performing a wonder, I dare say, when you had me reduced to an atrocious abstinence in what concerns *sin and the flesh*. Well, you were wrong. You have made me create phantoms I shall have to realize. That was beginning to happen anyhow, and it will only be that much nicer to start in all over again. When one turns up the fire under the pot you know very well it has got to boil over.

We see arbitrary imprisonment, an underground cell, helplessness, nakedness become the spirit's liberation.

1782: *Dialogue entre un prêtre et un moribond.* Composed at Vincennes. Manuscript lost, recovered, first published in 1926.

1785: *Les 120 Journées de Sodome.* Completed in thirty-seven days, at the Bastille. Manuscript lost when the crowd storms the Bastille; first French publication 1931–35. Three volumes.

1787: *Les Infortunes de la vertu.* Completed in fifteen days, at the Bastille; integral version first published in 1930.

1791: *Justine ou les malheurs de la vertu* printed.

1793: *Aline et Valcour ou le Roman philosophique, écrit à la Bastille un an avant la Révolution de France,* published in four volumes.

1795: *La Philosophie dans le boudoir.*

1797: *La Nouvelle Justine ou les malheurs de la vertu suivie de l'histoire de Juliette, sa soeur.* Published "in Holland." Ten volumes.

1800: *Les Crimes de l'amour* printed. Four volumes.

1802–03: In his notebooks Sade mentions a *Conrad ou le Jaloux en délire,* four volumes; a *Marcel ou le Cordelier,* four volumes. Neither text has ever been found. Some of *Le Portefeuille d'un homme de lettres,* intended to constitute three volumes, has survived; of *Mon Théâtre,* thirteen still unpublished plays plus *Oxtiern,* published in 1800; of *Mes confessions,* two volumes of diaries Sade kept between 1777 and 1790 while in prison, nothing; nothing either of his *Réfutation de Fénelon.*

1806: First volume of *Les Mémoires d'Emilie de Valrose ou les égarements du libertinage* completed at the Charenton asylum.

1807: Work terminated on *Emilie,* which makes up the four last volumes of a novel comprising ten, entitled *Les Journées de Florbelle ou la nature dévoilée, suivies des mémoires de l'abbé de Modose et des aventures d'Emilie de Volnange, etc.* Text definitively lost.

An *Histoire d'Isabelle, reine de la Bavière,* probably dating from the last years of Sade's life, was published in 1955.

Much of this, perhaps the greater share, was written under adverse, and sometimes the worst, circumstances: if not in a bedlam atmosphere, then alone in a dungeon, in personal danger, rapidly, furtively, without adequate light to see by, despite weakening health, under impossible circumstances; to help fill interminable hours of emptiness, and to bring to life the privileged creature of his dreams: that unimprisoned and unimprisonable, completely free, completely new "integral man of polymorphic sensibility" whose image, together with a prodigious thirst for revenge, kept him from despair.

5

The ideal universe, which in each of his novels Sade endeavors to refine, is the theater of a terrific struggle for absolute deliverance from all restraint and from all conditions, for sovereignty; only violence reigns here. Minski is an example of one of his heroes.

"Sensing myself made for better things than to vegetate in the back country of an obscure province like this that was my birthplace," become conscious of a world not vast enough for the scope of his desires, he set out to see the world and to learn. The vigorous young man, "born libertine and impious, debauched and perverse, bloodthirsty and ferocious," found in Africa that "depravity is neither more nor less than the natural state of man"; in America, he hunted men; in Asia, he acquired a taste for their flesh. He imitated the crimes of the polite societies he visited, and the atrocities of the barbaric ones; when he brought his "dangerous penchants" back with him to Europe he was condemned "to the stake in Spain, to be broken on the wheel in France, hanged in England, drawn and quartered in Italy"; however, he adds, "wealth is a guarantee against anything." Finally, he sought a place of retirement in Tuscany: "For surroundings I wanted something unusual, rustic, little frequented and where I could indulge my wanton imagination; and its caprices are not mild." To satisfy them he has equipped himself elaborately and collected a numerous retinue. "I have," he explains,

> two harems . . . the first contains two hundred girls from five to twenty years old; when by dint of lewd use they are sufficiently mortified, I eat them. Another ten score women of from twenty to thirty are in the second; you'll see how they are treated. Fifty servants of either sex look after this considerable store of pleasure-objects; and for purposes of recruitment I have one hundred agents posted in all the large cities of the world. . . . Much philosophy is needed to understand me, yes, I realize it, I am a monster, something vomited forth by Nature to aid her in the destruction whereof she gets the stuff she requires for creation; I am without peer in abomination, alone in my kind—oh, yes, all the invectives they gratify me with, I know them by heart; but powerful enough to have need of nobody, wise enough to find sufficiency in my solitude, to detest all mankind, to brave its censures, to jeer at its attitude toward me; experienced enough, intelligent enough to explode every creed, to

flout every religion, to send every God to hell; proud enough
to abhor every government, to refuse every tie, to ignore
every check, to consider myself above every ethical principle, I am happy in my little domain; in it I dispose of all
a sovereign's privileges, in it I enjoy all the pleasures of
despotism, I dread no man, and I live content. I have few
visitors, indeed none unless in the course of my outings I
encounter persons who, like you, strike me as philosophers
enough to take part in my amusements awhile. . . . It is
very far I am apt to rove on these excursions . . . captures,
rapes, burnings, murders, whatever the criminal opportunities
are I make the best of them. . . . Justice? Inexistent in this
country; that is why I chose it for my domicile . . . with
money, you do anything you like here, and I spend a lot.

In these dozens of "little domains" whereof Minski's infernal
paradise is a model, and which are merely demystified reconstruc-
tions of the world outside and therefore descriptions of that outside
world's truth, one finds a society divided into two rigid castes: the
libertine monsters and the prey they batten upon; the masters who
rule, and whose rule is unlimited, superior beings in whom material
and intellectual power is concentrated, and their defenseless slaves.[6]

[6] It is from the working class, from that "vile class" destined to annihilation, the capitalist Saint-Florent selects the "objects" he "sacrifices" to
his lust. "Furthermore, the species of individual is of infinite importance to
my lubricity: I must have them all got from those asylums of misery where
the need to keep alive and the impossibility of finding a way to do so eat
away courage, pride, delicacy, finally rot the soul and, in the hope of an
indispensable crumb, steel a spirit to anything that appears able to provide
it. I have all these nests ransacked, all these dungheaps combed pitilessly:
you've no idea what they yield: yes, Thérèse, I may even say that civil
activity, industry, manufacture, a little social ease would foil my suborna-
tions and rob me of a great proportion of my subjects: I combat such perils
with the influence I enjoy in this city, I promote commercial and economic
fluctuations or instigate the rise of prices which, enlarging the poverty-
stricken class, depriving it, on the one hand, of opportunities for work and
on the other rendering insoluble the problem of survival, increases according to a predictable ratio the total number of the individuals destitution
puts into my clutches. The strategy is a commonplace one, Thérèse: those
scarcities of firewood, dearths of wheat and other staples wherefrom Paris
has been suffering for so many years, have been created for the selfsame
purposes which animate me: avarice, libertinage, such are the passions
which, from the gilded halls of the rich, extend a multitude of nets to ensnare
the poor in their wretchedness." (*Justine*)

Superiority consists in no abstract quality, only in the palpable mani-festations of real strength; the criminal temper may be acquired, but it is only preserved through assiduous cultivation and untiring ex-ercise: greatness is a "career." To it there is no alternative but ruin.

The prosperous Dubois explains to a resolutely misfortunate Justine that

> 'Tis not a man's choice of virtue, which brings him happi-ness, dear girl, for virtue, like vice, is nothing beyond a scheme for getting along in the world; hence the question is not of adopting one course rather than another; but merely one of following the road generally taken; he who wanders from it is always wrong. In an entirely virtuous world, I would recommend virtue to you, because worldly rewards being associated therewith, happiness would infallibly be connected with it too; in a totally corrupt world, I would never advise anything but vice. He who does not walk along in step with others has inevitably to perish; everyone he encounters, he meets in head-on collision and, as he is weak, he has necessarily to be crushed. 'Tis in vain the law seeks to re-establish order and restore men to righteousness; too unjust to undertake the task, too insufficient to succeed in it, those laws will lure you away from the beaten path, but only temporarily; never will they make man abandon it. While the general interest of mankind drives it to corrup-tion, he who does not wish to be corrupted with the rest will therefore be combating the general interest; well, what happiness can he expect, who is in perpetual conflict with the interest of everyone else?

In order to survive in a competitive, strife-ridden society one has got to injure others; and it must be assumed that they will reply in kind, if they can. There is a natural sanction for crime; the universal prospect is of violence, if destruction; did not Nature design the uni-versal scheme? Into it did she not put suffering, cruelty, disorder, death? If there be evil there, does not evil please Nature? Is it not evident that human compassion, benevolence, goodness, even the propagation of the species are anti-natural? That what Nature, the Creator, asks of man is perversity, wickedness, vice, so as to be able to remake what he has undone? That this creation is the single joy Na-ture knows? That her creative lust requires infinite quantities of de-composed matter from which to fashion new beings? That there is no such thing as "death" or annihilation, but only mutation of forms, an efficient circulation of primary substance which, falling into her great crucible and springing forth renewed again, is in incessant motion? That this process is upset by the pernicious conservative efforts of virtuous men, facilitated by the great destroyers—human killers, plagues, quake, famine, fire—that are Nature's agents? Is it not by her express ordination that there are strong and weak: Nature's favorites and her enemies: the few pitted against the many, the many weak depressed to the last level of misery, the few strong raised to the level of gods?

Ah, Juliette! how delicious are the pleasures of the imagination! All the world is ours during these wonderful moments: not a single creature resists us, we devastate the planet, we repopulate it with new objects which we immolate in their turn. The means to every crime belongs to us, we use, we exhaust all, everything, we increase the horror an hundredfold.

That is our sublime duty; Nature and our desires bid us fulfill it. For others, all others stand leagued against you: they have their own interest to consider, their bodies to protect: all men are born into an ineluctable isolation, all their relations are aggressive, all their intentions murderous. These, for Sade, are the "things as they are"; all the rest is artifice, cant, dupery, self-deception. Social contracts, conventions, laws, religions: so many "prejudices" no intelligent man can harbor, of which no philosopher will let himself become the victim; they are compensations for popular weakness—they, together with notions of guilt, of justice, of conscience, of humaneness, of brotherhood are the weapons the weak use to deter the strong who, once made to waver, are lost.

The false ideas we have of the persons surrounding us are still the source of an incalculable number of erroneous moral judgments: we fabricate chimerical duties toward those persons, because it is believed that they bear some relation to us. We need but have the strength to renounce what we expect of others, and our obligations toward them evaporate at once. What, I ask you, what are all the creatures of the world when weighed against a single one of our desires? and for what reason ought I deprive the least of those desires so as to please a creature, a person which is nothing to me, which interests me not in the slightest? (*Justine*)

Again and again Sade warns against hesitation, against scruple, against remorse and what is certain to result if the criminal permits the bright edge of his faculties to dull. Clearly, he who wants intrepid courage or who is subject to misgivings is defeated in advance; but zeal and fire are not enough. No crime of passion has the value of the furtive, cold-blooded intellectual horror logically prepared and meticulously realized; the one betrays a dangerous enthusiasm which, if it waxes, must also wane; the other denotes the callousness and the industry of a mind that, while the hand is idle, keeps itself in a permanent state of viciousness. It is in moments of repose the criminal genius risks deterioration; hence Sade suggests that one

> do in a moment of *sang-froid* the very thing which, done in abandon, was able to afflict us with remorse afterward. In this way one clashes directly with virtue when it shows itself, and this habit of molesting it at the precise instant the senses' calm gives virtue the wish to appear, is one of the surest means to annihilating it forever. Employ this secret, it will not fail you: as soon as a moment of quiet enables virtue to rear itself in you, arriving in the form of remorse—for that is the guise it always wears in order to get its grip upon us—as soon as you perceive it, instantly do the thing you were going to regret. (*Justine*)

And with what regards the soul attributed to us—"because it is to their interest that we have one: the control they gain over souls is the means whereby they do as they please with men"—learn to cope with it by apathy:

> Stifle, extinguish your soul. . . . seek to make pleasure of all that alarms, of all that affrights your soul: having soon brought this stoicism to perfection, you will sense a host of new pleasures born of your apathy, delights very different from those you think are to be found in your baneful sensibility. Do you suppose that in my infancy I did not have a soul like your own? Well, I strangled its voice, and it is in this voluptuous callousness that I discovered the center of a multitude of irregularities, of frenzies, and of lecheries which are worth far, far more than my weaknesses. . . . I transformed my extravagant follies into principles, and from that moment I have known felicity. (*Juliette*)

What happens when precautions fail, when the unlikely occurs, and one of the mighty is overtaken by the human justice he despises?

> The true libertine loves his execrable actions even for the restitution of which they may someday be the cause. Have we not seen persons who cherished the very tortures human vengeance prepared for them? who joyously submitted to those ordeals, who beheld the scaffold as the throne of glory whereupon they would have been grief-stricken not to perish with the same unwavering courage that animated them in the committing of their crimes? There is the man who has attained the final stage of mediated depravity. (*Juliette*)

Or when such a personage meets his peer? Amélie confesses she likes the "firmness" Borchamps has displayed in flaying and then grilling his former mistress alive; she proposes herself as a suitable replacement for his dead companion. However, she adds:

> Swear to me that I too shall someday become your victim. I cannot help it, my imagination is what it is: delirious. My husband is too fond of me to satisfy it; I can stand no more: since the age of fifteen, the idea of perishing the victim of libertinage's cruel passions has been gnawing my brain. No, I don't want to die tomorrow, my extravagance doesn't go that far. But that is how I want to die, and only in that manner. To become, as I expire, the occasion of a crime—ah, my head reels at the thought.

And Borchamps reassures her that she will have cause to be content with him.

Each stage in the systematic articulation of this fictional counterworld marks a further advance in the profoundly dramatic emergence of an ideology that is at the same time an affective tonality. The demonstration moves toward an impasse. Only our "passions" count, and as for a man's "philosophy," he simply tailors it to fit his "temperament"; desire is infinite, but being is not. Being, erotically defined, turns into an infinite failure: the imagination, essential to that discovery, is forever a step beyond the science and the strength needed to achieve its imperatives: for

> is it possible to commit crimes as we have conceived them ... ? For my part, I must own that my imagination has always been in excess of my opportunities and my resources. I have

conceived a thousand times more than I have accomplished; I have always had grounds for complaint against the Nature who, giving me the desire to outrage her, always denies me the means. (*Juliette*)

Condemned by their human limitations, Sade's heroes recite a dirge:

We are confined to offending idols, creatures; but Nature is our quarry, and she lies outside our reach. What I want is the power to violate, to dislocate her scheme, to stem and reverse her career, to stop the round flight of the stars, to overwhelm the spheres drifting in space, to destroy what serves and to protect what injures Nature, in a word, to insult her in assaulting her works—and I am unable to do all that. (*Juliette*)

Being *is* its limitations.

6

To whom does the Marquis de Sade speak?

Official records note that on July 2, 1789, on the eve of the outbreak of the Revolution, the prisoner harangued the crowd gathered outside the Bastille;[7] two days later, in the middle of the night, he was removed to Charenton where, "surrounded by madmen and epileptics," he was to languish until April 2 of the following year. Upon being released he took stock of himself, found that

my eyes, my lungs have been ruined; for lack of exercise I have become so stout I am scarce able to stir; my sensations, they are all gone, I am incapable of feeling, I have no taste for anything any more; the world, which like a fool I so keenly regretted, seems to me so dull, so drab! There are moments when I am tempted by a desire to enter among the Trappists. . . . Never have I been such a misanthrope as since I have returned into the company of men and if, showing myself to them, I appear strangely, they may be very sure they produce the same impression upon me.[8]

[7] "*J'échauffais . . . par ma fenêtre l'esprit du peuple, je l'assemblais sous cette fenêtre, je l'avertissais des préparatifs qui se faisaient à la Bastille, je l'exhortais à venir jeter bas ce monument d'horreur.*" From a letter written in 1790.

[8] From a letter dated 1790.

And yet

> despair over not being able to communicate my ideas during
> these twelve years has amassed such a vast amount of them in
> my head that I have got to give birth, and I still sometimes
> speak aloud, to myself, when nobody is there. It is a real
> need, to speak . . .[9]

To whom? From this long exile there emerges a man of fifty,
friendless, estranged from his family, without a penny, knowing hardly
who he is; of what had been familiar—a regime, a milieu, laws, customs, prospects, a language—nothing has subsisted intact. Much of
it had been detestable; but from his struggle against it he had derived certitudes, from opposition he had built a personality, resistance
had oriented him. Freedom felt like falling into a void. Never hitherto
had he had a choice; now he was faced by one: retire into the silence
and obscurity he was used to, or begin afresh and attempt a public
existence. He was not long making up his mind. Before a year was
out *"le citoyen Sade"* had five plays on the stage in that many theaters,
was applying himself to attaining to *"la hauteur de la révolution,"* to
achieving a prominence in it, to fortifying his reputation with as many
"ouvrages patriotiques" as possible. He gave over all "impure pleasures"; as well, he observed that "one must be prudent in one's correspondence," sign one's letters *"fraternellement, votre concitoyen"*
and date them, for example, "this Fourth Year of Liberty and First
of Equality." Where did he stand? "The supreme good consists in
living independent of others"; that being out of the question, one had
to be clever, supple in order to live with them:

> As a man of letters, my everyday obligation to work
> sometimes for one party, sometimes in behalf of another, es-
> tablishes a mobility in my opinions that echoes my inner way
> of thinking. Would you really like me to sound it? It does not
> truly find itself favorable to any one party; rather, it is a com-
> posite of the attitudes entertained by them all. . . . What am
> I at present? Aristocrat, democrat? You will be so kind as to
> tell me, for I know nothing about the matter.[10]

Are we to believe that it was from cynicism that Sade, once so passive,
so reticent, so secretive, so lacking in initiative and skeptical, so modest

[9] From a letter dated 1790.
[10] From a letter dated December 5, 1791.

in his pretentions and reluctant to accept the role of a responsible member of society before he was banished from society, now put himself forward, energetically, zealously, and, a mere "opportunist," trying to efface his "complicated past," in the subtlest and most Machiavellian manner, feigned a revolutionary "enthusiasm" which Bourdin explains as his "prettiest lie"? He sought, he was offered one post after another: first a volunteer in the militia of Picques, the section of Paris where he lived, he was afterward made a commissar entrusted with organizing that section's cavalry unit, became president of the commission charged with the inspection and administration of hospitals, secretary then president of his section; upon the subject of revolutionary legislation he contributed an *Idée sur le mode de la sanction des lois;* it was he who was selected to compose and deliver the funeral oration of Marat and Le Pelletier. Ruse? Behind it, behind his behavior a fundamental contempt for the Revolution?

An impatience with it, doubtless. In a period of transition one stands nowhere: there is not yet anywhere to stand. Sade, who had foreseen a revolution, had wanted it and who, when it occurred, devoted himself to it, could at the same time be committed by these events of 1789–1793 and be dissatisfied with them; he could at the same time lend himself to a movement, even help direct it, and also harbor doubts that it would reach its final destination. While recognizing that a total change must be the objective, he could throw in his lot with men whom he knew incapable of perceiving it or afraid of going that far. They might alter structures, revise institutions, behead a king and transform a church into a barracks, a brothel, a Temple of Reason; well and good. Beyond all this lay the major task of changing men from within, of reinventing humanity. That is the exigency his writings contain. Sade.

> would have—he must have—the explosion take place once and for all; the weed must be brought to full growth so that the mind be able to uproot and consume it. In a word, evil must be made to reign one great and last time in the world in order that it be destroyed and Sade's spirit find peace at last.[11]

> *"L'un des hommes les plus rebelles et les plus rageurs qui aient jamais parlé de rébellion et de rage: un homme en un mot monstrueux, que la passion d'une liberté impossible possédait."*[12]

[11] Pierre Klossowski, *Sade mon prochain*, Paris: 1947.
[12] Georges Bataille, "Sade" in *La Littérature et le Mal*, Paris: 1957.

7

Having set down my "Notes for an Homage" I now find, to my irritation—for I foresaw this—that what had seemed to me unmistakably clear, implicit in everything I have said, is not; and that I cannot close without explicitly asserting, in some kind of resounding boldface, my hostility to Sade's message, that is, my disapproval of the doctrine he developed in his novels. "In the act of praising Sade, we edulcorate his philosophy," Georges Bataille writes in his essay "On Reading Sade." He goes on:

> As a matter of fact, to talk about Sade is itself paradoxical. It makes no difference whether we are, tacitly or wholeheartedly, doing the work of a proselyte. Is it less of a paradox to praise crime's apologist than to celebrate crime directly? . . . In as much as those who pronounce them remain well inside the compass of established morality, the hymns sung in praise of Sade tend to reinforce that morality: in some obscure way they give one the feeling that it is futile to seek to wreck or challenge it, that it is more solidly anchored than one would have suspected. All of which would have no importance if Sade's philosophy did not, in his disciples' hands, lose its underlying meaning, which is this: utter incompatibility with the moral values of any rational being.
>
> Sade devoted endless books to affirming inadmissible values; if one accepts his word for it, his entire life was a search after pleasure, and pleasure, for him, could be measured in proportion to the amount of life destroyed in the course of experiencing it. Phrased otherwise, life, for Sade, attained its highest degree of intensity in a monstrous negation of life's principle.
>
> How then can one fail to see that in order to be generally accepted, even generally proposed, so strange a doctrine should first have to be blunted, sugar-coated—emptied of sense and reduced to a vacant outburst? Who does not see that, taken seriously, none but an aberrant society could possibly adopt it for an instant? Actually, they who find a criminal in Sade respond more accurately to his intentions than do his admirers: Sade deliberately seeks to provoke a militant protest. Without that protest, the *paradox of pleasure* is mere poetry.[13]

[13] "On Reading Sade," introduction to *The 120 Days of Sodom*, Paris: 1954.

You too have read these books; you too have protested against them. But I ask you—for it is important to know: does your protest proceed from *a will not to know?* Is it against the demonstration you protest—these scenes of torture and murder, these acts of savagery and viciousness, these systematic eulogies of crime and evil pitched at their extreme of frenzy, at their logical extreme? Or against the conclusions that must perforce be drawn from this unique research? Do you protest against the truth of these images whose reality every war and much that is short of war reproduces, repeatedly, conventionally? Against the notion that peace is impossible so long as the aggressive impulses in man, uppermost among those we call "natural," continue to dominate him? Against the insinuation that aggression and freedom may be intimately, fatally connected, that to be rid of the one it may be necessary to renounce what we have always been in the custom of taking the other to be? This that is basic in us, this that is most precious, these desires and needs we consider rights, which we confound with life itself and without which "life as we know it" is inconceivable, at any rate "not worth living," do you protest against the idea that they are the undoing of man? And that man's salvation, by which I mean his physical survival first and then the rest, depends upon him becoming other than he is?

N.B. Rewriting this essay in 1961 (a first version of it was printed in the Autumn 1953 issue of the quarterly review, *Merlin*) I have tried only to give a greater coherence of expression to a line of thinking which, eight years ago, because of the situation then—the situation in general, my own—I did not feel able to avow openly. Speech is guilty until events confirm what speech wishes to convey, haven't you observed it? Speech remains clandestine until the action of History legitimates it. And in another eight years . . .

BAUDELAIRE

from *BAUDELAIRE*   by Jean-Paul Sartre

"He didn't have the life he deserved." Baudelaire's life seems at first a magnificent illustration of this comfortable saying. He certainly didn't deserve that mother, that perpetual want, that family council, that rapacious mistress or that syphilis. And what could have been more unjust than his premature end? Yet when we think it over, a doubt arises. If we consider the man himself, it appears that he was not without faults or contradictions. This perverse individual deliberately chose the most banal and the most rigid of moral codes. This refined man of the world went with the lowest harlots. A taste for squalor kept him hanging around Louchette's skinny body, and his love of the *affreuse Juive* anticipated his love of Jeanne Duval. This recluse had a horror of solitude; he never went a yard without a companion and longed for a home and a family. This apostle of effort was an "abulic" who was incapable of setting down to regular work. His poetry is full of "invitations to travel"; he clamored for escape from his surroundings, dreamed of undiscovered countries, but he hesitated for six months before making up his mind to go to Honfleur; and his one and only voyage seems to have been a long torment. He flaunted his contempt for, and even his hatred of, the solemn individuals who acted as his guardians, but he never made any real attempts to rid himself of their ministrations and never missed an opportunity of listening to their fatherly admonitions. Was his life really so alien to him? Supposing after all that he did deserve the sort of life he had? Supposing that contrary to the accepted view, men always have the sort of lives they deserve? We must look more closely into the matter.

Baudelaire was six when his father died. He worshiped his mother and was fascinated by her. He was surrounded by every care and

45

comfort; he did not yet realize that he existed as a separate person, but felt that he was united body and soul to his mother in a primitive mystical relationship. He was submerged in the gentle warmth of their mutual love. There was nothing but a home, a family and an incestuous couple. "I was always living in you," he wrote to her in later life; "you belonged to me alone. You were at once an idol and a friend."

It would be impossible to improve upon his description of the sacred nature of their union. The mother was an idol, the child *consecrated* by her affection for him. Far from feeling that his existence was vague, aimless, superfluous, he thought of himself as *son by divine right*. He was always living in her, which meant that he had found a sanctuary. He himself was nothing and did not want to be anything but an emanation of the divinity, a little thought which was always present in her mind. It was precisely because he was completely absorbed in a being who appeared to be a necessary being, to exist as of right, that he was shielded from any feeling of disquiet, that he melted into the absolute and was *justified*.

In November, 1828, the mother whom he worshiped remarried. Her second husband was a soldier. Baudelaire was sent to boarding school and it was from this period that his famous "flaw" dated. On this point Crépet quotes a significant comment of Buisson's. "Baudelaire was a very delicate soul—sensitive, original, tender—who had been flawed by the shock of his first contact with the world."[1]

His mother's second marriage was the one event of his life which he simply could not accept. He was always inexhaustible on the subject and his terrible logic always summed it up in these words: "When one has a son like me"—"like me" was understood—"one doesn't remarry."

The sudden break and the grief it caused forced him into a personal existence without any warning or preparation. One moment he was still enveloped in the communal religious life of the couple consisting of his mother and himself; the next, life had gone out like a tide leaving him high and dry. The justification for his existence had disappeared; he made the mortifying discovery that he was a single person, that his life had been given him for nothing. His rage at being driven out was colored by a profound sense of having fallen from grace. When later on he thought of this moment, he wrote in *Mon coeur mis à nu:* "Sense of solitude from childhood. In spite of the family —and above all when surrounded by children of my own age—I had a sense of being destined to eternal solitude." He already thought of

[1] E. Crépet, *Charles Baudelaire*, Paris, 1906, p. 11.

his isolation as a *destiny*. That meant that he did not accept it passively. On the contrary, he embraced it with fury, shut himself up in it and, since he was condemned to it, hoped that at any rate his condemnation was final. This brings us to the point at which Baudelaire chose the sort of person he would be—that irrevocable choice by which each of us decides in a particular situation what he will be and what he *is*. When he found himself abandoned and rejected, Baudelaire chose solitude deliberately as an act of self-assertion, so that his solitude should not be something inflicted on him by other people. The abrupt revelation of his individual existence made him *feel* that he was *another person;* but at the same time and in a mood of humiliation, rancor and pride, he asserted this otherness of his own accord. From this moment, he set to work with an obstinate, painful fury to *make* himself another person, to make himself into someone different from his mother, with whom he had been identical and who had rejected him; someone different from his coarse, carefree companions. He felt and was determined to feel that he was unique; and he pushed this sense of his uniqueness to the point of extreme solitary enjoyment and of terror.

But his sense of abandonment and isolation was not balanced by anything positive, by the discovery of some special virtue which would at once have placed him beyond comparison with other people. The white blackbird who is spurned by all the black blackbirds, at least has the consolation of looking out of the corner of its eye at the whiteness of its wings. Men are never white blackbirds. What the abandoned child experiences is a feeling of otherness which is purely formal; his experience is not even sufficient to distinguish him from other people. Each of us was able to observe in childhood the fortuitous and shattering advent of self-consciousness. . . .

Baudelaire's fundamental attitude was that of a man bending over himself—bending over his own reflection like Narcissus. With Baudelaire there was no immediate consciousness which was not pierced by his steely gaze. For the rest of us it is enough to see the tree or the house; we forget ourselves, completely absorbed in contemplation of them. Baudelaire was the man who never forgot himself. He watched himself see; he watched in order to see himself watch; it was his own consciousness of the tree and the house that he contemplated. He only saw things through this consciousness; they were paler, smaller and less touching as though seen through an eyeglass. They did not point to one another as a signpost points the way or a marker indicates the page, and Baudelaire's mind never became lost in their intricacies. On the contrary, their immediate function was to direct awareness back to the self. "What does it matter," he wrote, "what the reality outside me is made of provided that it helps me to feel that I am and what I am?" In his own art his one concern was to show things only as they appeared through a layer of human consciousness. . . .

The whole of Baudelaire's efforts were devoted to pushing to its last extreme this abortive duality which we call the reflective consciousness. If he was lucid from the first, it was not in order to make an exact inventory of his faults; it was *in order to be two people*. If he wanted to be two people, it was in order to realize in this couple the final possession of the Self by the Self. This meant that he exasperated his own lucidity. He was simply his own witness; he tried to become his own executioner, tried to become the *Heautontimoroumenos*. For torture brings into existence a closely united couple in which the executioner *appropriates* the victim. Because he did not succeed in his attempt to see *himself*, Baudelaire made up his mind at any rate he would explore himself as the knife explores the wound in the hope of reaching the "lonely depths" which constituted his true nature:

> *Je suis la plaie et le couteau*
> *Et la victime et le bourreau.*

Thus the tortures which he inflicted on himself simulated possession. They tended to make flesh—his own flesh—grow beneath his fingers so that in the very throes of its suffering it would recognize that it was his flesh. To cause suffering was just as much a form of possession and creation as destruction. The link between the victim and the inquisitor was sexual, but Baudelaire tried to transfer into his inner life a relationship which could only have had any meaning if it had existed between two separate persons. He attempted to make the reflective consciousness into the knife and the reflected consciousness into the wound. In a way they are identical. You cannot love, hate or torture yourself on your own. Victim and executioner disappear in a general blur when by a single voluntary act one demands and the other inflicts pain. By a reverse movement, which was nevertheless directed toward the same end, Baudelaire slyly tried to make himself the accomplice of his reflected consciousness against his reflective consciousness. When he stopped torturing himself it was because he was trying to take himself by surprise. He simulated a disconcerting spontaneity, pretended to surrender to the most gratuitous impulses so that he could suddenly appear in his own eyes as an opaque, unpredictable object, appear in fact as though he were *Another Person*. If he had succeeded in this, his task would have been more than half accomplished; he would have been able to derive enjoyment from himself. But here again he was identical with the person whom he wished to surprise. It would be an understatement to say that he divined his own plan before it was conceived; he foresaw and measured his own astonishment or, if one may say so, ran after his astonishment without ever catching up with it. Baudelaire was the man who chose to look upon himself as though he were another person; his life is simply the story of the failure of this attempt. . . .

He saw that he was incomparable, incommunicable, uncreated, absurd, useless, abandoned in the most complete isolation, bearing his burden alone, condemned to justify his existence all alone, and endlessly eluding himself, slipping through his own fingers, withdrawn in contemplation and, at the same time, dragged out of himself in an unending pursuit, a bottomless gulf without walls and without darkness, a mystery in broad daylight, unpredictable yet perfectly known. It was his misfortune that his image still eluded him. He was looking for the reflection of a certain Charles Baudelaire, the son of Mme. Aupick—the General's wife—a poet who had got into debt and the lover of the Negress Duval. His gaze encountered the human condition itself.

Translated by Martin Turnell

from *THE INTIMATE JOURNALS OF
CHARLES BAUDELAIRE*

III

Squibs. I believe I have already set down in my notes that Love
greatly resembles an application of torture or a surgical operation. But
this idea can be developed, and in the most ironic manner. For even
when two lovers love passionately and are full of mutual desire, one of
the two will always be cooler or less self-abandoned than the other.
He or she is the surgeon or executioner; the other, the patient or
victim. Do you hear these sighs—preludes to a shameful tragedy—
these groans, these screams, these rattling gasps? Who has not uttered
them, who has not inexorably wrung them forth? What worse sights
than these could you encounter at an inquisition conducted by adept
torturers? These eyes, rolled back like the sleepwalker's, these limbs
whose muscles burst and stiffen as though subject to the action of a
galvanic battery—such frightful, such curious phenomena are undoubtedly never obtained from even the most extreme cases of intoxication, of delirium, of opium-taking. The human face, which Ovid
believed fashioned to reflect the stars, speaks here only of an insane
ferocity, relaxing into a kind of death. For I should consider it indeed
a sacrilege to apply the word "ecstasy" to this species of decomposition.

A terrible pastime, in which one of the players must forfeit
possession of himself!

It was once asked, in my hearing, what was the greatest pleasure
in Love? Someone, of course, answered: To receive, and someone else:

To give oneself. The former said: The pleasure of pride, and the latter: The voluptuousness of humility. All those swine talked like *The Imitation of Jesus Christ*. Finally, there was a shameless Utopian who affirmed that the greatest pleasure in Love was to beget citizens for the State. For my part, I say: the sole and supreme pleasure in Love lies in the absolute knowledge of doing *evil*. And man and woman know, from birth, that in Evil is to be found all voluptuousness.

IX

Suggestions. Squibs. Nations—like families—produce great men in spite of themselves. They make every effort *not* to produce them. And thus the great man has need, if he is to exist, of a power of attack greater than the power of resistance developed by several millions of individuals.

XII

Are there mathematical lunacies and madmen who believe that two and two make three? In other words, can hallucination invade the realms of pure reason—if the words do not cry out (at being joined together)? If, when a man has fallen into habits of idleness, of daydreaming and of sloth, putting off his most important duties continually till the morrow, another man were to wake him up one morning with heavy blows of a whip and were to whip him unmercifully, until he who was unable to work for pleasure worked now for fear—would not that man, the chastiser, be his benefactor and truest friend? Moreover, one may go so far as to affirm that pleasure itself would follow, and this with much better reason than when it is said: love comes after marriage.

Similarly, in politics, the real saint is he who chastises and massacres the People, for the good of the People.

XVI

Squibs. I have found a definition of the Beautiful, of my own conception of the Beautiful. It is something intense and sad, something a little vague, leaving scope for conjecture. I am ready, if you will, to apply my ideas to a sentient object, to that object, for example, which Society finds the most interesting of all, a woman's face. A beautiful and seductive head, a woman's head, I mean, makes one dream, but in a confused fashion, at once of pleasure and of sadness; conveys an idea of melancholy, of lassitude, even of satiety—a contradictory impression, of an ardor, that is to say, and a desire for life together with a bitterness which flows back upon them as if from a sense of deprivation and hopelessness. Mystery and regret are also characteristics of the Beautiful.

A beautiful male head has no need to convey, to the eyes of man, at any rate—though perhaps to those of a woman—this impression of voluptuousness which, in a woman's face, is a provocation all the more attractive the more the face is generally melancholy. But this head also will suggest ardors and passions—spiritual longings—ambitions darkly repressed—powers turned to bitterness through lack of employment—traces, sometimes, of a revengeful coldness (for the archetype of the dandy must not be forgotten here), sometimes, also—and this is one of the most interesting characteristics of Beauty—of mystery, and last of all (let me admit the exact point to which I am a modern in my aesthetics) of Unhappiness. I do not pretend that Joy cannot associate with Beauty, but I will maintain that Joy is one of her most vulgar adornments, while Melancholy may be called her illustrious spouse—so much so that I can scarcely conceive (is my brain become a witch's miror?) a type of Beauty which has nothing to do with Sorrow. In pursuit of—others might say obsessed by—these ideas, it may be supposed that I have difficulty in not concluding from them that the most perfect type of manly beauty is Satan—as Milton saw him.

XVII

If a poet demanded from the State the right to have a few bourgeois in his stable, people would be very much astonished, but if a bourgeois asked for some roast poet, people would think it quite natural.

That would not scandalize our wives, our daughters or our sisters.

When I have inspired universal horror and disgust, I shall have conquered solitude.

This book is not for our wives, our daughters and our sisters. I have little to do with such things.

XXI

What can be more absurd than Progress, since man, as the event of each day proves, is forever the double and equal of man—is forever, that is to say, in the state of primitive nature! What perils have the forest and the prairie to compare with the daily shocks and conflicts of civilization? Whether man ensnares his dupe upon the boulevard or pierces his victim within the trackless forests, is he not everlasting man, the most perfect of the beasts of prey?

Man—all mankind, that is to say—is so *naturally* depraved that he suffers less from universal degradation than from the establishment of a reasonable hierarchy.

The world is about to end. Its sole reason for continuance is that it exists. And how feeble is this reason, compared with those which announce the contrary, particularly the following: What, under Heaven, has this world henceforth to do? Even supposing that it continued materially to exist, would this existence be worthy of the name or the Historical Dictionary? I do not say that the world will be reduced to the clownish shifts and disorders of a South American republic, or even that we shall perhaps return to a state of nature and roam the grassy ruins of our civilization, gun in hand, seeking our food. No; for these adventures would require a certain remnant of vital energy, echo of earlier ages. As a new example, as fresh victims of the inexorable moral laws, we shall perish by that which we have believed to be our means of existence. So far will machinery have Americanized us, so far will Progress have atrophied in us all that is spiritual, that no dream of the Utopians, however bloody, sacrilegious or unnatural, will be comparable to the result. I appeal to every thinking man to show me what remains of Life. As for religion, I believe it useless to speak of it or to search for its relics, since to give oneself the trouble of denying God is the sole disgrace in these matters. Ownership virtually disappeared with the suppression of the rights of the eldest son; but the time will come when humanity, like an avenging ogre, will tear their last morsel from those who believe themselves to be the legitimate heirs of revolution. And even that will not be the worst.

XXVII

Woman is the opposite of the Dandy. Therefore she should inspire horror.

Woman is hungry, and she wants to eat; thirsty, and she wants to drink.

She is in rut and she wants to be possessed.

What admirable qualities!

Woman is *natural*, that is to say abominable.

Thus she is always vulgar; the opposite, in fact, of the Dandy.

XXXIII

Politics. I have no convictions, as men of my century understand the word, because I have no ambition. There is no basis in me for a conviction.

There is a certain cowardice, a certain weakness, rather, among respectable folk.

Only brigands are convinced—of what? That they must succeed. And so they do succeed.

How should I succeed, since I have not even the desire to make the attempt?

Glorious empires may be founded upon crime and noble religions upon imposture.

Nevertheless, I have some convictions, in a higher sense, which could not be understood by the people of my time.

XXXVII

Belief in Progress is a doctrine of idlers and Belgians. It is the individual relying upon his neighbours to do his work.

There cannot be any Progress (true progress, that is to say, moral) except within the individual and by the individual himself.

But the world is composed of people who can think only in common, in the herd. Like the *Sociétés belges.*

There are also people who can only take their pleasures in a flock. The true hero takes his pleasure alone.

LXXIV

To be a great man and a saint by *one's own standards,* that is all that matters.

XCIII

The more a man cultivates the arts the less he fornicates. A more and more apparent cleavage occurs between the spirit and the brute.

Only the brute is really potent. Sexuality is the lyricism of the masses.

To fornicate is to aspire to enter into another; the artist never emerges from himself.

I have forgotten the name of that slut. Bah! I shall remember it at the last judgment.

XCV

Even when quite a child I felt two conflicting sensations in my heart: the horror of life and the esctasy of life. That, indeed, was the mark of a neurasthenic idler.

XCVIII

When Jesus Christ says, "Blessed are they that hunger, for they shall be filled," Jesus Christ is calculating on probabilities.

XCIX

The world only goes round by misunderstanding.

It is by universal misunderstanding that all agree.

For if, by ill luck, people understood each other, they would never agree.

The man of intelligence, who will never agree with anyone, should cultivate a pleasure in the conversation of imbeciles and the study of worthless books. From these he will derive a sardonic amusement which will largely repay him for his pains.

CVI

All these imbecile bourgeois who ceaselessly utter the words: immoral, immorality, morality in art, and other idiotic phrases, make me think of Louise Villedieu, the five-franc whore, who, having accompanied me one day to the Louvre, where she had never been before, began blushing and covering her face with her hands. And as we stood before the immortal statues and pictures she kept plucking me by the sleeve and asking how they could exhibit such indecencies in public.

The fig-leaves of Mr. Nieuwerkerke.

CIX

Hygiene. Projects. The more one desires, the stronger one's will.

The more one works, the better one works and the more one wants to work.

The more one produces, the more fecund one becomes.

After a debauch, one feels oneself always to be more solitary, more abandoned.

In the moral as in the physical world, I have been conscious always of an abyss, not only of the abyss of sleep, but of the abyss of action, of daydreaming, of recollection, of desire, of regret, of remorse, of the beautiful, of number . . . etc.

I have cultivated my hysteria with delight and terror. Now I suffer continually from vertigo, and today, 23rd of January, 1862, I have received a singular warning, I have felt the wind of the wing of madness pass over me.

Translated by Christopher Isherwood

DOSTOEVSKI

from *NOTES FROM THE UNDERGROUND*

I want now to tell you, gentlemen, whether you care to hear it or not, why I could not even become an insect. I tell you solemnly, that I have many times tried to become an insect. But I was not equal even to that. I swear, gentlemen, that to be too conscious is an illness—a real thorough-going illness. For man's everyday needs, it would have been quite enough to have the ordinary human consciousness, that is, half or a quarter of the amount which falls to the lot of a cultivated man of our unhappy nineteenth century, especially one who has the fatal ill-luck to inhabit Petersburg, the most theoretical and intentional town on the whole terrestrial globe. (There are intentional and unintentional towns.) It would have been quite enough, for instance, to have the consciousness by which all so-called direct persons and men of action live. I bet you think I am writing all this from affectation, to be witty at the expense of men of action; and what is more, that from ill-bred affectation, I am clanking a sword like my officer. But, gentlemen, whoever can pride himself on his diseases and even swagger over them?

Though, after all, every one does do that; people do pride themselves on their diseases, and I do, may be, more than any one. We will not dispute it; my contention was absurd. But yet I am firmly persuaded that a great deal of consciousness, every sort of consciousness, in fact, is a disease. I stick to that. Let us leave that, too, for a minute. Tell me this: why does it happen that at the very, yes, at the very moments when I am most capable of feeling every refinement of all that is "good and beautiful," as they used to say at one time, it would, as though of design, happen to me not only to feel but to do such ugly things, such that . . . Well, in short, actions that all, perhaps, commit; but which, as though purposely, occurred to me at the very time when I was most conscious that they ought not to be committed. The more conscious I was of goodness and of all that was "good and beautiful," the more deeply I sank into my mire and the more ready I was to sink in it altogether. But the chief point was that all this was, as it were, not accidental in me, but as though it were bound to be so. It was as though it were my most normal condition, and not in the least disease or depravity, so that at last all desire in me to struggle against this depravity passed. It ended by my almost believing (perhaps actually believing) that this was perhaps my normal condition. But at first, in the beginning, what agonies I endured in that struggle! I did not believe it was the same with other people, and all my life I hid this fact about myself as a secret. I was ashamed (even now, perhaps, I am ashamed): I got to the point of feeling a sort of secret abnormal, despicable enjoyment in returning home to my corner on some disgusting Petersburg night, acutely conscious that that day I had committed a loathsome action again, that what was done could never be undone, and secretly, inwardly gnawing, gnawing at myself for it, tearing and consuming myself till at last the bitterness turned into a sort of shameful accursed sweetness, and at last—into positive real enjoyment! Yes, into enjoyment, into enjoyment! I insist upon that. I have spoken of this because I kept wanting to know for a fact whether other people feel such enjoyment. I will explain: the enjoyment was just from the too intense consciousness of one's own degradation; it was from feeling oneself that one had reached the last barrier, that it was horrible, but that it could not be otherwise; that there was no escape for you; that you never could become a different man; that even if time and faith were still left you to change into something different you would most likely not wish to change; or if you did wish to, even then you would do nothing; because perhaps in reality there was nothing for you to change into.

And the worst of it was, and the root of it all, that it was all in accord with the normal fundamental laws of over-acute consciousness, and with the inertia that was the direct result of those laws, and that consequently one was not only unable to change but could do absolutely nothing. Thus it would follow, as the result of acute consciousness, that one is not to blame in being a scoundrel; as though that were any consolation to the scoundrel once he has come to realize that he actually is a scoundrel. But enough. . . . Ech, I have talked a lot of nonsense, but what have I explained? How is enjoyment in this to be explained? But I will explain it. I will get to the bottom of it! That is why I have taken up my pen. . . .

I, for instance, have a great deal of *amour propre*. I am as suspicious and prone to take offence as a humpback or a dwarf. But upon my word I sometimes have had moments when if I had happened to be slapped in the face I should, perhaps, have been positively glad of it. I say, in earnest, that I should probably have been able to discover even in that a peculiar sort of enjoyment—the enjoyment, of course, of despair; but in despair there are the most intense enjoyments, especially when one is very acutely conscious of the hopelessness of one's position. And when one is slapped in the face—why then the consciousness of being rubbed into a pulp would positively overwhelm one. The worst of it is, look at it which way one will, it still turns out that I was always the most to blame in everything. And what is most humiliating of all, to blame for no fault of my own but, so to say, through the laws of nature. In the first place, to blame because I am cleverer than any of the people surrounding me. (I have always considered myself cleverer than any of the people surrounding me, and sometimes, would you believe it, have been positively ashamed of it. At any rate, I have all my life, as it were, turned my eyes away and never could look people straight in the face.) To blame, finally, because even if I had had magnanimity, I should only have had more suffering from the sense of its uselessness. I should certainly have never been able to do anything from being magnanimous—neither to forgive, for my assailant would perhaps have slapped me from the laws of nature, and one cannot forgive the laws of nature; nor to forget, for even if it were owing to the laws of nature, it is insulting all the same. Finally, even if I had wanted to be anything but magnanimous, had desired on the contrary to revenge myself on my assailant, I could not have revenged myself on any one for anything because I should certainly never have made up my mind to do anything, even if I had been able to. Why should I not have made up my mind? About that in particular I want to say a few words.

With people who know how to revenge themselves and to stand up for themselves in general, how is it done? Why, when they are possessed, let us suppose, by the feeling of revenge, then for the time there is nothing else but that feeling left in their whole being. Such a gentleman simply dashes straight for his object like an infuriated bull with its horns down, and nothing but a wall will stop him. (By the way: facing the wall, such gentlemen—that is, the "direct" persons and men of action—are genuinely nonplussed. For them a wall is not an evasion, as for us people who think and consequently do nothing; it is not an excuse for turning aside, an excuse for which we are always very glad, though we scarcely believe in it ourselves, as a rule. No, they are nonplussed in all sincerity. The wall has for them something tranquillizing, morally soothing, final—maybe even something mysterious . . . but of the wall later.)

Well, such a direct person I regard as the real normal man, as his tender mother Nature wished to see him when she graciously brought him into being on the earth. I envy such a man till I am green in the face. He is stupid. I am not disputing that, but perhaps the normal man should be stupid, how do you know? Perhaps it is very beautiful, in fact. And I am the more persuaded of that suspicion, if one can call it so, by the fact that if you take, for instance, the antithesis of the normal man, that is, the man of acute consciousness, who has come, of course, not out of the lap of Nature but out of a retort (this is almost mysticism, gentlemen, but I suspect this, too), this retort-made man is sometimes so nonplussed in the presence of his antithesis that with all his exaggerated consciousness he genuinely thinks of himself as a mouse and not a man. It may be an acutely conscious mouse, yet it is a mouse, while the other is a man, and therefore, et caetera, et caetera. And the worst of it is, he himself, his very own self, looks on himself as a mouse; no one asks him to do so; and that is an important point. Now let us look at this mouse in action. Let us suppose, for instance, that it feels insulted, too (and it almost always does feel insulted), and wants to revenge itself, too. There may even be a greater accumulation of spite in it than in *l'homme de la nature et de la vérité*. The base and nasty desire to vent that spite on its assailant rankles perhaps even more nastily in it than in *l'homme de la nature et de la vérité*. For through his innate stupidity the latter looks upon his revenge as justice pure and simple; while in consequence of his acute consciousness the mouse does not believe in the justice of it. To come at last to the deed itself, to the very act of revenge. Apart from the one fundamental nastiness the luckless mouse succeeds in creating around it so many other nastinesses in the form of doubts and questions, adds to the one question so many unsettled questions, that there inevitably works up around it a sort of fatal brew, a stinking mess, made up of its doubts, emotions, and of the contempt spat upon it by the direct men of action who stand solemnly about it as judges and arbitrators, laughing at it till their healthy sides ache. Of course the only thing left for it is to dismiss all that with a wave of its paw, and, with a smile of assumed contempt in which it does not even itself believe, creep ignominiously into its mouse-hole. There in its nasty, stinking, underground home our insulted, crushed and ridiculed mouse promptly becomes absorbed in cold, malignant and, above all, everlasting spite. For forty years together it will remember its injury down to the smallest, most ignominious details, and every time will add, of itself, details still more ignominious, spitefully teasing and tormenting itself with its own imagination. It will itself be ashamed of its imaginings, but yet it will recall it all, it will go over and over every detail, it will invent unheard-of things against itself, pretending that those things might happen, and will forgive nothing. Maybe it will begin to revenge itself, too, but, as it were, piecemeal, in trivial ways, from behind the stove, incognito, without believing either in its own right to vengeance, or in the success of its revenge, knowing that from all its efforts at revenge it will suffer a hundred times more than he on whom it revenges itself, while he, I daresay, will not even scratch himself. On its death-bed it will recall it all over again, with interest accumulated over all the years and . . .

But it is just in that cold, abominable half despair, half belief, in that conscious burying oneself alive for grief in the underground for forty years, in that acutely recognized and yet partly doubtful hopelessness of one's position, in that hell of unsatisfied desires turned inward, in that fever of oscillations, of resolutions determined for ever and repented of again a minute later—that the savour of that strange enjoyment of which I have spoken lies. It is so subtle, so difficult of analysis, that persons who are a little limited, or even simply persons of strong nerves, will not understand a single atom of it. "Possibly," you will add on your own account with a grin, "people will not understand it either who have never received a slap in the face," and in that way you will politely hint to me that I too, perhaps, have had the experience of a slap in the face in my life, and so I speak as one who knows. I bet that you are thinking that. But set your minds at rest, gentlemen, I have not received a slap in the face, though it is absolutely a matter of indifference to me what you may think about it. Possibly, I even regret myself that I have given so few slaps in the face during my life. But enough . . . not another word on that subject of such extreme interest to you.

I will continue calmly concerning persons with strong nerves who do not understand a certain refinement of enjoyment. Though in certain circumstances these gentlemen bellow their loudest like bulls, though this, let us suppose, does them the greatest credit, yet, as I have said already, confronted with the impossible they subside at once. The impossible means the stone wall! What stone wall? Why, of course, the laws of nature, the deductions of natural science, mathematics. As soon as they prove to you, for instance, that you are descended from a monkey, then it is no use scowling, accept it for a fact. When they prove to you that in reality one drop of your own fat must be dearer to you than a hundred thousand of your fellow creatures, and that this conclusion is the final solution of all so-called virtues and duties and all such prejudices and fancies, then you have just to accept it, there is no help for it, for twice two is a law of mathematics. Just try refuting it.

"Upon my word," they will shout at you, "it is no use protesting: it is a case of twice two makes four! Nature does not ask your permission, she has nothing to do with your wishes, and whether you like her laws or dislike them, you are bound to accept her as she is, and consequently all her conclusions. A wall, you see, is a wall . . . and so on, and so on."

Merciful heavens! but what do I care for the laws of nature and arithmetic, when, for some reason, I dislike those laws and the fact that twice two makes four? Of course I cannot break through the wall by battering my head against it if I really have not the strength to knock it down, but I am not going to be reconciled to it simply because it is a stone wall and I have not the strength.

As though such a stone wall really were a consolation, and really did contain some word of conciliation, simply because it is as true as twice two makes four. Oh, absurdity of absurdities! How much better it is to understand it all, to recognize it all, all the impossibilities and the stone wall; not to be reconciled to one of those impossibilities and stone walls if it disgusts you to be reconciled to it; by the way of the most inevitable, logical combinations, to reach the most revolting conclusions on the everlasting theme, that even for the stone wall you are yourself somehow to blame, though again it is as clear as day you are not to blame in the least, and therefore grinding your teeth in silent impotence to sink into luxurious inertia, brooding on the fact that there is no one even for you to feel vindictive against, that you have not, and perhaps never will have, an object for your spite, that it is a sleight-of-hand, a bit of juggling, a card-sharper's trick, that it is simply a mess, no knowing what and no knowing who, but in spite of all these uncertainties and jugglings, still there is an ache in you, and the more you do not know, the worse the ache.

"Ha, ha, ha! You will be finding enjoyment in toothache next," you cry, with a laugh.

"Well? Even in toothache there is enjoyment," I answer. I had toothache for a whole month and I know there is. In that case, of course, people are not spiteful in silence, but moan; but they are not candid moans, they are malignant moans, and the malignancy is the whole point. The enjoyment of the sufferer finds expression in those moans; if he did not feel enjoyment in them he would not moan. It is a good example, gentlemen, and I will develop it. Those moans express in the first place all the aimlessness of your pain, which is so humiliating to your consciousness; the whole legal system of Nature on which you spit disdainfully, of course, but from which you suffer all the same while she does not. They express the consciousness that you have no enemy to punish, but that you have pain; the consciousness that in spite of all possible Vagenheims you are in complete slavery to your teeth; that if some one wishes it, your teeth will leave off aching, and if he does not, they will go on aching another three months; and that finally if you are still contumacious and still protest, all that is left you for your own gratification is to thrash yourself or beat your wall with your fist as hard as you can, and absolutely nothing more. Well, these mortal insults, these jeers on the part of some one unknown, end at last in an enjoyment which sometimes reaches the highest degree of voluptuousness. I ask you, gentlemen, listen sometimes to the moans of an educated man of the nineteenth century suffering from toothache, on the second or third day of the attack, when he is beginning to moan, not as he moaned on the first day, that is, not simply because he has toothache, not just as any coarse peasant, but as a man affected by progress and European civilization, a man who is "divorced from the soil and the national elements," as they express it nowadays. His moans become nasty, disgustingly malignant, and go on for whole days and nights. And of course he knows himself that he is doing himself no sort of good with his moans; he knows better than any one that he is only lacerating and harassing himself and others for nothing; he knows that even the audience before whom he is making his efforts, and his whole family, listen to him with loathing, do not put a ha'porth of faith in him, and inwardly understand that he might moan differently, more simply, without trills and flourishes, and that he is only amusing himself like that from ill-humour, from malignancy. Well, in all these recognitions and disgraces it is that there lies a voluptuous pleasure. As though he would say: "I am worrying you, I am lacerating your hearts, I am keeping every one in the house awake. Well, stay awake then, you, too, feel every minute that I have toothache. I am not a hero to you now, as I tried to seem before, but simply a nasty person, an impostor. Well, so be it, then! I am very glad that you see through me. It is nasty for you to hear my despicable moans: well, let it be nasty; here I will let you have a nastier flourish in a minute. . . ." You do not understand even now, gentlemen? No, it seems our development and our consciousness must go further to understand all the intricacies of this pleasure. You laugh? Delighted. My jests, gentlemen, are of course in bad taste, jerky, involved, lacking self-confidence. But of course that is because I do not respect myself. Can a man of perception respect himself at all?

Come, can a man who attempts to find enjoyment in the very feeling of his own degradation possibly have a spark of respect for himself? I am not saying this now from any mawkish kind of remorse. And, indeed, I could never endure saying, "Forgive me, Papa, I won't do it again," not because I am incapable of saying that—on the contrary, perhaps just because I have been too capable of it, and in what a way, too! As though of design I used to get into trouble in cases when I was not to blame in any way. That was the nastiest part of it. At the same time I was genuinely touched and penitent, I used to shed tears and, of course, deceived myself, though I was not acting in the least and there was a sick feeling in my heart at the time. . . . For that one could not blame even the laws of nature, though the laws of nature have continually all my life offended me more than anything. It is loathsome to remember it all, but it was loathsome even then. If course, a minute or so later I would realize wrathfully that it was all a lie, a revolting lie, an affected lie, that is, all this penitence, this emotion, these vows of reform. You will ask why did I worry myself with such antics: answer, because it was very dull to sit with one's hands folded, and so one began cutting capers. That is really it. Observe yourselves more carefully, gentlemen, then you will understand that it is so. I invented adventures for myself and made up a life, so as at least to live in some way. How many times it has happened to me—well, for instance, to take offense simply on purpose, for nothing; and one knows oneself, of course, that one is offended at nothing, that one is putting it on, but yet one brings oneself, at last, to the point of being really offended. All my life I have had an impulse to play such pranks, so that in the end I could not control it in myself. Another time, twice, in fact, I tried hard to be in love. I suffered, too, gentlemen, I assure you. In the depth of my heart there was no faith in my suffering, only a faint stir of mockery, but yet I did suffer, and in the real, orthodox way; I was jealous, beside myself . . . and it was all from *ennui*, gentlemen, all from *ennui*; inertia overcame me. You know the direct, legitimate fruit of consciousness is inertia, that is, conscious sitting-with-the-hands-folded. I have referred to this already. I repeat, I repeat with emphasis: all "direct" persons and men of action are active just because they are stupid and limited. How explain that? I will tell you: in consequence of their limitation they take immediate and secondary causes for primary ones, and in that way persuade themselves more quickly and easily than other people do that they have found an infallible foundation for their activity, and their minds are at ease and you know that is the chief thing. To begin to act, you know, you must first have your mind completely at ease and no trace of doubt left in it. Why, how am I, for example, to set my mind at rest? Where are the primary causes on which I am to build? Where are my foundations? Where am I to get them from? I exercise myself in reflection, and consequently with me every primary cause at once draws after itself another still more primary, and so on to infinity. That is just the essence of every sort of consciousness and reflection. It must be a case of the laws of nature again. What is the result of it in the end? Why, just the same. Remember I spoke just now of vengeance. (I am sure you did not take it in.) I said that a man revenges himself because he sees justice in it. Therefore he has found a primary cause, that is, justice. And so he is at rest on all sides, and consequently he carries out his revenge calmly and successfully, being persuaded that he is doing a just and honest thing. But I see no justice in it, I find no sort of virtue in it either, and consequently if I attempt to revenge myself, it is only out of spite. Spite, of course, might overcome everything, all my doubts, and so might serve quite successfully in place of a primary cause, precisely because it is not a cause. But what is to be done if I have not even spite (I began with that just now, you know)? In consequence again of those accursed laws of consciousness, anger in me is subject to chemical disintegration. You look into it, the object flies off into air, your reasons evaporate, the criminal is not to be found, the wrong becomes not a wrong but a phantom, something like the toothache, for which no one is to blame, and consequently there is only the same outlet left again—that is, to beat the wall as hard as you can. So you give it up with a wave of the hand because you have not found a fundamental cause. And try letting yourself be carried away by your feelings, blindly, without reflection, without a primary cause, repelling consciousness at least for a time; hate or love, if only not to sit with your hands folded. The day after to-morrow, at the latest, you will begin despising yourself for having knowingly deceived yourself. Result: a soap-bubble and inertia. Oh, gentlemen, do you know, perhaps I consider myself an intelligent man only because all my life I have been able neither to begin nor to finish anything. Granted I am a babbler, a harmless vexatious babbler, like all of us. But what is to be done if the direct and sole vocation of every intelligent man is babble, that is, the intentional pouring of water through a sieve?

But these are all golden dreams. Oh, tell me, who was it first announced, who was it first proclaimed, that man only does nasty things because he does not know his own interests; and that if he were enlightened, if his eyes were opened to his real normal interests, man would at once cease to do nasty things, would at once become good and noble because, being enlightened and understanding his real advantage, he would see his own advantage in the good and nothing else, and we all know that not one man can, consciously, act against his own interests, consequently, so to say, through necessity, he would begin doing good? Oh, the babe! Oh, the pure, innocent child! Why, in the first place, when in all these thousands of years has there been a time when man has acted only from his own interest? What is to be done with the millions of facts that bear witness that men, *consciously*, that is, fully understanding that real interests, have left them in the background and have rushed headlong on another path, to meet peril and danger, compelled to this course by nobody and by nothing, but, as it were, simply disliking the beaten track, and have obstinately, wilfully, struck out another difficult, absurd way, seeking it almost in the darkness. So, I suppose, this obstinancy and perversity were pleasanter to them than any advantage. . . . Advantage! What is advantage?

And will you take it upon yourself to define with perfect accuracy in what the advantage of man consists? And what if it so happens that a man's advantage, *sometimes*, not only may, but even must, consist in his desiring in certain cases what is harmful to himself and not advantageous. And if so, there can be such a case, the whole principle falls into dust. What do you think—are there such cases? You laugh; laugh away, gentlemen, but only answer me: have man's advantages been reckoned up with perfect certainty? Are there not some which not only have not been included but cannot possibly be included under any classification? You see, you gentlemen have, to the best of my knowledge, taken your whole register of human advantages from the averages of statistical figures and politico-economical formulas. Your advantages are prosperity, wealth, freedom, peace—and so on, and so on. So that the man who should, for instance, go openly and knowingly in opposition to all that list would, to your thinking, and indeed mine too, of course, be an obscurantist or an absolute madman: would not he? But, you know, this is what is surprising: why does it so happen that all these statisticians, sages and lovers of humanity, when they reckon up human advantages invariably leave out one? They don't even take it into their reckoning in the form in which it should be taken and the whole reckoning depends upon that. It would be no great matter, they would simply have to take it, this advantage, and add it to the list. But the trouble is, that this strange advantage does not fall under any classification and is not in place in any list. I have a friend for instance . . . Ech! gentlemen, but of course he is your friend, too; and indeed there is no one, no one, to whom he is not a friend!

When he prepares for any undertaking this gentleman immediately explains to you, elegantly and clearly, exactly how he must act in accordance with the laws of reason and truth. What is more, he will talk to you with excitement and passion of the true normal interests of man; with irony he will upbraid the short-sighted fools who do not understand their own interests, nor the true significance of virtue; and, within a quarter of an hour, without any sudden outside provocation, but simply through something inside him which is stronger than all his interests, he will go off on quite a different tack —that is, act in direct opposition to what he has just been saying about himself, in opposition to the laws of reason, in opposition to his own advantage—in fact, in opposition to everything. . . . I warn you that my friend is a compound personality, and therefore it is difficult to blame him as an individual. The fact is, gentlemen, it seems there must really exist something that is dearer to almost every man than his greatest advantages, or (not to be illogical) there is a most advantageous advantage (the very one omitted of which we spoke just now) which is more important and more advantageous than all other advantages, for the sake of which a man if necessary is ready to act in opposition to all laws; that is, in opposition to reason, honour, peace, prosperity—in fact, in opposition to all those excellent and useful things if only he can attain that fundamental, most advantageous advantage which is dearer to him than all. "Yes, but it's advantage all the same" you will retort. But excuse me, I'll make the point clear, and it is not a case of playing upon words. What matters is, that this advantage is remarkable from the very fact that it breaks down all our classifications, and continually shatters every system constructed by lovers of mankind for the benefit of mankind. In fact, it upsets everything. But before I mention this advantage to you, I want to compromise myself personally, and therefore I boldly declare that all these fine systems—all these theories for explaining to mankind their real normal interests, in order that inevitably striving to pursue these interests they may at once become good and noble —are, in my opinion, so far, mere logical exercises! Yes, logical exercises. Why, to maintain this theory of the regeneration of mankind by means of the pursuit of his own advantage is to my mind almost the same thing as . . . as to affirm, for instance, following Buckle, that through civilization mankind becomes softer, and consequently less bloodthirsty, and less fitted for warfare.

Logically it does seem to follow from his arguments. But man has such a predilection for systems and abstract deductions that he is ready to distort the truth intentionally, he is ready to deny the evidence of his senses only to justify his logic. I take this example because it is the most glaring instance of it. Only look about you: blood is being spilt in streams, and in the merriest way, as though it were champagne. Take the whole of the nineteenth century in which Buckle lived. Take Napoleon—the Great and also the present one. Take North America—the eternal union. Take the farce of Schleswig-Holstein. . . . And what is it that civilization softens in us? The only gain of civilization for mankind is the greater capacity for variety of sensations—and absolutely nothing more. And through the development of this many-sidedness man may come to finding enjoyment in bloodshed. In fact, this has already happened to him. Have you noticed that it is the most civilized gentlemen who have been the subtlest slaughterers, to whom the Attilas and Stenka Razins could not hold a candle, and if they are not so conspicuous as the Attilas and Stenka Razins it is simply because they are so often met with, are so ordinary and have become so familiar to us. In any case civilization has made mankind if not more bloodthirsty, at least more vilely, more loathsomely blood-thirsty. In old days he saw justice in bloodshed and with his conscience at peace exterminated those he thought proper. Now we do think bloodshed abominable and yet we engage in this abomination, and with more energy than ever. Which is worse? Decide that for yourselves.

They say that Cleopatra (excuse an instance from Roman history) was fond of sticking gold pins into her slave-girls' breasts and derived gratification from their screams and writhings. You will say that that was in the comparatively barbarous times; that these are barbarous times too, because also, comparatively speaking, pins are stuck in even now; that though man has now learned to see more clearly than in barbarous ages, he is still far from having learnt to act as reason and science would dictate. But yet you are fully convinced that he will be sure to learn when he gets rid of certain old bad habits, and when common sense and science have completely re-educated human nature and turned it in a normal direction. You are confident that then man will cease from *intentional* error and will, so to say, be compelled not to want to set his will against his normal interests. That is not all; then, you say, science itself will teach man (though to my mind it's a superfluous luxury) that he never has really had any caprice or will of his own, and that he himself is something of the nature of a piano-key or the stop of an organ, and that there are, besides, things called the laws of nature; so that everything he does is not done by his willing it, but is done of itself, by the laws of nature. Consequently we have only to discover these laws of nature, and man will no longer have to answer for his actions and life will become exceedingly easy for him. All human actions will then, of course, be tabulated according to these laws, mathematically, like tables of logarithms up to 108,000, and entered in an index; or, better still, there would be published certain edifying works of the nature of encyclopaedic lexicons, in which everything will be so clearly calculated and explained that there will be no more incidents or adventures in the world.

Then—this is all what you say—new economic relations will be established, all ready-made and worked out with mathematical exactitude, so that every possible question will vanish in the twinkling of an eye, simply because every possible answer to it will be provided. Then the "Palace of Crystal" will be built. Then . . . In fact, those will be halcyon days. Of course there is no guaranteeing (this is my comment) that it will not be, for instance, frightfully dull then (for what will one have to do when everything will be calculated and tabulated?), but on the other hand everything will be extraordinarily rational. Of course boredom may lead you to anything. It is boredom sets one sticking golden pins into people, but all that would not matter. What is bad (this is my comment again) is that I dare say people will be thankful for the gold pins then. Man is stupid, you know, phenomenally stupid; or rather he is not at all stupid, but he is so ungrateful that you could not find another like him in all creation. I, for instance, would not be in the least surprised if all of a sudden, apropos of nothing, in the midst of general prosperity a gentleman with an ignoble, or rather with a reactionary and ironical, countenance were to arise and putting his arms akimbo, say to us all: "I say, gentlemen, hadn't we better kick over the whole show and scatter rationalism to the winds, simply to send these logarithms to the devil, and to enable us to live once more at our own sweet foolish will!" That again would not matter; but what is annoying is that he would be sure to find followers—such is the nature of man. And all that for the most foolish reason, which, one would think, was hardly worth mentioning: that is, that man everywhere and at all times, whoever he may be, has preferred to act as he chose and not in the least as his reason and advantage dictated. And one may choose what is contrary to one's own interests, and sometime one *positively ought* (that is my idea). One's own free unfettered choice, one's own caprice —however wild it may be, one's own fancy worked up at times to frenzy—is that very "most advantageous advantage" which we have overlooked, which comes under no classification and against which all systems and theories are continually being shattered to atoms. And how do these wiseacres know that man wants a normal, a virtuous choice? What has made them conceive that man must want a rationally advantageous choice? What man wants is simply *independent* choice, whatever that independence may cost and wherever it may lead. And choice, of course, the devil only knows what choice. . . .

HERMANN HESSE

Unlike Pascal's postulated man—neither angel nor beast, but static between the two—Steppenwolf, eternally ambivalent, lives in a state of constant tension. The man lies in ambush for the wolf, and the wolf stalks the man, and repose, if ever found, is fleeting and derisory. Agony and ecstasy are the twin poles of his existence: he prowls in darkness and dreads the dawn, covets solitude and refuses to be alone.

"There are in every man at every moment two simultaneous postulations," writes Baudelaire, who is Steppenwolf, "one toward God, the other toward Satan. The invocation to God, or spirituality is a desire to ascend; that of Satan or animality is a joy in descending."

Neither saint nor devil, Steppenwolf disdains the crowd, the common man, the world from which he comes, but such is his ambivalence he never divorces himself completely from it: renouncing the standards of that world, he nonetheless accepts its trappings. The Steppenwolfs aspire, or believe they aspire, to anonymity, at least on the surface. Sade, the "monster author," can write: "What living man would not instantly revise his tastes, his affections, his penchants and bring them into harmony with the general scheme, what man, rather than continue a freak, would not prefer to be like everyone else, were it in his power to do so." And although Sade's subsequent conduct may seem a total refutation of this declaration, the will, the temptation, to conform is undeniable. Baudelaire too speaks seriously of his desire for a home and family, and yet frequents the most miserable prostitutes; was a recluse and trembled to be alone. Jean-Paul Sartre, doubtless this age's most constant and vehement revolutionary, eternally at war with the bourgeois *status quo*, has never

71

denied his bourgeois origins or moved to divest himself of his middle-class accouterments. Perhaps this is why he is so drawn to Genet, why he calls his book *Saint Genet*, for Genet has shorn himself of these attachments, flouted the laws, declared war, renounced the Steppenwolf ambivalence, plunged deep, soared high, profligate and angel, undiluted. But Genet, after all, is not Steppenwolf, the ambivalent, for Steppenwolf is Everyman.

from *STEPPENWOLF*

TREATISE ON THE STEPPENWOLF

There was once a man, Harry, called the Steppenwolf. He went on two legs, wore clothes and was a human being, but nevertheless he was in reality a wolf of the Steppes. He had learnt a good deal of all that people of a good intelligence can, and was a fairly clever fellow. What he had not learnt, however, was this: to find contentment in himself and his own life. The cause of this apparently was that at the bottom of his heart he knew all the time (or thought he knew) that he was in reality not a man, but a wolf of the Steppes. Clever men might argue the point whether he truly was a wolf, whether, that is, he had been changed, before birth perhaps, from a wolf into a human being, or had been given the soul of a wolf, though born as a human being; or whether, on the other hand, this belief that he was a wolf was no more than a fancy or a disease of his. It might, for example, be possible that in his childhood he was a little wild and disobedient and disorderly, and that those who brought him up had declared a war of extinction against the beast

in him; and precisely this had given him the idea and the belief that
he was in fact actually a beast with only a thin covering of the human. On this point one could speak at length and entertainingly, and
indeed write a book about it. The Steppenwolf, however, would be
none the better for it, since for him it was all one whether the wolf
had been bewitched or beaten into him, or whether it was merely
an idea of his own. What others chose to think about it or what he
chose to think himself was no good to him at all. It left the wolf
inside him just the same.

And so the Steppenwolf had two natures, a human and a wolfish
one. This was his fate, and it may well be that it was not a very
exceptional one. There must have been many men who have had a
good deal of the dog or the fox, of the fish or the serpent in them
without experiencing any extraordinary difficulties on that account.
In such cases, the man and the fish lived on together and neither
did the other any harm. The one even helped the other. Many a man
indeed has carried this condition to such enviable lengths that he has
owed his happiness more to the fox or the ape in him than to the
man. So much for common knowledge. In the case of Harry, however, it was just the opposite. In him the man and the wolf did not
go the same way together, but were in continual and deadly enmity.
The one existed simply and solely to harm the other, and when there
are two in one blood and in one soul who are at deadly enmity, then
life fares ill. Well, to each his lot, and none is light.

Now with our Steppenwolf it was so that in his conscious life
he lived now as a wolf, now as a man, as indeed the case is with all
mixed beings. But, when he was a wolf, the man in him lay in ambush, ever on the watch to interfere and condemn, while at those
times that he was man the wolf did just the same. For example, if
Harry, as man, had a beautiful thought, felt a fine and noble emotion, or performed a so-called good act, then the wolf bared his
teeth at him and laughed and showed him with bitter scorn how
laughable this whole pantomime was in the eyes of a beast, of a wolf
who knew well enough in his heart what suited him, namely, to trot
alone over the Steppes and now and then to gorge himself with blood
or to pursue a female wolf. Then, wolfishly seen, all human activities
became horribly absurd and misplaced, stupid and vain. But it was
exactly the same when Harry felt and behaved as a wolf and showed
others his teeth and felt hatred and enmity against all human beings
and their lying and degenerate manners and customs. For then the
human part of him lay in ambush and watched the wolf, called him

brute and beast, and spoiled and embittered for him all pleasure in his simple and healthy and wild wolf's being.

Thus it was then with the Steppenwolf, and one may well imagine that Harry did not have an exactly pleasant and happy life of it. This does not mean, however, that he was unhappy in any extraordinary degree (although it may have seemed so to himself all the same, inasmuch as every man takes the sufferings that fall to his share as the greatest). That cannot be said of any man. Even he who has no wolf in him, may be none the happier for that. And even the unhappiest life has its sunny moments and its little flowers of happiness between sand and stone. So it was, then, with the Steppenwolf too. It cannot be denied that he was generally very unhappy; and he could make others unhappy also, that is, when he loved them or they him. For all who got to love him, saw always only the one side of him. Many loved him as a refined and clever and interesting man, and were horrified and disappointed when they had come upon the wolf in him. And they had to because Harry wished, as every sentient being does, to be loved as a whole and therefore it was just with those whose love he most valued that he could least of all conceal and belie the wolf. There were those, however, who loved precisely the wolf in him, the free, the savage, the untamable, the dangerous and strong, and these found it peculiarly disappointing and deplorable when suddenly the wild and wicked wolf was also a man, and had hankerings after goodness and refinement, and wanted to hear Mozart, to read poetry and to cherish human ideals. Usually these were the most disappointed and angry of all; and so it was that the Steppenwolf brought his own dual and divided nature into the destinies of others besides himself whenever he came into contact with them.

Now, whoever thinks that he knows the Steppenwolf and that he can imagine to himself his lamentably divided life is nevertheless in error. He does not know all by a long way. He does not know that, as there is no rule without an exception and as one sinner may under certain circumstances be dearer to God than ninety and nine righteous persons, with Harry too there were now and then exceptions and strokes of good luck, and that he could breathe and think and feel sometimes as the wolf, sometimes as the man, clearly and without confusion of the two; and even on very rare occasions, they made peace and lived for one another in such fashion that not merely did one keep watch whilst the other slept but each strengthened and confirmed the other. In the life of this man, too, as well as in all things else in the world, daily use and the accepted and common knowledge seemed sometimes to have no other aim than to be arrested now and again for an instant, and broken through, in order to yield the place of honor to the exceptional and miraculous. Now whether these short and occasional hours of happiness balanced and allevi- ated the lot of the Steppenwolf in such a fashion that in the upshot happiness and suffering held the scales even, or whether perhaps the short but intense happiness of those few hours outweighed all suffering and left a balance over is again a question over which idle persons may meditate to their hearts' content. Even the wolf brooded often thereover, and those were his idle and unprofitable days.

In this connection one thing more must be said. There are a good many people of the same kind as Harry. Many artists are of his kind. These persons have two souls, two beings within them. There is God and the devil in them; the mother's blood and the father's; the capacity for happiness and the capacity for suffering; and in just such a state of enmity and entanglement towards and within each other as were the wolf and man in Harry. And these men, for whom life has no repose, live at times in their rare moments of happiness with such strength and indescribable beauty, the spray of their moment's happi- ness is flung so high and dazzlingly over the wide sea of suffering, that the light of it, spreading its radiance, touches others too with its enchantment. Thus, like a precious, fleeting foam over the sea of suffering arise all those works of art, in which a single individual lifts himself for an hour so high above his personal destiny that his happiness shines like a star and appears to all who see it as some- thing eternal and as a happiness of their own. All these men, what- ever their deeds and works may be, have really no life; that is to say, their lives are not their own and have no form. They are not heroes, artists or thinkers in the same way that other men are judges, doctors, shoemakers or schoolmasters. Their life consists of a perpetual tide, unhappy and torn with pain, terrible and meaningless, unless one is ready to see its meaning in just those rare experiences, acts, thoughts and works that shine out above the chaos of such a life. To such men the desperate and horrible thought has come that perhaps the whole of human life is but a bad joke, a violent and ill-fated abortion of the primal mother, a savage and dismal catastrophe of nature. To them, too, however, the other thought has come that man is perhaps not merely a half-rational animal but a child of the gods and destined to immortality.

Men of every kind have their characteristics, their features, their virtues and vices and their deadly sins. It was part of the sign manual of the Steppenwolf that he was a night prowler. The morning was a bad time of day for him. He feared it and it never brought him any good. On no morning of his life has he ever been in good spirits nor done any good before midday, nor ever had a happy idea, nor devised any pleasure for himself or others. By degrees during the afternoon he warmed and became alive, and only towards evening, on his good days, was he productive, active and, sometimes, aglow with joy. With this was bound up his need for loneliness and independence. There was never a man with a deeper and more passionate craving for independence than he. In his youth when he was poor and had difficulty in earning his bread, he preferred to go hungry and in torn clothes rather than endanger his narrow limit of independence. He never sold himself for money or an easy life or to women or to those in power; and had thrown away a hundred times what in the world's eyes was his advantage and happiness in order to safeguard his liberty. No prospect was more hateful and distasteful to him than that he should have to go to an office and conform to daily and yearly routine and obey others. He hated all kinds of offices, governmental or commercial, as he hated death, and his worst nightmare was confinement in barracks. He contrived, often at great sacrifice, to avoid all such predicaments. It was here that his strength and his virtue rested. On this point he could neither be bent nor bribed. Here his character was firm and indeflectable. Only, through this virtue, he was bound the closer to his destiny of suffering. It happened to him as it does to all; what he strove for with the deepest and stubbornest instinct of his being fell to his lot, but more than is good for men. In the beginning his dream and his happiness, in the end it was his bitter fate. The man his life even had anyone wished it. For the air of lonely men surrounded him now, a still atmosphere in which the world around him slipped away, leaving him incapable of relationship, an atmosphere again which neither will nor longing availed.

It still remains to elucidate the Steppenwolf as an isolated phenomenon, in his relation, for example, to the bourgeois world, so that his symptoms may be traced to their source. Let us take as a starting point, since it offers itself, his relation to the bourgeoisie.

To take his own view of the matter, Steppenwolf stood entirely outside the world of convention, since he had neither family life nor social ambitions. He felt himself to be single and alone, whether as a queer fellow and a hermit in poor health, or as a person removed from the common run of men by the prerogative of talents that had something of genius in them. Deliberately, he looked down upon the ordinary man and was proud that he was not one. Nevertheless his life in many aspects was thoroughly ordinary. He had money in the bank and supported poor relations. He was dressed respectably and inconspicuously, even though without particular care. He was glad to live on good terms with the police and the tax collectors and other such powers. Besides this, he was secretly and persistently attracted to the little bourgeois world, to those quiet and respectable homes with tidy gardens, irreproachable staircases and their whole modest air of order and comfort. It pleased him to set himself outside it, with his little vices and extravagances, as a queer fellow or a genius, but he never had his domicile in those provinces of life where the bourgeoisie had ceased to exist. He was not at ease with violent and exceptional persons nor with criminals and outlaws, and he took up his abode always among the middle classes, with whose habits and standards and atmosphere he stood in a constant relation, even though it might be one of contrast and revolt. Moreover, he had been brought up in a provincial and conventional home and many of the notions and much of the examples of those days had never left him. In theory he had nothing whatever against the servant class; yet in practice it would have been beyond him to take a servant quite seriously as his equal. He was capable of loving the political criminal, the revolutionary or intellectual seducer, the outlaw of state and society, as his brother, but as for theft and robbery, murder and rape, he would not have known how to deplore them otherwise than in a thoroughly bourgeois manner.

In this way he was always recognizing and affirming with one half of himself, in thought and act, what with the other half he fought against and denied. Brought up, as he was, in a cultivated home in the approved manner, he never tore part of his soul loose from its conventionalities even after he had long since individualized himself to a degree beyond its scope and freed himself from the substance of its ideals and beliefs.

Now what we call "bourgeois," when regarded as an element always to be found in human life, is nothing else than the search for a balance. It is the striving after a mean between the countless extremes and opposites that arise in human conduct. If we take any one of these coupled opposites, such as piety and profligacy, the analogy is immediately comprehensible. It is open to a man to give himself up wholly to spiritual views, to seeking after God, to the ideal of saintliness. On the other hand, he can equally give himself up entirely to the life of instinct, to the lusts of the flesh, and so direct all his efforts to the attainment of momentary pleasures. The one path leads to the saint, to the martyrdom of the spirit and surrender to God. The other path leads to the profligate, to the martyrdom of the flesh, the surrender to corruption. Now it is between the two, in the middle of the road, that the bourgeois seeks to walk. He will never surrender himself either to lust or to asceticism. He will never be a martyr nor agree to his own destruction. On the contrary, his ideal is not to give up but to maintain his own identity. He strives neither for the saintly nor its opposite. The absolute is his abhorrence. He may be ready to serve God, but not by giving up the fleshpots. He is ready to be virtuous, but likes to be easy and comfortable in this world as well. In short, his aim is to make a home for himself between two extremes in a temperate zone without violent storms and tempests; and in this he succeeds though it be at the cost of that intensity of life and feeling which an extreme life affords. A man cannot live intensely except at the cost of the self. Now the bourgeois treasures nothing more highly than the self (rudimentary as his may be). And so at the cost of intensity he achieves his own preservation and security. His harvest is a quiet mind which he prefers to being possessed by God, as he does comfort to pleasure, convenience to liberty, and a pleasant temperature to that deathly inner consuming fire. The bourgeois is consequently by nature a creature of weak impulses, anxious, fearful of giving himself away and easy to rule. Therefore, he has substituted majority for power, law for force, and the polling booth for responsibility.

It is clear that this weak and anxious being, in whatever numbers he exists, cannot maintain himself, and that qualities such as his can play no other rôle in the world than that of a herd of sheep among free roving wolves. Yet we see that, though in times when commanding natures are uppermost, the bourgeois goes at once to the wall, he never goes under; indeed at times he even appears to rule the world. How is this possible? Neither the great numbers of the herd, nor virtue, nor common sense, nor organization could avail to save it from destruction. No medicine in the world can keep a pulse beating that from the outset was so weak. Nevertheless the bourgeoisie prospers. Why?

The answer runs: Because of the Steppenwolves. In fact, the vital force of the bourgeoisie resides by no means in the qualities of its normal members, but in those of its extremely numerous "outsiders" who by virtue of the extensiveness and elasticity of its ideals it can embrace. There is always a large number of strong and wild natures who share the life of the fold. Our Steppenwolf, Harry, is a characteristic example. He who is developed far beyond the level possible to the bourgeois, he who knows the bliss of meditation no less than the gloomy joys of hatred and self-hatred, he who despises law, virtue and common sense, is nevertheless captive to the bourgeoisie and cannot escape it. And so all through the mass of the real bourgeoisie are interposed numerous layers of humanity, many thousands of lives and minds, every one of whom, it is true, would have outgrown it and have obeyed the call to unconditioned life, were they not fastened to it by sentiments of their childhood and infected for the most part with its less intense life; and so they are kept lingering, obedient and bound by obligation and service. For with the bourgeoisie the opposite of the formula for the great is true: He who is not against me is with me.

If we now pause to test the soul of the Steppenwolf, we find him distinct from the bourgeois in the higher development of his individuality—for all extensions of the individuality revolve upon the self and tend to destroy it. We see that he had in him a strong impulse both to the saint and the profligate; and yet he could not, owing to some weakness or inertia, make the plunge into the untrammelled realms of space. The parent constellation of the bourgeoisie binds him with its spell. This is his place in the universe and this his bondage. Most intellectuals and most artists belong to the same type. Only the strongest of them force their way through the atmosphere of the Bourgeois-Earth and attain to the cosmic. The others all resign themselves, or make compromises. Despising the bourgeoisie, and yet belonging to it, they add to its strength and glory; for in the last resort they have to share their beliefs in order to live. The lives of these infinitely numerous persons make no claim to the tragic; but they live under an evil star in a quite considerable affliction; and in this hell their talents ripen and bear fruit. The few who break free seek their reward in the unconditioned and go down in splendor. They wear the thorn crown and their number is small. The others, however, who remain in the fold and from whose talents the bourgeoisie reaps much gain, have a third kingdom left open to them, an imaginary and yet a sovereign world, humor. The lone wolves who know no peace, these victims of unceasing pain to whom the urge for tragedy has been denied and who can never break through the starry space, who feel themselves summoned thither and yet cannot survive in its atmosphere—for them is reserved, provided suffering has made their spirits tough and elastic enough, a way of reconcilement and an escape into humor. Humor has always something bourgeois in it, although the true bourgeois is incapable of understanding it. In its imaginary realm the intricate and many-faceted ideal of all Steppenwolves finds its realization. Here it is possible not only to extol the saint and the profligate in one breath and to make the poles meet, but to include the bourgeois, too, in the same affirmation. Now it is possible to be possessed by God and to affirm the sinner, and vice versa, but it is not possible for either saint or sinner (nor for any other of the unconditioned) to affirm as well that lukewarm mean, the bourgeois. Humor alone, that magnificent discovery of those who are cut short in their calling to highest endeavor, those who falling short of tragedy are yet as rich in gifts as in affliction, humor alone (perhaps the most inborn and brilliant achievement of the spirit) attains to the impossible and brings every aspect of human existence within the rays of its prism. To live in the world as though it were not the world, to respect the law and yet to stand above it, to have possessions as though "one possessed nothing," to renounce as though it were no renunciation, all these favorite and often formulated propositions of an exalted worldly wisdom, it is in the power of humor alone to make efficacious.

And supposing the Steppenwolf were to succeed, and he has gifts and resources in plenty, in decocting this magic draught in the sultry mazes of his hell, his rescue would be assured. Yet there is much lacking. The possibility, the hope only are there. Whoever loves him and takes his part may wish him this rescue. It would, it is true, keep him forever tied to the bourgeois world, but his suffering would be bearable and productive. His relation to the bourgeois world would lose its sentimentality both in its love and its hatred, and his bondage to it would cease to cause him the continual torture of shame.

To attain to this, or, perhaps it may be, to be able at last to dare the leap into the unknown, a Steppenwolf must once have a good look at himself. He must look deeply into the chaos of his own soul and plumb its depths. The riddle of his existence would then be revealed to him at once in all its changelessness, and it would be impossible for him ever after to escape first from the hell of the flesh to the comforts of a sentimental philosophy and then back to the blind orgy of his wolfishness. Man and wolf would then be compelled to recognize one another without the masks of false feeling and to look one another straight in the eye. Then they would either explode and separate forever, and there would be no more Steppenwolf, or else they would come to terms in the dawning light of humor.

It is possible that Harry will one day be led to this latter alternative. It is possible that he will learn one day to know himself. He

may get hold of one of our little mirrors. He may encounter the
Immortals. He may find in one of our magic theatres the very thing
that is needed to free his neglected soul. A thousand such possibilities
await him. His fate brings them on, leaving him no choice; for those
outside of the bourgeoisie live in the atmosphere of these magic possibilities. A mere nothing suffices—and the lightning strikes.

And all this is very well known to the Steppenwolf, even though
his eye may never fall on this fragment of his inner biography. He
has a suspicion of his allotted place in the world, a suspicion of the
Immortals, a suspicion that he may meet himself face to face; and
he is aware of the existence of that mirror in which he has such bitter
need to look and from which he shrinks in such deathly fear.

The division into wolf and man, flesh and spirit, by means of
which Harry tries to make his destiny more comprehensible to himself is a very great simplification. It is a forcing of the truth to suit
a plausible, but erroneous, explanation of that contradiction which
this man discovers in himself and which appears to himself to be
the source of his by no means negligible sufferings. Harry finds in
himself a "human being," that is to say, a world of thoughts and
feelings, of culture and tamed or sublimated nature, and besides this
he finds within himself also a "wolf," that is to say, a dark world of
instinct, of savagery and cruelty, of unsublimated or raw nature. . . .
To explain so complex a man as Harry by the artless division into
wolf and man is a hopelessly childish attempt. Harry consists of a
hundred or a thousand selves, not of two. His life oscillates, as everyone's does, not merely between two poles, such as the body and the
spirit, the saint and the sinner, but between thousand and thousands. . . .

When Faust, in a line immortalized among schoolmasters and
greeted with a shudder of astonishment by the Philistine, says: "Two
souls, alas, inhabit in my breast!" he has forgotten Mephisto and a
whole crowd of other souls that he has in his breast likewise. The
Steppenwolf, too, believes that he bears two souls (wolf and man)
in his breast and even so finds his breast disagreeably cramped because of them. The breast and the body are indeed one, but the
souls that dwell in it are not two, nor five, but countless in number. . . .

That man is not yet a finished creation but rather a challenge of
the spirit; a distant possibility dreaded as much as it is desired; that
the way towards it has only been covered for a very short distance
and with terrible agonies and ecstasies even by those few for whom

it is the scaffold today and the monument tomorrow—all this the Steppenwolf, too, suspected. . . .

It is as much a matter for surprise and sorrow that men of such possibilities should fall back on Steppenwolves and "Two souls, alas!" as that they reveal so often that pitiful love for the bourgeoisie. A man who can understand Buddha and has an intuition of the heaven and hell of humanity ought not to live in a world ruled by "common sense" and democracy and bourgeois standards. It is only from cowardice that he lives in it; and if its dimensions are too cramping for him and the bourgeois parlour too confined, he lays it at the wolf's door, and refuses to see that the wolf is as often as not the best part of him. All that is wild in himself he calls wolf and considers it wicked and dangerous and the bugbear of all decent life. He cannot see, even though he thinks himself an artist and possessed of delicate perceptions, that a great deal else exists in him besides and behind the wolf. He cannot see that not all that bites is wolf and that fox, dragon, tiger, ape and bird of paradise are there also. Yet he allows this whole world, a garden of Eden in which are manifestations of beauty and terror, of greatness and meanness, of strength and tenderness, to be huddled together and shut away by the wolf-legend, just as is the real man in him by the shams and pretenses of a bourgeois existence.

Man designs for himself a garden with a hundred kinds of trees, a thousand kinds of flowers, a hundred kinds of fruit and vegetables. Suppose, then, that the gardener of this garden knew no other distinction than between edible and inedible, nine-tenths of this garden would be useless to him. He would pull up the most enchanting flowers and hew down the noblest trees and even regard them with a loathing and envious eye. This is what the Steppenwolf does with the thousand flowers of his soul. What does not stand classified as either man or wolf he does not see at all. And consider all that he imputes to "man"! All that is cowardly and apish, stupid and mean —while to the wolf, only because he has not succeeded in making himself its master, is set down all that is strong and noble.

Now we bid Harry good-bye and leave him to go on his way alone. Were he already among the immortals—were he already there at the goal to which his difficult path seems to be taking him, with what amazement he would look back to all this coming and going, all this indecision and wild zig-zag trail. With what a mixture of encouragement and blame, pity and joy, he would smile at this Steppenwolf.

ARTAUD

NO MORE MASTERPIECES

One of the reasons for the asphyxiating atmosphere in which we live without possible escape or remedy—and in which we all share, even the most revolutionary among us—is our respect for what has been written, formulated, or painted, what has been given form, as if all expression were not at last exhausted, were not at a point where things must break apart if they are to start anew and begin fresh.

We must have done with this idea of masterpieces reserved for a self-styled elite and not understood by the general public; the mind has no such restricted districts as those so often used for clandestine sexual encounters.

Masterpieces of the past are good for the past: they are not good for us. We have the right to say what has been said and even what has not been said in a way that belongs to us, a way that is immediate and direct, corresponding to present modes of feeling, and understandable to everyone.

It is idiotic to reproach the masses for having no sense of the sublime, when the sublime is confused with one or another of its formal manifestations, which are moreover always defunct manifestations. And if for example a contemporary public does not understand *Oedipus Rex*, I shall make bold to say that it is the fault of *Oedipus Rex* and not of the public.

In *Oedipus Rex* there is the theme of incest and the idea that nature mocks at morality and that there are certain unspecified powers at large which we would do well to beware of, call them *destiny* or anything you choose.

There is in addition the presence of a plague epidemic which is a physical incarnation of these powers. But the whole in a manner

84

and language that have lost all touch with the rude and epileptic rhythm of our time. Sophocles speaks grandly perhaps, but in a style that is no longer timely. His language is too refined for this age, it is as if he were speaking beside the point.

However, a public that shudders at train wrecks, that is familiar with earthquakes, plagues, revolutions, wars; that is sensitive to the disordered anguish of love, can be affected by all these grand notions and asks only to become aware of them, but on condition that it is addressed in its own language, and that its knowledge of these things does not come to it through adulterated trappings and speech that belong to extinct eras which will never live again.

Today as yesterday, the public is greedy for mystery: it asks only to become aware of the laws according to which destiny manifests itself, and to divine perhaps the secret of its apparitions.

Let us leave textual criticism to graduate students, formal criticism to esthetes, and recognize that what has been said is not still to be said; that an expression does not have the same value twice, does not live two lives; that all words, once spoken, are dead and function only at the moment when they are uttered, that a form, once it has served, cannot be used again and asks only to be replaced by another, and that the theater is the only place in the world where a gesture, once made, can never be made the same way twice.

If the public does not frequent our literary masterpieces, it is because those masterpieces are literary, that is to say, fixed; and fixed in forms that no longer respond to the needs of the time.

Far from blaming the public, we ought to blame the formal screen we interpose between ourselves and the public, and this new form of idolatry, the idolatry of fixed masterpieces which is one of the aspects of bourgeois conformism.

This conformism makes us confuse sublimity, ideas, and things with the forms they have taken in time and in our minds—in our snobbish, precious, aesthetic mentalities which the public does not understand.

How pointless in such matters to accuse the public of bad taste because it relishes insanities, so long as the public is not shown a valid spectacle; and I defy anyone to show me *here* a spectacle valid —valid in the supreme sense of the theater—since the last great romantic melodramas, i.e., since a hundred years ago.

The public, which takes the false for the true, has the sense of the true and always responds to it when it is manifested. However it is not upon the stage that the true is to be sought nowadays, but in the street; and if the crowd in the street is offered an occasion to show its human dignity, it will always do so.

If people are out of the habit of going to the theater, if we have all finally come to think of theater as an inferior art, a means of popular distraction, and to use it as an outlet for our worst instincts, it is because we have learned too well what the theater has been, namely, falsehood and illusion. It is because we have been accustomed for four hundred years, that is since the Renaissance, to a purely descriptive and narrative theater—storytelling psychology; it is because every possible ingenuity has been exerted in bringing to life on the stage plausible but detached beings, with the spectacle on one side, the public on the other—and because the public is no longer shown anything but the mirror of itself.

Shakespeare himself is responsible for this aberration and decline, this disinterested idea of the theater which wishes a theatrical performance to leave the public intact, without setting off one image that will shake the organism to its foundations and leave an ineffaceable scar.

If, in Shakespeare, a man is sometimes preoccupied with what transcends him, it is always in order to determine the ultimate consequences of this preoccupation within him, i.e., psychology.

Psychology, which works relentlessly to reduce the unknown to the known, to the quotidian and the ordinary, is the cause of the theater's abasement and its fearful loss of energy, which seems to me to have reached its lowest point. And I think both the theater and we ourselves have had enough of psychology.

I believe furthermore that we can all agree on this matter sufficiently so that there is no need to descend to the repugnant level of the modern and French theater to condemn the theater of psychology.

Stories about money, worry over money, social careerism, the pangs of love unspoiled by altruism, sexuality sugar-coated with an eroticism that has lost its mystery have nothing to do with the theater, even if they do belong to psychology. These torments, seductions, and lusts before which we are nothing but Peeping Toms gratifying our cravings, tend to go bad, and their rot turns to revolution: we must take this into account.

But this is not our most serious concern.

If Shakespeare and his imitators have gradually insinuated the idea of art for art's sake, with art on one side and life on the other, we can rest on this feeble and lazy idea only as long as the life outside endures. But there are too many signs that everything that used to sustain our lives no longer does so, that we are all mad, desperate, and sick. And I call for *us* to react.

This idea of a detached art, of poetry as a charm which exists only to distract our leisure, is a decadent idea and an unmistakable symptom of our power to castrate.

Our literary admiration for Rimbaud, Jarry, Lautréamont, and a few others, which has driven two men to suicide, but turned into café gossip for the rest, belongs to this idea of literary poetry, of detached art, of neutral spiritual activity which creates nothing and produces nothing; and I can bear witness that at the very moment when that kind of personal poetry which involves only the man who creates it and only at the moment he creates it broke out in its most abusive fashion, the theater was scorned more than ever before by poets who have never had the sense of direct and concerted action, nor of efficacity, nor of danger.

We must get rid of our superstitious valuation of texts and *written* poetry. Written poetry is worth reading once, and then should be destroyed. Let the dead poets make way for others. Then we might even come to see that it is our veneration for what has already been created, however beautiful and valid it may be, that petrifies us, deadens our responses, and prevents us from making contact with that underlying power, call it thought-energy, the life force, the determinism of change, lunar menses, or anything you like. Beneath the poetry of the texts, there is the actual poetry, without form and without text. And just as the efficacity of masks in the magic practices of certain tribes is exhausted—and these masks are no longer good for anything except museums—so the poetic efficacity of a text is exhausted; yet the poetry and the efficacity of the theater are exhausted least quickly of all, since they permit the *action* of what is gesticulated and pronounced, and which is never made the same way twice.

It is a question of knowing what we want. If we are prepared for war, plague, famine, and slaughter we do not even need to say so, we have only to continue as we are; continue behaving like snobs, rushing en masse to hear such and such a singer, to see such and such an admirable performance which never transcends the realm of art (and even the Russian ballet at the height of its splendor never transcended the realm of art), to marvel at such and such an exhibition of painting in which exciting shapes explode here and there but at random and without any genuine consciousness of the forces they could rouse.

This empiricism, randomness, individualism, and anarchy must cease.

Enough of personal poems, benefitting those who create them much more than those who read them.

Once and for all, enough of this closed, egoistic, and personal art.

Our spiritual anarchy and intellectual disorder is a function of the anarchy of everything else—or rather, everything else is a function of this anarchy.

I am not one of those who believe that civilization has to change in order for the theater to change; but I do believe that the theater, utilized in the highest and most difficult sense possible, has the power to influence the aspect and formation of things: and the encounter upon the stage of two passionate manifestations, two living centers, two nervous magnetisms is something as entire, true, even decisive, as, in life, the encounter of one epidermis with another in a timeless debauchery.

That is why I propose a theater of cruelty.—With this mania we all have for depreciating everything, as soon as I have said "cruelty," everybody will at once take it to mean "blood." But *"theater of cruelty"* means a theater difficult and cruel for myself first of all. And, on the level of performance, it is not the cruelty we can exercise upon each other by hacking at each other's bodies, carving up our personal anatomies, or, like Assyrian emperors, sending parcels of human ears, noses, or neatly detached nostrils through the mail, but the much more terrible and necessary cruelty which things can exercise against us. We are not free. And the sky can still fall on our heads. And the theater has been created to teach us that first of all.

Either we will be capable of returning by present-day means to this superior idea of poetry and poetry-through-theater which underlies the Myths told by the great ancient tragedians, capable once more of entertaining a religious idea of the theater (without meditation, unless contemplation, and vague dreams), capable of attaining awareness and a possession of certain dominant forces, of certain notions that control all others, and (since ideas, when they are effective, carry their energy with them) capable of recovering within ourselves those energies which ultimately create order and increase the value of life, or else we might as well abandon ourselves now, without protest, and recognize that we are no longer good for anything but disorder, famine, blood, war, and epidemics.

Either we restore all the arts to a central attitude and necessity, finding an analogy between a gesture made in painting or the theater, and a gesture made by lava in a volcanic explosion, or we must stop painting, babbling, writing, or doing whatever it is we do.

I propose to bring back into the theater this elementary magical idea, taken up by modern psychoanalysis, which consists in effecting a patient's cure by making him assume the apparent and exterior attitudes of the desired condition.

I propose to renounce our empiricism of imagery, in which the unconscious furnishes images at random, and which the poet arranges at random too, calling them poetic and hence hermetic images, as if the kind of trance that poetry provides did not have its reverberations throughout the whole sensibility, in every nerve, and as if poetry were some vague force whose movements were invariable.

I propose to return through the theater to an idea of the physical knowledge of images and the means of inducing trances, as in Chinese medicine which knows, over the entire extent of the human anatomy, at what points to puncture in order to regulate the subtlest functions.

Those who have forgotten the communicative power and magical mimesis of a gesture, the theater can reinstruct, because a gesture carries its energy with it, and there are still human beings in the theater to manifest the force of the gesture made.

To create art is to deprive a gesture of its reverberation in the organism, whereas this reverberation, if the gesture is made in the conditions and with the force required, incites the organism and, through it, the entire individuality, to take attitudes in harmony with the gesture.

The theater is the only place in the world, the last general means we still possess of directly affecting the organism and, in periods of neurosis and petty sensuality like the one in which we are immersed, of attacking this sensuality by physical means it cannot withstand.

If music affects snakes, it is not on account of the spiritual notions it offers them, but because snakes are long and coil their length upon the earth, because their bodies touch the earth at almost every point; and because the musical vibrations which are communicated to the earth affect them like a very subtle, very long massage; and I propose to treat the spectators like the snakecharmer's subjects and conduct them *by means of their organisms* to an apprehension of the subtlest notions.

At first by crude means, which will gradually be refined. These immediate crude means will hold their attention at the start.

That is why in the "theater of cruelty" the spectator is in the center and the spectacle surrounds him.

In this spectacle the sonorisation is constant: sounds, noises, cries are chosen first for their vibratory quality, then for what they represent.

Among these gradually refined means light is interposed in its turn. Light which is not created merely to add color or to brighten, and which brings its power, influence, suggestions with it. And the light of a green cavern does not sensually dispose the organism like the light of a windy day.

After sound and light there is action, and the dynamism of action: here the theater, far from copying life, puts itself whenever possible in communication with pure forces. And whether you accept or deny them, there is nevertheless a way of speaking which gives the name of "forces" to whatever brings to birth images of energy in the unconscious, and gratuitous crime on the surface.

A violent and concentrated action is a kind of lyricism: it summons up supernatural images, a bloodstream of images, a bleeding spurt of images in the poet's head and in the spectator's as well.

Whatever the conflicts that haunt the mind of a given period, I defy any spectator to whom such violent scenes will have transferred their blood, who will have felt in himself the transit of a superior action, who will have seen the extraordinary and essential movement of his thought illuminated in extraordinary deeds—the violence and blood having been placed at the service of the violence of the thought —I defy that spectator to give himself up, once outside the theater, to ideas of war, riot, and blatant murder.

So expressed, this idea seems dangerous and sophomoric. It will be claimed that example breeds example, that if the attitude of cure induces cure, the attitude of murder will induce murder. Everything depends upon the manner and the purity with which the thing is done. There is a risk. But let it not be forgotten that though a theatrical gesture is violent, it is disinterested; and that the theater teaches precisely the uselessness of the action which, once done, is not to be done, and the superior use of the state unused by the action and which, *restored*, produces a purification.

I propose then a theater in which violent physical images crush and hypnotize the sensibility of the spectator seized by the theater as by a whirlwind of higher forces.

A theater which, abandoning psychology, recounts the extraordinary, stages natural conflicts, natural and subtle forces, and presents itself first of all as an exceptional power of redirection. A theater that induces trance, as the dances of Dervishes induce trance, and that addresses itself to the organism by precise instruments, by the same means as those of certain tribal music cures which we admire on records but are incapable of originating among ourselves.

There is a risk involved, but in the present circumstances I believe it is a risk worth running. I do not believe we have managed to revitalize the world we live in, and I do not believe it is worth the trouble of clinging to; but I do propose something to get us out of our marasmus, instead of continuing to complain about it, and about the boredom, inertia, and stupidity of everything.

Translated by Mary Caroline Richards

CÉLINE

What Henry Miller has done in literature for the language, Céline has attempted to do for the emotions. He has managed to free certain emotions—"cowardice," "lust," "selfishness"—from the trap of stigma and taboo that made them inhuman; he has shown how it is possible for a character to possess these feelings and still retain the reader's sympathy, if not, in fact, become all the more acceptable because of them. Céline is the first modern author to have done this on such a vast and unrelenting scale; his work, long considered wholly perverse and despicable, opened the door for an entire school of popular fiction, whose heroes, like Lucky Jim Dixon, Jimmy Porter and the Ginger Man, have an unwholesomeness of character (by traditional literary standards) which is matched only by their warmth and credibility as human beings.

In the existentialist hero—Mathieu, Roquentin, Mersault—we see men who tend to reject not merely conventional values but ordinary semantics as well; they will not acknowledge any legitimate tendency even to think in terms of "right" and "wrong," or in terms of "love," "patriotism," and "courage"—terms, that is to say, which their authors wish to prove outmoded and inadequate. Céline's hero, on the other hand, is more diabolic in his revolt, and more subtle; he recognizes the existence of these new rules-of-the-game and, without questioning their validity, he simply refuses to play—taking a rather detached, and often bemused, interest in his own lonely failure to measure up to the standards professed by the crowd . . . standards which, as Céline has revealed, are usually the mouthings of fools and liars.

from *JOURNEY TO THE END OF THE NIGHT*

Once one's in it, one's in it up to the neck. They put us on horse-back and then, after two months of that, they put us back on foot. Perhaps because it cost too much. Anyway, one morning the colonel was looking for his horse; his orderly had gone off with it, no one knew where, somewhere no doubt where bullets sang less merrily than in the middle of the road. Because that's exactly where we finished up, the colonel and I, plumb in the middle of the road, with me holding the forms on which he wrote out orders.

Far away up the road, as far as you could see, there were two black dots, in the middle of it, like us—only they were two Germans, very busy shooting. They'd been doing that for a good quarter of an hour.

The colonel perhaps knew why those two fellows were firing and the Germans maybe knew it too; but as for me, quite frankly, I didn't at all. However far back I remembered, the Germans had nothing against me. I had always been quite friendly and polite to them. I knew the Germans a bit, I'd even been to school with them as a kid, near Hanover. I'd talked their language. They were then a lot of noisy little idiots, with the pale and furtive eyes of wolves; we all used to go and neck the girls in the woods near by, where we'd also shoot with bows or with the little pistols you could get for four marks. We used to drink sweet beer. But that was one thing and now letting fly at each other, without even coming over to talk first, and right in the middle of the road, was another—not the same thing at all. It was altogether too damn different.

The war, in fact, was everything that one didn't understand. It couldn't go on.

Had something extraordinary then come over these people? Something which I didn't feel at all? I must have failed to notice it.

At any rate, my feelings towards them had not changed. In spite of everything, I felt I wanted to understand their brutal behaviour; but even more I wanted, I terribly wanted, to go away, it all suddenly seemed so much the result of a tremendous mistake.

"In this sort of business there's nothing for it; the only thing to do is to shove out of it." That's what I said to myself. After all . . .

Over our heads, an inch or half an inch away, one after the other those long tentative steel strings which bullets make when they want to kill you came twanging in the warm air of summer.

Never have I felt so futile as among all those bullets in that sunshine. A vast, a universal ramp.

I wasn't more than twenty at the time. In the distance were deserted farmhouses and open and empty churches, as if the peasants every one of them had left these hamlets for the day, to go to some gathering at the other end of the canton and had left in our keeping all they possessed—their countryside, their carts and upturned shafts, their fields and patches, the road, the trees and even the cows, a dog on its chain, everything. So that we should not be disturbed and could do what we wanted while they were away. It seemed a kindly thought on their part. "All the same," said I to myself, "if only they hadn't gone off, if only there was still somebody about around here, we surely shouldn't be behaving so badly—so disgracefully! We wouldn't have dared with them here. Only there's no one to see us. We're by ourselves like newly married folk doing dirty things when every one's left."

And I thought too (behind a tree) that I should love to have the biggest Jingo of the lot here with me, to explain what *he* would do when a bullet hit him slap in the pan.

These Germans, squatting on the road, sniping away so obstinately, weren't shooting well but they seemed to have ammunition enough and to spare, stacks of it obviously. No, the war wasn't by any means over. Our colonel, I must say, was showing amazing coolness. He walked about, right in the middle of the road, up and down in the thick of these bullets, just as carelessly as if he were waiting for a friend on a station platform; a little impatiently, that's all.

As a matter of fact, I may as well admit that I've never liked the country, anyway; I've always found it depressing, with all its endless puddles and its houses where nobody's ever in and its roads leading nowhere. But with a war on as well, it's intolerable. The wind had come up fiercely from both sides of the embankment, the gusts in the poplar leaves mingling with the rustle that was directed against us from up the road. They were missing us all the time, these unknown soldiers of ours, yet they put a thousand deaths round about us so close that they were almost a garment. I didn't dare move.

What a monster that colonel must be, though. I was sure that, like a dog, he had no idea of death. It struck me at the same time that there must be lots like him, as gallant as he, in our army, and as many again, no doubt, on the opposite side. One wondered how many. A million—or two? Several millions in all, perhaps. From that moment, my terror became panic. With creatures like that about the place, this hellish idiocy might go on indefinitely. . . . Why should they stop? Never had I felt the way of men and things to be so implacable.

Could it be that I was the only coward on earth, I wondered. The thought was terrifying. Lost in the midst of two million madmen, all of them heroes, at large and armed to the teeth! With or without helmets, without horses, on motor bicycles, screeching, in cars, whistling, sniping, plotting, flying, kneeling, digging, taking cover, wheeling, detonating, shut in on earth as in an asylum cell; intending to wreck everything in it, Germany, France, the whole world, every breathing thing; destroying, more ferocious than a pack of mad dogs and adoring their own madness (which no dog does), a hundred, a thousand times fiercer than a thousand dogs and so infinitely more vicious! What a mess we were in! Clearly it seemed to me that I had embarked on a crusade that was nothing short of an apocalypse.

One is as innocent of Horror as one is of sex. How could I possibly have guessed this horror when I left the Place Clichy? Who could have foreseen, before getting really into the war, what was inside the foul and idle, heroic soul of man? There I was, caught up into a general rush towards murder for all, towards fire. . . . It was a thing that had come up from the depths and here it was on top of us.

All this while the colonel never faltered; I watched him receive little messages from the general, there on the embankment, where he straightway tore them up after reading them without haste, amid the bullets. Did none of them contain the order to put an immediate stop to this frightfulness? Was he not being told by H.Q. that there was some misunderstanding, some ghastly mistake? That the cards had been wrongly dealt and something was wrong? That we were meant to have engaged on manœuvres, for fun, and not in this business of killing? Not at all.

"Carry on, Colonel! Go right ahead as you are." That must be what General Des Entrayes, our Chief of Division, was telling him in these messages which were brought to him every five minutes by a runner, who each time looked greener and more liverish. He could have been my brother in fear, that boy; but there wasn't the time to fraternize, either.

What, was there nothing wrong then? This shooting at each other like this without a word—it was all O.K. It was one of the things you can do without getting hauled over the coals good and proper. It was actually accepted, it was probably encouraged by decent folk, like drawing lots in conscription or getting engaged or beagling! There was nothing for it. I had suddenly discovered, all at once, what the war was, the whole war. I'd lost my innocence. You need to be pretty well alone with it face to face, as I was then, to see the filthy thing properly, in the round. They'd touched off the war between us and the other side, and now it was flaring! Like the current between the two carbons in an arc lamp. And it wasn't going to be put out soon, either. We would all be going through it, the colonel along with the rest, for all his fine airs, and his guts would look the same as mine when the current from opposite flashed through his middle.

There are a lot of ways of being condemned to death. What wouldn't I have given at that moment to be in gaol instead of where I was! If only, fool that I was, if only I'd gone and stolen something, looking ahead when it was still so easy, when there was still time. One thinks of nothing! You come out of gaol alive, but not out of a war. That's a fact and everything else hot air.

If only I'd still had the time, but I hadn't it any longer! There was nothing left to steal. How cosy it would be in a dear little prison cell, I told myself, where no bullets ever came. No bullets, ever. I knew of one all ready and warm, facing the sun. In my mind I could see it, the Saint-Germain it was actually, closed to the woods; I knew it well; I used to pass by it often at one time. How one changes! I was a kid in those days and the prison used to frighten me. I didn't yet know what men were like. I shall never again believe what they say or what they think. It is of men, and of them only, that one should always be frightened.

How long would the delirium of these monsters need to last for them to stop in the end, exhausted? How long could a fit of frenzy like this go on? A few months? A few years? Perhaps until every one was dead, every one of these madmen. To the very last of all? Well, since things were taking this desperate turn, I decided to risk everything at one throw, to try the final, the supreme move, and on my own, alone, to try and stop the war! My small section of it, at any rate.

The colonel was walking about, two yards away. I would go and speak to him. I'd never done that before. Now was the time to dare to do it, though. Where we were, there was hardly anything further to lose. "What do you want?" I could see him saying it, very surprised, of course, by my cheek in interrupting him. Then I should explain it all to him as I saw it. We'd see what his views on the matter were. The all-important thing in life is to say what's in your mind. And two heads would be better than one.

I was about to take this decisive step when, at that very moment, hurrying along towards us came a dismounted cavalryman (as they were called in those days), limping, hobbling, with his upturned helmet in his hand like a blind beggar, and properly spattered with mud, his face even greener than the company runner's. He was muttering as if sick at heart or as if he were suffering the pains of hell, and was trying somehow to struggle up out of a grave. So here was a ghost who disliked the bullets as much as I did, eh? Perhaps he could foresee them, like I could.

"What's up?" The colonel savagely stopped him short, glaring coldly at this apparition. To see this deplorable trooper in such slovenly undress and shuddering with excitement thoroughly irritated the colonel. Fear was not to the colonel's liking in the least, one could see that. And then above all, that helmet held in his hand like a felt hat, when ours was a front-line regiment, a regiment on the attack— that was the last straw. He looked as if he were taking off his hat to the war, this cavalryman, as he walked into it on foot.

Under this stare of disapproval, our uncertain messenger came to attention, with his little fingers along the seams of his trousers, which is the proper thing to do in such cases. He stood there on the road, stiff and swaying, with the sweat running down his throat, and his jaws were working so hard that he uttered little grunting cries like a puppy dreaming. You couldn't make out whether he wanted to say something to us or whether he was crying.

The Germans squatting at the end of the road had just changed weapons. They were now carrying on their pranks with a machine gun; it crackled like a lot of big boxes of matches, and infuriated bullets swarmed all around us, pricking the air like wasps.

All the same the man managed at last to get out something intelligible.

"Quartermaster Sergeant Barousse has been killed, sir," he said in one gasp.

"Well?"

"He was killed on his way to meet the bread waggon on the Étrapes road, sir."

"Well?"

"He's been blown up by a shell."

"Well, good God, and what then?"

"Well, that's what it is, sir."

"Is that all?"

"Yes sir, that's all, sir."

"And what about the bread?" asked the colonel.

That was the end of the conversation, because I distinctly remember that he had time to say, "And what about the bread?" Then that was all. After that there was only a flash and then the noise that came with it. But it was the sort of noise that you never would believe existed. My eyes, ears, nose and mouth were so full of it suddenly that I really believed it was all over and that I had been turned into fire and noise myself.

But no, after a while the fire had gone and the noise stayed a long time in my head, and then my arms and legs were shaking as if some one from behind me were waggling them. They seemed to be leaving me but in the end they stayed where they were. In the smoke which pricked my eyes for a long time the smell of powder and sulphur was strong enough to kill all the bugs and fleas in the whole world.

Directly after that, I thought of Quartermaster Sergeant Barousse who the other fellow had told us had been blown up. That was good news. So much the better, I thought to myself. "That's rid the regiment of one more bastard." He'd tried to have me up for a tin of jam. "Every one has his own war to wage," I said to myself. Looked at in some ways, there seemed at times to be some point in the war. I certainly knew of three or four other swine in our company whom I'd have been very willing to help find a shell, like Barousse had.

As for the colonel, I had nothing against him. Nevertheless, he was dead too. I couldn't see where he was at first. He'd been flung onto the embankment on his side and the explosion had thrown him into the arms of the despatch bearer, who was dead also. They were in each other's arms and would continue the embrace for ever, but the cavalryman hadn't his head any more, only his neck open at the top with blood bubbling in it like stew in a pot. The colonel's stomach was slit open and he was making an ugly face about that. It must have been painful when that happened. So much the worse for him. If he'd gone away when the firing began, he wouldn't have had it.

All this heap of flesh was bleeding like the deuce. Shells were still bursting to right and left of the picture.

I wasn't slow to leave the place after that. I was delighted to have such a good excuse to clear out. In fact, I sang a bit as I walked, tottering slightly as one does after a hard afternoon's rowing when one's legs are behaving rather funnily. "Just one shell; it doesn't take long for just one shell to do the trick," I told myself. "Well, I'm damned!" I kept repeating all the time. "Well, I'm damned!"

There was nobody left at the end of the road. The Germans had gone away. But just that once had taught me pretty quick to keep to the cover of the trees in future. I was in a hurry to get back to the lines to find out whether any others in our lot had been killed while out reconnoitering. Besides, I went on, there must be some pretty smart ways of getting yourself taken prisoner! . . . Here and there wisps of bitter smoke were wreathed around the earth clods. "Perhaps they're all dead by now." I wondered whether they were. "As they're such obstinate fools, that would be the best and most practical way out, that they should all have been killed without delay. . . . Then we should be through with it at once. . . . We'd go off home. We'd go through the Place Clichy again maybe, in triumph. . . . The two or three of us who had survived . . . That's what I hoped. Just a few good fine-looking fellows swinging along with the general in front. All the others would have been killed. Like the colonel—like Barousse, like Vanaille (another sod) and all the rest. . . . They'd cover us with decorations and flowers and we'd march through the Arc de Triomphe. We'd walk into a restaurant and they'd serve us free. We'd never have to pay for anything any more, never again. 'We're your heroes,' we'd say, when the bill came, 'the saviours of our country!' And that would be enough. Little French flags would do for payment. Why, the girl at the cash desk would refuse to take money from heroes; she'd even make us a present of some and kiss us as we went past her till. Life would be worth living."

As I was escaping, I noticed that my arm was bleeding, but only slightly, from a scratch, not a decent wound. It wouldn't be enough; I should have to carry on.

It began to rain again and the Flemish fields seemed to dribble dirty water. For a long time I still hadn't met anybody, only the wind and a little later on the sun. From time to time, I couldn't think from where, a bullet would come after me, gaily through the sunny air, looking for me in all this emptiness, determined to kill me. Why? Never again, even if I lived to be a hundred, would I go for a walk in the country. That I promised myself.

As I walked along, I remembered the ceremony that had taken place the day before. It had been in a meadow on the side of a hill; the colonel in his loud voice had harangued the regiment: "Up, boys, and at 'em! And long live France!"

If you've no imagination, dying doesn't matter much; if you have, it's too much. That's what I think. Never had I understood so many things at once.

The colonel never had had any imagination. All his bad luck was due to that, and ours especially. Was I then the only one in our regiment to have any idea what death meant? I preferred my own taste in death, a leisurely one. . . . To come in twenty years' time, or thirty or maybe longer. Better than the one they planned for me to have right away, swallowing a full mouthful of Flanders mud, more than a mouthful, my face split from ear to ear in one flash. One has surely the right to have an opinion about one's own death. But where could I go? Straight ahead? With my back to the enemy? If the M.P.'s were to catch me at a loose end like that, I should be in for a good time. I should be given a rough-and-ready trial that very evening in a secondary-school classroom. There were plenty of empty ones wherever we went. They would have played at justice with me as one does when the master is out of the room. The N.C.O.'s would be seated on the dais, while I stood handcuffed in front of the little desks. At dawn I should have been shot; a dozen rounds plus one. What then?

I thought again of the colonel and how fine the fellow looked, with his cuirass and his helmet and his moustaches. Put him on at a music hall, walking about among the bullets and shells as I had seen him, and the turn would have filled the Alhambra those days. He'd have wiped the floor with Fragson herself, though at the time I'm speaking of she was tremendously popular. That's what I was thinking. Down, boys, and leave 'em alone, I thought.

After hours and hours of carefully sneaking forward, at last I caught sight of our men by a group of farmhouses. It was one of our advance posts, part of a squadron billeted thereabouts. Not one of them had been killed, they told me. Everybody alive and kicking. But it was I who had the big piece of news. "The colonel's dead!" I yelled to them, as soon as I was within distance.

"There's no shortage of colonels!" Lance Corporal Pistil, who was on duty, and also on fatigue, snapped back at me.

"And while waiting for the colonel to be replaced, I'll tell you what you can do, me lad. You get on with fetching the grub, together with Empouille and Kerdoncuff here. There's a couple of sacks for each of you, and it's behind the church over there that you'll find it. . . . And you can see to it you don't get handed a bag of bloody bones, as you did yesterday. And I'll thank you to get a move on with it and not come bleedin' in here after nightfall, you stiffs. . . ."

So off we went again, all three of us.

"I sha'n't ever tell them anything in future," I said to myself. I was annoyed. There was clearly no point in telling their sort about such a thing as I'd just seen; one only got bawled at for one's pains. It was already too long past to be of any interest. And when you think that a week before I would have had four columns in the papers, along with my photograph, for announcing the death of a colonel like that. Just a brainless lot of sods, that's all!

It was in a cherry orchard dried up by the August sun that the meat for the whole regiment was being doled out. On sacks and on tent canvas spread out on the ground and on the grass itself were pounds and pounds of tripe and whitish-yellow fat and whole disembowelled sheep in a havoc of entrails which oozed curious little streams into the surrounding grass. The carcass of an ox had been cut in two and hung in a tree. The four butchers of the regiment were still clambering around it, swearing and tugging at portions of its flesh. There was any amount of brawling between sections over morsels of rich meat, and kidneys in particular, amid clouds of those flies which are only seen at such moments and are as lusty and clamorous as sparrows.

And then, too, there was blood everywhere, softly flowing through the grass in search of sloping ground. The last pig was being killed near by. Four men and one of the butchers were already squabbling over some of the bits to come.

"Damn your eyes, it was you pinched the sirloin yesterday. . . ."

I had time to glance twice at this discussion of food values, as I leant against a tree, and then I had to give way to an overwhelming desire to vomit—more than a little, until I fainted.

Well, they took me back to camp on a stretcher, but not without making good use of the opportunity to rummage through my two rubber-lined meat sacks.

I awoke into another of Pistil's cursing fits. The war was still in full swing.

Translated by JOHN H. P. MARKS

MALAPARTE

Malaparte often quoted Verlaine:

"Ce qui m'intéresse n'est pas toujours ce qui m'importe."

It was in this manner that he dealt with history. His concern was the tone, or fundamental truths, of history rather than its particulars; and if the facts did not always measure up to the authenticity of the tone, he was, like Herodotus, not above their embellishment —though never their mere invention. And therein lay his discipline and his dangerous art, on the high wire of truth between the sordid and the fantastic; it is not recorded that he ever fell.

from *THE SKIN*

It was not my fault, however, if the price of Negroes' flesh was increasing every day. A dead Negro cost nothing; he cost much less than a dead white man—even less than a live Italian! He cost pretty much the same as twenty Neapolitan children who had died of hunger. It was indeed strange that a dead Negro should cost so little. A dead Negro is very handsome. He is glossy, massive, immense, and when he is stretched out on the ground he occupies almost twice as much space as a dead white man. Even if a Negro, when he was alive in America, was only a poor Harlem bootblack, or a worker whose job was to unload coal in the docks, or a fireman on the railways, in death he took up almost as much space as the huge, magnificent corpses of the Homeric heroes. At heart I was pleased to think that the corpse of a Negro took up almost as much ground as the corpse of Achilles, Hector or Ajax would have done. And I could not resign myself to the idea that a dead Negro should cost so little.

But a live Negro cost a small fortune. Within the last few days the price of live Negroes had risen in Naples from two hundred to a thousand dollars, and its tendency was to increase. It was only necessary to see the hungry expressions with which the poor people eyed a Negro—a live Negro—to appreciate that the price of live Negroes was very high, and was still rising. The dream of all the poor people of Naples, especially the street arabs and the boys, was to be able to hire a "black," if only for a few hours. Hunting Negro soldiers was the favorite sport of the boys. Naples, to them, was a vast equatorial forest, redolent with a warm, heavy odor of sweet fritters, where ecstatic Negroes promenaded, swaying their hips, their eyes fixed upon the heavens. When a street arab managed to seize a Negro by the sleeve of his tunic and drag him along behind him from bar to bar, from inn to inn, from brothel to brothel, all the windows, doorsteps and street corners in the maze of alleys that constitutes Toledo and Forcella would fill with eyes, hands and voices crying: "Sell me your black! I'll give you twenty dollars! Thirty dollars! Fifty dollars!" This was what was called the "flying market." Fifty dollars was the maximum price that was paid for the hire of a Negro for a day, that is for a few hours—the time needed to make him drunk, to strip him of everything he had on, from his cap to his shoes, and then, after nightfall, to abandon him naked on the pavement of an alley.

The Negro suspects nothing. He is not conscious of being bought and resold every quarter of an hour, and he walks about innocently and happily, very proud of his shoes, which glitter as though made of gold, his smart uniform, his yellow gloves, his rings and gold teeth, his great white eyes, viscous and translucent like the eyes of an octopus. He walks along with a smile on his face, his head inclined on his shoulder and his eyes lost in contemplation of a green cloud drifting far away through the sea-blue sky, his sharp, dazzlingly white teeth seeming to cut like scissors the blue fringe of the roofs, the bare legs of the girls leaning against the railings of the balconies, the red carnations that protrude from the terracotta vases on the window sills. He walks like a somnambulist, savoring with delight all the smells, colors, tastes, sights and sounds that make life sweet: the smell of fritters, wine and fried fish, a pregnant woman sitting on her doorstep, a girl scratching her back, another girl looking for a flea in her bosom, the crying of a baby in its cradle, the laughter of a street arab, the flashing of the sunlight on a windowpane, the music of a gramophone, the flames of the papier-mâché Purgatories in which the damned burn at the feet of the Madonnas in the chapels at the corners of the alleys, a boy who with knifelike teeth, snow-white and dazzling, produces from a curved slice of melon, as from a mouth organ, a half-moon of green and red sounds that sparkle against the gray sky of a wall, a girl combing her hair at a window, singing *"Ohi Marì"* and gazing at her image reflected in the sky as in a mirror.

The Negro does not notice that the boy who holds his hand

and strokes his wrist, talking to him softly and looking up at him with mild eyes, from time to time changes his identity. (When the boy sells his "black" to another street arab he slips the Negro's hand into that of the buyer and loses himself in the crowd.) The price of a Negro on the flying market is based on the lavishness and recklessness of his expenditure, on his avidity for food and drink, on the way in which he smiles, lights a cigarette or looks at a woman. A hundred expert, eager eyes follow the Negro's every gesture, count the coins that he draws from his pocket, observe his pink-and-black fingers with their pale cuticles. There are boys who are very expert at the precise and rapid calculation which the traffic entails. (In two months Pasquale Mele, a boy of ten, earned from the purchase and resale of Negroes on the flying market about six thousand dollars, with which he acquired a house in the vicinity of the Piazza Olivella.) As he wanders from bar to bar, from inn to inn, from brothel to brothel, as he smiles, drinks and eats, as he caresses the arms of a girl, the Negro is oblivious of the fact that he has become a medium of exchange, he does not even suspect that he has been bought and sold like a slave.

It was certainly not dignified, the position of the Negro soldiers in the American army—so kind, so black, so respectable—who had won the war, landed at Naples as conquerors, and now found themselves being bought and sold like unfortunate slaves. But in Naples this kind of thing has been happening for a thousand years. Such was the experience of the Normans, the Angevins and the Aragonese, of Charles VIII of France, and of Garibaldi and Mussolini themselves. The people of Naples would have perished of hunger centuries ago if every so often they had not been lucky enough to be able to buy and resell all those, Italians and foreigners, who presumed to land at Naples as conquerors and overlords.

If the cost of hiring a Negro soldier on the flying market for a few hours was only twenty or thirty dollars, the cost of hiring him for one or two months was high, ranging from three hundred to a thousand dollars or even more. An American Negro was a gold mine. The owner of a Negro slave possessed a sure income and a source of easy gain. He had solved the problem of making a living, and often grew rich. The risk, certainly, was great, since the M.P.s, who understood nothing about the affairs of Europe, nourished an inexplicable aversion to the traffic in Negroes. But in spite of the M.P.s the Negro trade was held in high honor in Naples. There was not a family in the city, however poor, which did not possess its Negro slave.

A Negro's master treated his slave as an honored guest. He offered him food and drink, filled him with wine and fritters, let him dance with his own daughters to the strains of an old gramophone, made him sleep, along with all the members of his family, male and female, in his own bed—one of those vast beds which occupy a large part of every Neapolitan basso. And the Negro would come home every evening with gifts of sugar, cigarettes, spam, bacon, bread, white flour, vests, stockings, shoes, uniforms, bedspreads, overcoats, and vast quantities of caramels. The "black" was delighted by the quiet family life, the decorousness and warmth of his welcome, the smiles of the women and children, the sight of the table laid for supper beneath the lamp, the wine, the pizza cheese, the sweet fritters. After a few days the fortunate Negro, having become the slave of this poor, warmhearted Neapolitan family, would become engaged to one of his master's daughters; and he would return home every evening laden with gifts for his fiancée—cases of corned beef, bags of sugar and flour, cartons of cigarettes, and treasures of every kind, which he filched from the military stores, and which the father and brothers of his fiancée sold to dealers on the black market. It was also possible to buy white slaves in the jungle that was Naples; but they showed little return, and so cost less. Still, a white soldier from the P.X. cost as much as a colored driver.

Drivers were the most expensive of all. A black driver cost up to two thousand dollars. There were drivers who presented their fiancées with complete vehicles laden with flour, sugar, tires and cans of gas. One day a black driver gave his fiancée, Concetta Esposito, of the Vicolo della Torretta, situated at the end of the Riviera di Chiaia, a heavy tank—a Sherman. In two hours the tank, which had been hidden in a yard, was stripped of all its bolts and dismantled. In two hours it disappeared: not a trace was left of it save for a patch of oil on the flagstones of the yard. One night a Liberty ship, which had arrived from America a few hours before in convoy with ten other ships, was stolen from Naples harbor. Not only was the cargo stolen, but the ship itself. It vanished, and was never heard of again. All Naples, from Capodimonte to Posilipo, rocked with tumultuous laughter, as if convulsed by an earthquake. The Muses, the Graces, Juno, Minerva, Diana and all the Goddesses from Olympus, who in the cool of the evening appear among the clouds above Vesuvius and look down on Naples, could be seen laughing and clasping their bosoms with both hands, while Venus made the heavens shimmer with the flashing of her white teeth.

"How much does a Liberty ship cost on the black market, Jack?"

"*Oh, ça ne coûte pas cher,* you damned fool!" Jack would reply, turning red.

"You were right to post sentries on the bridges of your battle-ships. If you aren't careful they'll steal your fleet."

"To hell with you, Malaparte."

When, each evening, we came to the end of Via Toledo and arrived outside the famous Caffè Caflisch, which the French had requisitioned and turned into their *foyer du soldat,* we used to slacken our pace in order to listen to General Juin's soldiers talking French among themselves. It was a pleasure to us to hear the French language articulated by French voices. (Jack always spoke French to me. When, immediately after the Allied landing at Salerno, I was appointed liaison officer between the Italian Corps of Liberation and General Headquarters of the Peninsular Base Section, Jack, Staff Colonel Jack Hamilton, had at once asked me if I spoke French, and at my *"Oui, mon colonel"* he had flushed with joy *"Vous savez,"* he said to me, *"il fait bon de parler français. Le français est une langue très, très respectable. C'est très bon pour la santé."*) At every hour of the day a small crowd of soldiers and sailors from Algeria, Madagascar, Morocco, Senegal, Tahiti and Indochina would be standing about on the pavement outside the Caffè Caflisch, but their French was not that of La Fontaine, and we could not understand a word they said. Sometimes, however, if we strained our ears, we were lucky enough to catch a few French words pronounced with a Parisian or Marseillais accent. Jack would flush with joy, and seizing me by the arm would say: *"Ecoute, Malaparte, écoute, voilà du français, du véritable français!"* We would both stop, deeply moved, and listen to those French voices, those French words, with their Ménilmontant or La Cannebière intonation, and Jack would say: *"Ah, que c'est bon! Ah, que ça fait du bien!"*

Often, each lending the other courage, we would cross the threshold of the Caffè Caflisch. Timidly Jack would go up to the French sergeant who ran the foyer du soldat and ask him with a blush: *"Est-ce que, par hasard . . . est-ce qu'on a vu par là le lieutenant Lyautey?"*

"Non, mon colonel," the sergeant would reply, *"on ne l'a pas vu depuis quelques jours. Je regrette."*

"Merci," Jack would say. *"Au revoir, mon ami."*

"Au revoir, mon colonel," the sergeant would say.

"Ah, que ça fait du bien, d'entendre parler français!" Jack would say, red-faced, as we walked out of the Caffè Caflisch.

The Pendino is a dismal alley. It owes its character not so much to its narrowness, carved out as it is between the high, mildewed walls of ancient, sordid houses, or to the eternal darkness that reigns within it even on sunny days, as to the strangeness of its inhabitants.

In point of fact, the Pendino di Santa Barbara is famous for the many female dwarfs who reside in it. They are so small that they barely come up to the knee of a man of average height. Repulsive and wrinkled, they are among the ugliest of their kind in the world. There are in Spain female dwarfs of great beauty, with well-proportioned limbs and features. And I have seen some in England who are truly exquisite, pink-skinned and fair-haired, like miniature Venuses. But the female dwarfs of the Pendino di Santa Barbara are frightful creatures. All of them, even the youngest, look like very old women, so wizened are their faces, so creased their foreheads, so thin and faded their disheveled locks.

The most astounding thing about that noisome alley, with its horrible population of dwarf women, is the handsomeness of the men, who are tall and have very dark eyes and hair, leisurely, noble gestures, and clear, resonant voices. There are no male dwarfs to be seen on the Pendino di Santa Barbara, a fact which encourages the belief that they die in infancy or that this lack of inches is a monstrous legacy inherited only by the women.

These dwarf women spend the whole day sitting on the doorsteps of the bassi or squatting on tiny stools at the entrances to their lairs, croaking to one another in froglike voices. Their shortness of stature seems prodigous against the background of the furniture that fills their dark caverns—chests of drawers, vast cupboards, beds that look like giants' couches. To reach the furniture the dwarf women climb on chairs and benches; they hoist themselves up with their arms, making use of the ends of the high iron beds. And anyone climbing the steps of the Pendino di Santa Barbara for the first time feels like Gulliver in the Kingdom of Lilliput, or a servant at the Court of Madrid among Velasquez's dwarfs. The foreheads of these female dwarfs are scored with the same deep wrinkles as furrow the foreheads of the horrible old women portrayed by Goya. Nor should this Spanish analogy be thought arbitrary, for the district is Hispanic in character and still alive with memories of the long years when Naples was subject to Castilian domination. There is an air of old Spain about the streets, alleys, houses and mansions, the strong, sweet smells, the gutteral voices, the long, musical laments that echo from balcony to balcony, and the raucous strains of the gramophones that issue from the depths of the dark caverns.

Taralli are little cakes made of sweet pastry; and the bakery halfway up the steps of the Pendino, from which at all hours of the day there emanates the appetizing smell of fresh, crisp taralli, is famous throughout Naples. When the baker thrusts his long wooden shovel into the red-hot mouth of the oven the dwarf women run up, stretching out their little hands, which are as dark and wrinkled as the hands of monkeys. Uttering loud cries in their raucous little voices they seize the dainty taralli, all hot and steaming, hobble rapidly to different parts of the alley, and deposit the taralli on shining brass trays. Then they sit on the doorsteps of their hovels with the trays on their knees and wait for customers, singing *"Oh li taralli! oh li taralli belli cauri!"* The smell of the taralli spreads all through the Pendino di Santa Barbara, and the dwarf women, squatting on their doorsteps, croak and laugh among themselves. And one, a young one perhaps, sings at a little window high up, and looks like a great spider poking its hairy head out of a crack in the wall.

Bald, toothless dwarf women go up and down the slimy stairway, supporting themselves with sticks or crutches, reeling along on their little short legs, lifting their knees up to their chins in order to mount the steps, or drag themselves along on all fours, whimpering and slobbering. They look like little monsters in the paintings of Breughel or Bosch, and one day Jack and I saw one of them sitting on the threshold of a cavern with a sick dog in her arms. As it lay on her lap, in her tiny arms, it seemed a gigantic animal, a monstrous wild beast. Up came a companion of hers, and the two of them seized the sick dog, the one by the hind legs, the other by the head, and with great difficulty carried it into the hovel. It seemed as if they were carrying a wounded dinosaur. The voices that ascend from the depths of the caverns are shrill and guttural, and the wails of the dreadful children, who are tiny and wrinkled, like old dolls, resemble the mewling of a dying kitten. If you enter one of these hovels you see, in the fetid half-light, those great spiders with enormous heads dragging themselves across the floor, and you have to take care not to crush them beneath the soles of your shoes.

Occasionally we saw some of these dwarf women climbing the steps of the Pendino in the company of gigantic American soldiers, white or colored, with moist, shining eyes. Tugging them along by the trouser legs they would push them into their lairs. (The white soldiers, thank God, were always drunk.) I shuddered when I visualized the strange unions of those enormous men and those little monsters, on those high, vast beds.

And I would say to Jimmy Wren: "I am glad to see that those little dwarfs and your handsome soldiers like each other. Aren't you glad too, Jimmy?"

"Of course I'm glad too," Jimmy would answer, furiously chewing his gum.

"Do you think they'll get married?" I would say.

"Why not?" Jimmy would answer.

"Jimmy is a nice guy," Jack would say, "but you mustn't provoke him. He flares up easily."

"I'm a nice guy too," I would say, "and I'm glad to think that you have come from America to improve the Italian race. But for you those poor dwarfs would have remained spinsters. By ourselves, we poor Italians couldn't have done anything about it. It's a lucky thing that you people have come from America to marry our dwarf women."

"You will certainly be invited to the wedding breakfast," Jack would say. *"Tu pourras prononcer un discours magnifique."*

"Oui, Jack, un discours magnifique. But don't you think, Jimmy," I would say, "that the Allied military authorities ought to encourage marriages between these dwarf women and your handsome soldiers? It would be an excellent thing if your soldiers married those little dwarfs. As a race you are too tall. America needs to come down to our level, don't you think so, Jimmy?"

"Yes, I think so," Jimmy would answer, giving me a sidelong glance.

"You are too tall," I would say, "too handsome. It's immoral that the world should contain a race of men who are so tall, so handsome and so healthy. I should like all the American soldiers to get married to those little dwarfs. Those 'Italian brides' would score a tremendous hit in America. American civilization needs shorter legs."

"To hell with you," Jimmy would say, spitting on the ground.

"Il va te caresser la figure, si tu insistes," Jack would say.

"Yes, I know. Jimmy is a nice guy," I would say, laughing to myself.

It made me feel sick at heart to laugh in that way. But I should have been happy, truly happy, if all the American soldiers had one day gone back to America arm in arm with all the little dwarf women of Naples, Italy and Europe.

The "plague" had broken out in Naples on October 1, 1943— the very day on which the Allied armies had entered that ill-starred city as liberators. October 1, 1943, is a memorable date in the history of Naples, both because it marks the beginning of the liberation of Italy and Europe from the anguish, shame and sufferings of war and slavery, and because it exactly coincided with the outbreak of the terrible plague which gradually spread from the unhappy city all over Italy and all over Europe.

The appalling suspicion that the fearful disease had been brought to Naples by the liberators themselves was certainly unjust; but it became a certainty in the minds of the people when they perceived, with a mixture of amazement and superstitious terror, that the Allied soldiers remained strangely immune from the contagion. Pink-faced, calm and smiling, they moved about in the midst of the plague-stricken mob without contracting the loathsome disease, which gathered its harvest of victims solely from among the civilian population, not only in Naples itself, but even in the country districts, spreading like a patch of oil into the territory liberated by the Allied armies as they laboriously drove the Germans northward.

But it was strictly forbidden, under threat of the severest penalties, to insinuate in public that the plague had been brought to Italy by the liberators. And it was dangerous to repeat the allegation in private, even in an undertone, since among the many loathsome effects of the plague the most loathsome was that it engendered in its victims a mad passion, a voluptuous avidity for delation. No sooner were they stricken with the disease than one and all began to inform against fathers, mothers, brothers, sons, husbands, lovers, relations and dearest friends—but never against themselves. Indeed, one of the most surprising and repulsive characteristics of this extraordinary plague was that it transformed the human conscience into a horrible, noisome ulcer.

The only remedy which the British and American military authorities had discovered for the disease was to forbid the Allied soldiers to enter the most seriously infected areas of the city. On every wall one read the legends "Off Limits" and "Out of Bounds," surmounted by the aulic emblem of the plague—a black circle within which were depicted two black bars in the form of a cross, similar to the pair of crossed shinbones that appears beneath a skull on the saddlecloth of a funeral carriage.

Within a short space of time the whole of Naples was declared "off limits" with the exception of a few streets in the center of the city. But the areas most frequented by the liberators were in fact those which were "off limits," i.e., the most infected and therefore forbidden areas, since it is in the nature of man, and especially of the soldiers of all ages and every army, to prefer forbidden things to those that are permitted. And so the contagion, whether it had been brought to Naples by the liberators, or whether the latter carried it from one part of the city to another, from the infected areas to the healthy, very soon reached a terrible pitch of violence, rendered abominable, almost diabolical, by its grotesque, obscene manifestations, which were suggestive of a macabre public celebration, a funereal kermis. Drunken soldiers danced with women who were almost or completely naked in the squares and streets, in the midst of the wreckage of the houses that had been destroyed in the air raids. There was a mad orgy of drinking, eating, gaiety, singing, laughing, prodigality and revelry, amid the frightful stench that emanated from the countless hundreds of corpses buried beneath the ruins.

This was a plague profoundly different from, but no less horrible than, the epidemics which from time to time devastated Europe during the Middle Ages. The extraordinary thing about this most modern of diseases was that it corrupted not the body but the soul. The limbs remained seemingly intact, but within the integument of the healthy flesh the soul festered and rotted. It was a kind of moral plague, against which it seemed there was no defense. The first to be infected were the women, who in every nation constitute the weakest bulwark against vice, and an open door to every form of evil. And this seemed an amazing and most lamentable thing, inasmuch as during the years of slavery and war, right up to the day of the promised and eagerly awaited liberation, the women—not only in Naples, but throughout Italy and Europe—had proved, amid the universal wretchedness and misfortune, that they possessed greater dignity and greater strength of mind than the men. In Naples and in every other city of Europe the women had refused to give themselves to the Germans. Only the prostitutes had had relations with the enemy, and even they had not done so openly, but in secret, either to avoid having to endure the sharp revulsion of popular feeling or because they themselves considered that to have such relations was to be guilty of the most infamous crime that a woman could commit during those years.

And now, as a result of this loathsome plague, which first corrupted the feminine sense of honor and dignity, prostitution on the most appalling scale had brought shame to every hovel and every mansion. But why call it shame? Such was the baneful power of the contagion that self-prostitution had become a praiseworthy act, almost a proof of patriotism, and all, men and women, far from blushing at the thought of it, seemed to glory in their own and the universal degradation. True, many, whose sense of justice was warped by despair, almost made excuses for the plague, implying that the women used the disease as a pretext for becoming prostitutes, and that they sought in the plague the justification of their shame.

But a more intimate knowledge of the disease subsequently revealed that such a suspicion was mischievous. For the first to despair of their lot were the women; and I myself have heard many bewailing and cursing this pitiless plague which drove them, with an irresistible violence their feeble virtue was powerless to withstand, to prostitute themselves like bitches. Such, alas, is the nature of women, who often seek to buy with tears forgiveness for their deeds of shame, and pity too. But in this case one must perforce forgive them and have pity on them.

If such was the lot of the women, no less piteous and horrible was that of the men. No sooner were they infected than they lost all self-respect. They lent themselves to the most ignoble transactions and committed the most sordid acts of self-abasement; they dragged themselves on all fours through the mire, kissing the boots of their "liberators" (who were disgusted by such extreme and unasked-for abjectness), not only to obtain pardon for the sufferings and humiliations which they had undergone during the years of slavery and war, but so that they might have the honor of being trampled underfoot by their new masters; they spat on their own country's flag and publicly sold their own wives, daughters and mothers. They did all this, they said, to save their country. Yet those who seemed on the surface to be immune from the disease fell sick of a nauseating malady which made them ashamed of being Italians and even of belonging to the human race. It must be admitted that they did all they could to be unworthy of the name of men. Few indeed were those who remained free from taint, their consciences seemingly impervious to the disease; and they went about in fear and trembling, despised by all, unwelcome witnesses of the universal shame.

The suspicion, which later became a conviction, that the plague had been brought to Europe by the liberators themselves had filled the people with profound and heartfelt grief. Although it is an ancient tradition that the vanquished hate their conquerors, the people of Naples did not hate the Allies. They had awaited them with longing, they had welcomed them with joy. Their thousand-year-long experience of wars and foreign invasions had taught them that it is the habit of conquerors to reduce those whom they have vanquished to slavery. Instead of slavery, the Allies had brought them freedom. And the people had immediately loved these magnificent soldiers—so young, so handsome, so well groomed—whose teeth were so white and whose lips were so red. In all those centuries of invasions, of wars won and lost, Europe had never seen such elegant, clean, courteous soldiers. Always they were newly shaven; their uniforms were impeccable; their ties were tied with meticulous care; their shirts were always spotless; their shoes were eternally new and shining; they had never a tear in their trousers or at their elbows, never a button missing. Such were these wonderful armies, born, like Venus, of the sea foam. They contained not a soldier who had a boil, a decayed tooth, even a pimple on his face. Never had Europe seen soldiers who were so free from infection, without the smallest microbe either in the folds of their skin or in the recesses of their consciences. And what hands they had—white, well looked after, always protected by immaculate shammy-leather gloves! But what touched the people of Naples most of all was the kindliness of their liberators, especially the Americans: their urbane nonchalance, their humanity, their innocent, cordial smiles—the smiles of honest, goodhearted, ingenuous, overgrown boys. If ever it was an honor to lose a war, it was certainly a great honor for the people of Naples, and for all the other conquered peoples of Europe, to have lost this one to soldiers who were so courteous, elegant and neatly dressed, so goodhearted and generous.

And yet everything that these magnificent soldiers touched was at once corrupted. No sooner did the luckless inhabitants of the liberated countries grasp the hands of their liberators than they began to fester and to stink. It was enough that an Allied soldier should lean out of his jeep to smile at a woman, to give her face a fleeting caress, and the same woman, who until that moment had preserved her dignity and purity, would change into a prostitute. It was enough that a child should put into its mouth a caramel offered to it by an American soldier, and its innocent soul would be corrupted.

The liberators themselves were terrified and deeply affected by this dire scourge. "It is human to feel compassion for the afflicted," writes Boccaccio in his introduction to the *Decameron,* with reference to the terrible plague which swept Florence in 1348. But the Allied soldiers, especially the Americans, faced with the pitiable spectacle of the plague of Naples, did not only feel compassion for the unhappy people of that city: they felt compassion for themselves as well. The reason was that for some time past the suspicion had been growing in their ingenuous and honest minds that the source of the terrible contagion was in their frank, timid smiles, in their eyes, so full of human sympathy, in their affectionate caresses. The source of the plague was in their compassion, in their very desire to help these unfortunate people, to alleviate their miseries, to succor them in the tremendous disaster that had overtaken them. The source of the disease was in the very hand which they stretched out in brotherhood to this conquered people.

Perhaps it was written that the freedom of Europe must be born not of liberation, but of the plague. Perhaps it was written that, just as liberation had been born of the sufferings of war and slavery, so freedom must be born of the new and terrible sufferings caused by the plague which liberation had brought with it. The price of freedom is high—far higher than that of slavery. And it is not paid in gold, nor in blood, nor in the most noble sacrifices, but in cowardice, in prostitution, in treachery, and in everything that is rotten in the human soul.

At about eleven o'clock on the evening of July 25, 1943, the Secretary of the Royal Italian Embassy in Berlin, Michele Lanza, was reclining comfortably in an armchair near the open window in the little bachelor apartment occupied by the Press attaché, Cristiano Ridomi.

It was stiflingly hot, and the two friends, having extinguished the light and thrown the window wide open, were sitting in the dark room, smoking and chatting. Angela Lanza had left for Italy with her little girl a few days before, intending to pass the summer in her villa near Lake Como. (The families of foreign diplomats had left Berlin at the beginning of July in order to avoid not so much the suffocating heat of the Berlin summer as the air raids, which were becoming heavier each day.) And Michele Lanza, like the other Embassy officials, had got into the habit of spending his nights at the homes of various colleagues so as not to be left alone, shut up in a room, during the hours of darkness, which are the slowest of all to pass, and so that he might share with a friend, with a human being, the anguish and dangers of the raids.

That evening Lanza was in Ridomi's apartment, and the two friends were sitting in the darkness, discussing the massacre of Hamburg. The happenings described in the reports from the Royal Italian Consul in Hamburg were terrible. Whole districts of the city had been set alight by phosphorus bombs, which had claimed a great number of victims. There was nothing strange about that: even the Germans are mortal. But thousands and thousands of unfortunate people, dripping with burning phosphorus, had thrown themselves into the canals which cross Hamburg in every direction, into the river, the harbor, into ponds, even into the basins in the public gardens, hoping thereby to extinguish the flames that were devouring them; or they had had themselves covered over with earth in the trenches that had been dug here and there in the squares and streets to provide immediate shelter in the event of sudden raids. Clinging to the banks and to boats and immersed in the water up to their mouths, or buried in the earth up to their necks, they waited for the authorities to find some antidote to those treacherous flames. For the nature of phosphorus is such that it adheres to the skin like a sticky leprous crust, and burns only when it comes in contact with the air. As soon as those wretched beings stuck an arm out of the ground or out of the water it started to burn like a torch. To protect themselves from the scourge the hapless victims were forced to remain immersed in the water or buried in the earth like the damned in Dante's *Inferno*. Rescue squads went from one to another of them, offering them food and drink, fastening those who were immersed in the water to the bank with ropes lest, overcome by weariness, they should collapse and drown, and experimenting with all sorts of ointments. But their efforts were in vain; for while they were anointing an arm, or a leg, or a shoulder, having momentarily pulled it out of the water or out of the ground, the flames at once flared up again like little fiery serpents, and nothing availed to check the spread of that terrible burning corruption.

For a few days Hamburg presented the appearance of Dis, the infernal city. Here and there in the squares, in the streets, in the canals, in the Elbe, thousands and thousands of heads projected from the water and from the ground, looking as though they had been lopped off by the headsman's axe. Livid with terror and pain, they moved their eyes, opened their mouths and spoke. Those horrible heads, wedged between the paving stones of the streets or floating on the surface of the water, were visited night and day by their doomed owners' relatives, an emaciated, ragged throng, who spoke in low voices, as if to avoid intensifying their excruciating agony. Some brought food, drink and ointments, others brought cushions to place beneath the heads of their dear ones; some sat beside those who were buried in the ground and fanned their faces to bring them comfort in the heat of the day, while others sheltered their heads from the sun with umbrellas, or mopped their perspiring brows, or moistened their lips with soaking handkerchiefs, or straightened their hair with combs; some leaned from boats or from the bank of the canal or the river and consoled the doomed victims as they clung to their lines and moved to and fro with the current. Packs of dogs ran hither and thither, barking and licking the faces of their interred masters, or jumping into the water and swimming out to help them. Sometimes one of the doomed creatures, seized with impatience or despair, would utter a loud cry and attempt to escape from the water or from the ground, to put an end to the torment of his useless waiting; but immediately his limbs came in contact with the air they flared up, and dreadful scuffles broke out between the desperate victims and their relatives, who punched them with their fists, struck them with stones and sticks, or exerted the whole weight of their bodies in their efforts to push those dreadful heads back into the warter or into the earth.

The bravest and the most patient were the children. They did not cry or call out, but looked about them with serene eyes, gazing at the fearful spectacle, and smiled at their relatives, with that wonderful resignation so characteristic of children, who forgive the impotence of their seniors, and pity those who cannot help them. As soon as night fell a whispering arose on all sides, a murmuring, as of the wind in the grass, and those thousands and thousands of heads watched the sky with eyes that were bright with terror.

On the seventh day the order was given for the removal of the civilian population from the localities where the doomed beings were buried in the ground or immersed in the water. The crowd of relatives silently withdrew, urged on gently by the soldiers and orderlies. The doomed victims were left alone. A terrified muttering, a gnashing of teeth, a stifled sobbing came from those horrible heads, which protruded above the water and the ground along the banks of the canals and the river, in the streets and the deserted squares. All day those heads talked among themselves, wept, cried out, with their

mouths just above the surface of the ground, making frightful gri-
maces, putting out their tongues at the schupos on guard at the crossroads; and they seemed to be eating earth and spitting stones. Then
night fell: and mysterious shadows moved among the doomed creatures and silently bent over them. Columns of trucks arrived with
their lights extinguished, and stopped. From every side arose the
sound of spades and shovels, and a splashing, and the dull plop of
oars, and cries that were at once stifled, and moans, and the staccato
crack of pistols.

After the liberation of Naples the Allies, for military reasons, had
prohibited fishing in the bay. From Sorrento to Capri, from Capri
to Ischia, the sea was blocked by mine fields and infested with drifting mines which made fishing dangerous. Moreover, the Allies, especially the British, considered it unsafe to let the fishermen go out
to sea, fearing that they might carry information to the German
submarines, or supply them with oil, or in some way endanger the
hundreds and hundreds of warships, troop transports and Liberty
ships which were anchored in the bay. To think that they could distrust the fishermen of Naples—that they could believe them to be
capable of such crimes! But there it was: fishing was prohibited.

In the whole of Naples it was impossible to find a fishbone, let
alone a fish: there was not a sardine, not a hogfish, not a lobster,
a mullet or a cuttlefish—there was nothing. Consequently, when General Cork gave a dinner in honor of some high Allied officer, like
Field Marshal Alexander, General Juin or General Anders, or some
important politician, a Churchill, a Vishinsky or a Bogomolov, or
some commission of American senators who had come by air from
Washington to hear what the soldiers of the Fifth Army had to say
in criticism of their generals and to collect their opinions and suggestions with regard to the most serious problems of the war, he was
in the habit of having the fish for his table caught in the Naples
Aquarium, which, apart from that at Munich, is perhaps the most
important aquarium in Europe.

It followed that the fish served at General Cork's dinners was
always very fresh and of a rare species. At the dinner which he had
given in honor of General Eisenhower we had eaten the famous "giant
octopus" presented to the Naples Aquarium by the Emperor William
II of Germany. The celebrated Japanese fish known as "dragons,"
a gift from the Emperor Hirohito of Japan, had been sacrificed on
General Cork's table in honor of a party of American senators. The

enormous mouths of those monstrous fish, their yellow gills, their black and scarlet fins, which resembled the wings of a bat, their green and gold tails, and their heads, bristling with prickles and crested like the helmet of Achilles, had profoundly depressed the spirits of the senators, who were already preoccupied with the progress of the war against Japan. But General Cork, who in addition to his military virtues possessed the qualities of the perfect diplomat, had restored his guests' morale by intoning "Johnny Got a Zero," the famous song of the American airmen in the Pacific, and they had all sung it in chorus.

In the early days General Cork had had the fish for his table caught from the tanks in the Lucrine Lake—famous for the ferocious and exquisite murries which Lucullus, whose villa was near Lucrino, fed on the flesh of his slaves. But the American newspapers, which lost no opportunity of harshly criticizing the High Command of the U.S. Army, had accused General Cork of mental cruelty in that he had compelled his guests—"respectable American citizens"—to eat Lucullus's murries. "Can General Cork tell us," some papers had ventured to say, "on what kind of meat he feeds his murries?"

It was in consequence of this accusation that General Cork had given orders to the effect that in future the fish for his table should be caught in the Naples Aquarium. Thus, one by one, all the rarest and most famous fish in the Aquarium had been sacrificed to General Cork's mental cruelty, including even the heroic swordfish, a gift from Mussolini (which had been served steamed with a border of boiled potatoes), and the strikingly beautiful tunny, a gift from His Majesty King Victor Emmanuel III, and the lobsters from the Isle of Wight, the gracious gift of His Britannic Majesty King George V.

The valuable pearl oysters which His Highness the Duke of Aosta, Viceroy of Ethiopia, had sent as a gift to the Naples Aquarium (they came from that part of the coast of Arabia which lies opposite Massawa) had enlivened the dinner which General Cork had given in honor of Vishinsky, the Soviet Vice-Commissar for Foreign Affairs, who at the time was representing the U.S.S.R. on the Allied Commission in Italy. Vishinsky had been much astonished to find in each of his oysters a pink pearl of the color of the new moon. And he had raised his eyes from his plate and looked at General Cork with the same expression with which he might have looked at the Emir of Bagdad had he been present at one of the banquets described in the *Thousand and One Nights.*

"Don't spit out the stone," General Cork had said to him. "It's delicious."

"But it's a pearl!" Vishinsky had exclaimed.

"Of course it's a pearl! Don't you like it?"

Vishinsky had gulped down the pearl, muttering between his teeth, in Russian: "These decadent capitalists!"

No less great, it seemed, was the amazement of Churchill when, having been invited to dinner by General Cork, he found on his plate a strange fish, round, slender and of a steely hue, like the quoits which the ancient discoboli used to throw.

"What is it?" asked Churchill.

"A fish," replied General Cork.

"A fish?" said Churchill, looking closely at the extraordinary fish.

"What is the name of this fish?" General Cork asked the major-domo.

"It's a torpedo," replied the major-domo.

"What?" said Churchill.

"A torpedo," said General Cork.

"A torpedo?" said Churchill.

"Yes, of course—a torpedo," said General Cork, and turning to the major-domo he asked him what a torpedo was.

"An electric fish," replied the major-domo.

"Ah, yes, of course—an electric fish!" said General Cork, turning to Churchill. And the two men smiled at each other, their fish knives and forks suspended in mid-air, not daring to touch the "torpedo."

"Are you sure it isn't dangerous?" asked Churchill after a few moments' silence.

General Cork turned to the major-domo. "Do you think it's dangerous to touch it?" he said. "It's charged with electricity."

"Electricity," replied the major-domo in English, which he pronounced with a Neapolitan accent, "is dangerous when it is raw. When it is cooked it is harmless."

"Ah!" exclaimed Churchill and General Cork with one voice; and heaving sighs of relief they touched the electric fish with the ends of their forks.

But one fine day the supply of fish in the Aquarium ran out. There only remained the famous Siren (a very rare example of that species of "sirenoids" which, because of their almost human form, gave rise to the ancient legend about the Sirens) and a few wonderful stems of coral.

General Cork, who had the praiseworthy habit of concerning himself personally with the smallest details, had asked the major-domo what kind of fish it would be possible to catch in the Aquarium for the dinner he was giving in honor of Mrs. Flat.

"There's very little left," the major-domo had replied. "Only a Siren and a few stems of coral."

"Is it a good fish, the Siren?"

"Excellent!" the major-domo had replied, without batting an eyelid.

"And coral?" General Cork had asked. (When he concerned himself with his dinners he was especially meticulous.) "Is it good to eat?"

"No—not coral. It's a little indigestible."

"Very well, then—no coral."

"We can use it as a border," the major-domo had suggested imperturbably.

"That's fine!"

And the major-domo had written on the menu: "Siren mayonnaise with a border of coral."

At that moment the door opened and four liveried footmen appeared in the entrance, preceded by the major-domo. On a kind of stretcher, covered with magnificent red brocade on which was designed the crest of the Dukes of Toledo, they carried, in the traditional manner, an immense solid silver tray, containing an enormous fish. A gasp of joy and admiration passed down the table. "Here is the Siren!" exclaimed General Cork, turning to Mrs. Flat and bowing.

The major-domo, assisted by the footmen, deposited the tray in the middle of the table, in front of General Cork and Mrs. Flat, and withdrew a few steps.

We all looked at the fish, and we turned pale. A feeble cry of horror escaped the lips of Mrs. Flat, and General Cork blanched.

In the middle of the tray was a little girl, or something that resembled a little girl. She lay face upwards on a bed of green lettuce leaves, encircled by a large wreath of pink coral stems. Her eyes were open, her lips half closed; and she was gazing with an expression of wonderment at Luca Giordano's painting of the "Triumph of Venus" which adorned the ceiling. She was naked; but her dark, shining skin, which was of the same purple color as Mrs. Flat's gown, was exactly like a well-fitted dress in the way in which it outlined her still callow yet already well-proportioned form, the gentle curve of her hips, her slightly protruding belly, her little virginal breasts, and her broad, plump shoulders.

She might have been not more than eight or ten years old, though at first sight, owing to the precocious development of her body, which was that of a grown woman, she looked fifteen. Here and there, especially about the shoulders and hips, the skin had been torn or pulpified by the process of cooking, and through the cracks and fissures a glimpse was afforded of the tender flesh, which in some places was silvery, in others golden, so that she looked as if she were clad in purple and yellow, just like Mrs. Flat. And, like Mrs. Flat's, her face (which the heat of the boiling water had caused to burst out of its skin like an over-ripe fruit from its rind) resembled a shining mask of old porcelain, while her lips pouted, and her brow was deep and narrow, her eyes round and green. She had short, fin-like arms, pointed at the ends and similar in shape to hands with no fingers. Hairlike bristles protruded in a tuft from the top of her head and grew sparsely down the sides of her small face. About her mouth the flesh was all puckered and, as it were, congealed in a kind of grimace that resembled a smile. Her flanks were long and slender, and terminated, exactly as Ovid says, *in piscem*—in a fish's tail. The little girl lay on her silver bier; she seemed to be asleep. But, owing to the unpardonable negligence of the cook, she slept as the dead sleep when no one has performed the merciful duty of lowering their eyelids: she slept with her eyes open. And she gazed at Luca Giordano's Tritons as they blew into their sea shells; at the dolphins as they galloped over the waves, dragging Venus's coach behind them; at Venus herself, sitting naked in her golden coach, and her retinue of pink and white nymphs; at Neptune, grasping his trident as he raced across the sea, drawn by his mettlesome white horses, still athirst for the innocent blood of Hippolytus. She gazed at the painting of the "Triumph of Venus" which adorned the ceiling—at the blue sea, the silvery fishes, the green sea monsters, the white clouds that drifted across the horizon; and she smiled ecstatically. This was *her* sea, this was her lost country, the land of her dreams, the happy kingdom of the Sirens.

It was the first time I had ever seen a little girl who had been cooked, a little girl who had been boiled; and I was silent, gripped by a holy fear. All the diners were pale with horror.

General Cork raised his eyes and looked at his guests. "But it isn't a fish . . . ! It's a little girl!" he exclaimed in a trembling voice.

"No," I said, "it's a fish."

"Are you sure it's a fish—a *real* fish?" said General Cork.

Walking along the miserable alleys of Naples one often catches a glimpse, through the open door of some basso, of a dead man lying on a bed, encircled by a wreath of flowers. And it is not unusual to see the corpse of a little girl. But I had never seen the corpse of a little girl encircled by a wreath of coral. How many poor Neapolitan mothers would have coveted such a wonderful wreath of coral for their own dead babes! Coral stems are like the branches of a flowering peach tree. They are a joy to behold; they lend a gay, springlike air to the dead bodies of little children. I looked at that poor boiled child, and I trembled inwardly with pity and pride. A wonderful country, Italy! I thought. What other people in the world can permit itself the luxury of offering Siren mayonnaise with a border of coral to a foreign army that has destroyed and invaded its country? Ah! It was worth losing the war just to see those American officers and that proud American woman sitting pale and horror-stricken round the table of an American general, on which, in a silver tray, reposed the body of a Siren, a sea goddess!

"Disgusting!" exclaimed Mrs. Flat, covering her eyes with her hands.

"Yes . . . I mean . . . yes . . ." stammered General Cork, pale and trembling.

"Take it away—take this horrible thing away!" cried Mrs. Flat.

"Why?" I said. "It's an excellent fish."

"But there must be some mistake! Please forgive me . . . but . . . there must be some mistake . . . Please forgive me . . ." stammered poor General Cork, with a wail of distress.

"I assure you that it's an excellent fish," I said.

"But we can't eat that . . . that girl . . . that poor girl!" said Colonel Eliot.

"It isn't a girl," I said. "It's a fish."

"General," said Mrs. Flat in a stern voice, "I hope you won't force me to eat that . . . this . . . that poor girl!"

"But it's a fish!" said General Cork. "It's a first-rate fish! Malaparte says it's excellent. He knows . . ."

"I haven't come to Europe to be forced to eat human flesh by *your* friend Malaparte, *or by you*," said Mrs. Flat, her voice trembling with indignation. "Let's leave it to these barbarous Italians to eat children at dinner. I refuse. I am an honest American woman. I don't eat Italian children!"

"I'm sorry—I'm terribly sorry," said General Cork, mopping his brow, which was dripping with perspiration. "But in Naples every-one eats this species of child . . . yes . . . I mean . . . no . . . I mean . . . that species of fish . . . ! Isn't it true, Malaparte, that that species of child . . . of fish . . . is excellent?"

"It's an excellent fish," I replied, "and what does it matter if it looks like a child? It's a fish. In Europe a fish doesn't have to look like a fish . . ."

"Nor in America!" said General Cork, glad to find at last someone who would stick up for him.

"What?" cried Mrs. Flat.

"In Europe," I said, "fish at least are free! No one says that a fish mustn't look like—what shall I say?—a man, a child, or a woman. And this is a fish, even if . . . Anyhow," I added, "what did you expect to eat when you came to Italy? The corpse of Mussolini?"

"Ha! ha! ha! That's funny!" roared General Cork, but his laughter was too shrill to be genuine. "Ha! ha! ha!" And all the others joined in, their laughter a strangely conflicting blend of dismay, doubt and merriment. I have never loved the Americans, I shall never love them, in the way I did that evening, as I sat at that table, confronted by that horrible fish.

"You don't intend, I hope," said Mrs. Flat, pale with anger and horror, "you don't intend to make me eat that horrible thing! You forget that I am an American! What would they say in Washington, General, what would they say at the War Department, if they knew that the guests at your dinners ate boiled girls?"

"I mean . . . yes . . . of course . . ." stammered General Cork, giving me a look of supplication.

"Boiled girls with mayonnaise!" added Mrs. Flat in an icy voice.

"You are forgetting the border of coral," I said, as if I thought thereby to absolve General Cork.

"I am not forgetting the coral!" said Mrs. Flat, giving me a dev-astating look.

"Take it away!" shouted General Cork suddenly to the major-domo, pointing to the Siren. "Take that thing away!"

"General, wait a moment, please," said Colonel Brown, the chap-lain attached to G.H.Q. "We must bury that . . . that poor kid."

"What?" exclaimed Mrs. Flat.

"We must bury this . . . this . . . I mean . . ." said the chaplain.

"Do you mean . . . ?" said General Cork.

"Yes I mean bury," said the chaplain.

"But . . . it's a fish . . ." said General Cork.

"It may be a fish," said the chaplain, "but it looks more like a little girl . . . Allow me to insist: it is our duty to bury this little girl . . . I mean, this fish. We are Christians. Are we not Christians?"

"I have my doubts!" said Mrs. Flat, gazing at General Cork with an expression of cold contempt.

"Yes, I suppose . . ." replied General Cork.

"We must bury it," said Colonel Brown.

"All right," said General Cork. "But where should we bury it? I would say, throw it on the ash heap. That seems the simplest thing to me."

"No," said the chaplain. "One never knows. It's not at all certain that it is a real fish. We must give it a more decent burial."

"But there are no cemeteries for fish in Naples!" said General Cork, turning to me.

"I don't think there are any," I said. "The Neapolitans don't bury fish—they eat them."

"We could bury it in the garden," said the chaplain.

"That's a good idea," said General Cork, his face clearing. "We can bury it in the garden." And turning to the major-domo he added: "Please go and bury this thing . . . this poor fish in the garden."

"Yes, General," said the major-domo, bowing, and meanwhile the footmen lifted the gleaming solid silver bier on which the poor dead Siren lay and put it on the stretcher.

"I said bury it," said General Cork. "I forbid you to eat it in the kitchen!"

"Yes, General," said the major-domo. "But it's a pity! Such a lovely fish!"

"We don't know for certain that it is a fish," said General Cork, "and I forbid you to eat it."

The major-domo bowed, the footmen set off in the direction of the door, carrying the gleaming silver bier on the stretcher, and we all followed that strange funeral procession with sad eyes.

"It will be as well," said the chaplain, rising, "if I go and supervise the burial. I don't want to have anything on my conscience."

"Thank you, Reverend," said General Cork, mopping his brow, and with a sigh of relief he glanced timidly at Mrs. Flat.

"Oh, Lord!" exclaimed Mrs. Flat, raising her eyes to heaven.

She was pale, and the tears glistened in her eyes. I was glad that she was moved; I was deeply grateful to her for her tears. I had misjudged her: Mrs. Flat was a woman with a heart. If she wept for a fish, it was certain that in the end, some day or other, she would also feel compassion for the people of Italy, that she would also be moved to tears by the sorrows and sufferings of my own unhappy people.

A dead man is a dead man. He is just a dead man. He is more, and perhaps less too, than a dead dog or cat. Many times, on the roads of Serbia, Bessarabia and the Ukraine, I had seen in the mud of the street the imprint of a dog that had been killed and crushed by the caterpillars of a tank. The outline of a dog drawn on the slate of the road with a red pencil. A carpet made of the skin of a dog.

In July, 1941, I had seen a carpet of human skin lying in the dust of the street right in the center of Yampol, a village on the Dniester, in the Ukraine. It was a man who had been crushed by the caterpillars of a tank. The face had assumed a square shape, and the chest and stomach were splayed out at the sides in the form of a diamond. The outspread legs and the arms, which were a little apart from the torso, were like the trousers and sleeves of a newly pressed suit, stretched out on the ironingboard. It was a dead man—something more, or something less, than a dead dog or cat. I cannot say now in what respect that dead man was more, or less, than a dead dog or cat. But then, on that evening, at the moment at which I saw his imprint in the dust of the street, in the center of the village of Yampol, I could perhaps have said what it was that made him something more, or something less, than a dead dog or cat.

Here and there gangs of Jews in black caftans, armed with spades and shovels, were collecting the dead whom the Russians had left behind them in the village. Sitting on the doorstep of a ruined house I watched the light, transparent mist ascending from the marshy banks of the Dniester, while in the distance, on the other bank, beyond the bend of the river, the black clouds of smoke that rose from the houses of Soroca slowly spiraled up into the air. The sun revolved like a red wheel in a whirlwind of dust at the far end of the plain, where cars, men, horses and wagons were clearly silhouetted against the brilliant, dust-filled sunset sky.

In the middle of the street, there in front of me, lay the man who had been crushed by the caterpillars of a tank. Some Jews came up and began to remove the outline of the dead man from the dust. Very slowly they lifted the edges of the pattern with the ends of their spades, as one lifts the edges of a carpet. It was a carpet of human skin, and the fabric consisted of a fine network of bones, a spider's web of crushed bones. It was like a starched suit, a starched human skin. It was an appalling and at the same time delicate, exquisite, unreal scene. The Jews talked among themselves, and their voices sounded distant, soft, muffled. When the carpet of human skin had been completely detached from the dusty street one of the Jews impaled the head on the end of his spade and moved off, carrying the remains like a flag.

The standard-bearer was a young Jew with long hair that hung loosely over his shoulders. His eyes shone forth from his pale, lean face with a melancholy, unwavering stare. He walked with his head high, and on the end of his spade, like a flag, he carried that human skin, which flapped and fluttered in the wind exactly as a flag does.

I said to Lino Pellegrini, who was sitting beside me: "That's the flag of Europe. It's our flag."

"It isn't my flag," said Pellegrini. "A dead man isn't the flag of a living man."

"What is the inscription on that flag?" I said.

"It says that a dead man is a dead man."

"No," I said. "Read it carefully. It says that a dead man is not a dead man."

"No," said Pellegrini, "a dead man is just a dead man. What do you suppose a dead man is?"

"Ah, you don't know what a dead man is. If you knew what a dead man was you would never sleep again."

"Now I see," said Pellegrini, "what the inscription on that flag is. It says: The dead must bury the dead."

"No, it says that this is our country's flag, the flag of our true country. A flag made of human skin. Our true country is our skin."

HENRY MILLER

It is not unlikely that at the close of this epoch, the literature of the American which will stand, in many respects, as a pinnacle among aborted towers, will be that of Henry Miller. America has produced, like most other nations of the West, a fair amout of literature to receive international acclaim; there is no longer any dearth, certainly, of American Nobel Prize winners. What is rare, however, and quite possibly unique, is for a culture to have at its bosom an artist whose major work has not merely gone unpublished in his own country, but has actually been outlawed there; work, that is to say, hailed throughout the rest of the world as of the very first importance, and more widely read, according to the University of California Librarian, Lawrence Powell, than any American living other than Upton Sinclair, or any dead, other than Mark Twain and Jack London. Yet it is only within the past year, through the sustaining wisdom and courage of Mr. Rosset's Grove Press, that *Tropic of Cancer* and *Tropic of Capricorn* have at last appeared in the open market; this leaves *Black Spring, Quiet Days in Clichy, The World of Sex,* and at least two volumes of *The Rosy Crucifixion*—or a total of several thousand pages—still on the dark side of the horizon.

The influence of this work on contemporary American literature has been immeasurable. The English language itself has always presented a problem peculiar to American creative writing in that it is the only Western language which contains words that are, of themselves, indadmissible, that is to say, the so-called four-letter words. In languages of equal currency—French, German, Italian and Spanish—it is, of course, possible to construct, out of existing and acceptable words, images which are wholly offensive and, as such, inadmissible, but the structure of the language is always such that there cannot exist an instance of an isolated word, of high-frequency usage, which is of itself so potently taboo that it cannot be employed, either in everyday converse or in creative work for any form of communicative or art mass media—stage, film, radio, television and books. One of the crucial problems then in American literary creation has been how to avoid the use of these words with the minimum loss of verisimilitude (in dialogue) and without too seriously crippling the chance for genuine and meaningful self-expression. Genuine artists, certainly, have deplored these arbitrarily imposed limits as nothing less than primitive superstition; and giants, of course, have ignored them, so that one aspect of Henry Miller's life and art has been consecrated to overthrowing this tyranny of words. Let us look at how he was writing, back in the 1930's. . . .

ON HENRY MILLER by Lawrence Durrell

An invitation to give some account of the writings of Henry Miller comes very appositely since I have just completed a rereading of all his available work with a view to making a representative selection from it for his American publishers. On the other hand I should make it clear at once that my own association and friendship with him has, in the opinion of many common friends, made me over-indulgent to what they consider his defects as a writer. I rate him too highly, they tell me. He lacks all sense of form . . . ("They say I must have form, blast them," writes D. H. Lawrence somewhere. "They mean their own miserable skin-and-grief form"). Miller, in the same context, replied to a criticism of mine thus: "You keep bellyaching about form. I'm against the form that's imposed from the outside, the dead structure. My books represent germination in all its phases."

"Germination," the word is a key to many of the intentions of Miller in his writings; it is the key to what Miller feels himself to be— a fecundating force expressing itself through writing, not a "literary man" or an "artist." The distinction is worth underlining for the shape and colour of this writer's work is dictated by his attitude to art and the world of which that art is a reflection.

There seem to be two distinct types of creative man. The first controls his material and shapes it. The second delivers himself over, bound hand and foot to his gifts. The first belongs to the family of Pope, the second to the family of Lawrence, of Blake. With this second type of artist it is useless to agitate for measure, form, circumspection. They are entirely mantic, delivered over to their pneuma. It is very exasperating, for almost any one of us talented fellows could show Blake how to improve his work, or Lawrence how to achieve the form he lacked with the artificial aid of a blue pencil. But we should then be guilty, I have no doubt, of missing the whole meaning and content of the work of such artists—for the meaning resides not only in the work as a whole unit, but also in the life of its creator, and in the struggle that went into the making of the work. Unless we are prepared to admit that this type of creative man is *making use* of his art in order to grow by it, in order to expand the domains of his own sensibility, we will be unable to profit by what he has to offer us, which is the vicarious triumph of *finding ourselves* in reading him. The imperfections of his art come from an honourable admission that he wishes to grow. He does not wish to sever the umbilical cord connecting him to his creation. He wraps himself more and more deeply in the coloured cocoon of his personal mythology until it is quite impossible for you to do more than reject him utterly, or accept him unreservedly. With the other type of artist, the great formalist who resides in a Joyce or a Proust, you find another attitude—that of the embalmer. Such artists are tied to a memory, to location, to a precise age and cultus. They condense and refine. They sum up their lives in a great complete metaphor from one determined standpoint. They are the real artists, says a friend, while the others are "adventurers in literature" properly speaking, whose topic is growth, efflorescence, being. This may well be true. Certainly the latter type of artist makes a greater demand upon us. We have to accustom ourselves to his tone of voice, which is often irritating or unpleasant. Yet in an age where our literature is coming more and more to resemble an exchange of common-room debating-points wrapped in impeccable prose or verse, the work of such hungry time-spirits as Miller and Lawrence has a very special function. The new psyche of the age will be born of their desperate struggles, one feels. Merit and defect are somehow irrelevant to their work. What matters is the personality, the key, the tone of voice. They remind us that literature is something more than an electric massage for the over-educated ego, or a formal garden in which the critic can take his Peke for a run. It is a wilderness in which one can find or lose oneself, and where the object of creation is not only to produce "works of art" but to become more and more oneself in doing so.

The comparison of Lawrence and Miller is inevitable. Despite many differences of temperament and talent there are several points of reference worth noting. They both belong to the generation which, under the influence of Bergson and Spengler, opted for a vitalist view of history, and an anti-intellectual metaphysic. One makes such ascriptions light-heartedly enough in critical essays—but here I would like to emphasize that for the creative man the whole world of philosophical or religious ideas is simply a sort of harem from which he chooses now this pretty concubine, now that. We say that X is Theosophist or a Bergsonian: but it would be very difficult to criticize his work entirely in terms of either proposition. Readers of Mr. Louis MacNeice's excellent study of Yeats will perhaps remember the closing chapters in which the author confesses to a certain bewilderment at the *inconsistency* of his subject. The truth is that the artist is at his most amoral when he reaches the domain of ideas. He is concerned, of course, not with the dialectical truth of ideas, but simply with their beauty and appositeness to his own temperamental make-up. He chooses often exactly the *opposite* of what he is, simply in order to provide a counter-balance to his own overbalanced sensibility. Yeats felt an almost sensual attraction for the calm of the Indian sages. His own rosy, romantic Irish sensibility needed something of the sort to contain its disorders. With this reservation in mind one might ascribe Miller's intellectual pedigree partly to Bergson and Spengler, partly to Freud, and partly to Hindu and Chinese religion. Certain elements are easier to isolate than others. The following quotations from *The Hamlet Letters* outline his attitude more clearly than I could do.

"It's your marvellous analytic mind which will not rest content until the subject has been torn to tatters . . . You must take it between your fingers, metaphorically speaking, and rend it to bits . . . You are like a savage who takes the watch apart to find out what makes it go, but like the savage again you neither find out what makes it go nor can you put the watch together again. You are left with a beautiful piece of destruction on your hands—a capable job, but what avail? Listen, *must* we know what makes the watch go? Isn't it enough to know what time it is? . . . Of course I am against the known . . . When you say that Knowledge is my great Bugaboo, you are absolutely right. But to go on and say that I detest science, metaphysics, religion, etc—sticking one's finger into the Unknown, as you say—because I might bring up something horrible, *the truth,* that is not true. The fact is that truth is not arrived at that way. The exploration of the unknown yields only the known. We discover only what we set out to find, nothing more. Truth on the other hand comes instantaneously, without search. *Truth is,* as Krisnamurti says. You don't win it. It comes to you as a gift, and to receive it you must be in the proper state. All this is nonsense to you, I know . . . It's just a piece of mysticism, if you like, which keeps me gay and fit. The unknown is constant and the advances we make into it are illusory. I love the unknown precisely because it is a 'beyond,' because it *is* impenetrable."

The surrender to the flux of individual life; the life which marks the history of individual and nation alike, is an article of faith with both Miller and Lawrence; and in both of them we see, over and over again, the attempt to emphasize the creative rebirth of the *individual,* and the rise of the human spirit to full consciousness. That both share a didactic purpose goes without saying. Their work offers us what is really a religious message. To be reborn with every breath one draws and every line one writes, suggests the spiritual athletic of the mystic rather than the patient and prescient interest of an artist in a form determined, in a tract of experience digested and finished with.

"Suddenly your whole life seems like a grand eclipse; the sun was blacked out and you had never imagined that there was a sun but only this black spot in front of your eyes, only you yourself and your idea of life. Then suddenly the cataract is removed, and suddenly you see . . . The labour of putting two and two together you leave to the blind . . . When a man gets this sight havoc seizes the world. The philosophers and the historians may say that the time is not ripe—the time is never ripe for the historians and philosophers, except in the past—but the man who suddenly sees announces the time and the time is always ripe because it is one with his vision. To break this man, to destroy this vision, requires centuries and centuries of future time. And even then the vision is never completely destroyed. Another man arises and it is the same vision. No time for writing books, no time for building philosophies. The man simply says what he sees and goes straight to his death. He walks seeing and saying, each step he makes, each word he utters a clear, clean break with the past. He has no memory, no hope, no regrets. Neither has he wife nor friends. Nor has he loyalty. He moves straight on with ice-cold compassion, the supreme master of irony, the chief actor in the drama of man. When we attempt to describe the pattern of such a life we create a spider-web in which we are strangled . . ."

"Man has a pattern but he seldom lives according to it. Man's pattern is God, but he refuses to recognize it as a creation . . . Man oscillates between God and the Devil. He is seldom man . . ."

"Man is a creator. And to create means to destroy at the same time. To destroy usually gives us pleasure but to create produces a sense of guilt. Why? Because to create entails responsibility. We create out of a sense of insufficiency. Our longing to be understood is only a reflection of our fear of trespassing. A creative act is in the nature of a trespass. It is a violation of the static order of things. We say we want to be understood, but in reality it is the anticipation of war which makes us tremble with joy and apprehension. Every creative act is a declaration of war. And war is man's pattern."

But the Heraclitean proposition expresses a paradox: that it is only by the acceptance of the war, the reconciliation of the warring selves, that the individual ever reaches the road to peace in the self. This rare understanding of the problem gives Miller's work a less scolding rancorous quality than that of Lawrence; he is temperamentally a larger man and consequently less hard on himself and the world; he takes time off to develop his comic gifts; he devotes a great deal of his time to buffoonery which irritates the "serious reader." But his intentions are very strictly honourable in all that he does, while an essential childishness of spirit makes him rather enjoy being caught in awkward or ridiculous positions. In Lawrence's work the gradual curve towards self-reconciliation as man and artist was not completely carried out. His death cut him off at perhaps the most important stage in his career if we are to judge the temper of stories like *The Man Who Died* and poems like *The Ship of Death*, which breathe an entirely new air of calm and relaxation: as if every rancour and every disenchantment had suddenly given place to a new understanding of the artist's role. It is this core of self-realization which Miller has had time to examine and develop, and which forms the theme of his latest work and much that he promises us for the future; like Lawrence, however, he values art as a method of self-realization, not as an end in itself. ("I always say: Art For *My Sake*" barks Lawrence somewhere.) Miller writes: "Concerning every bold act one may raise the reproach of vulgarity. Everything dramatic is in the nature of an appeal, a frantic appeal for communion. Violence, whether in deed or speech, is an inverted sort of prayer . . . Initiation itself is a violent process of purification and union. Whatever demands radical treatment demands God, and always through some form of death or annihilation. Whenever the obscene crops out one can smell the imminent death of a form. Those who possess the highest clue are not impatient, even in the presence of death; the artist in words, however, is not of this order, he is only at the vestibule, as it were, of the palace of wisdom . . . When he fully understands his role as creator he substitutes his own being for the medium of words" . . .

The artist, then, is not for Miller the supreme figure of the age. He is only a stage towards a fuller self-realization—a self-realization which he can only reach by coming to terms with himself as a man.

I have avoided so far any reference to the obscenity of Miller's writings, because I was anxious to establish his *bona fides* as a serious practitioner of the arts in order to present, if possible, a fairly proportioned picture. For the average reader he is, of course, a "banned writer," a little of whose work is available in bowdlerized collections. The problem which faces a critic of Miller is to give some idea of his comparative stature to a public which has so far only seen one hundredth part of his work. (How would one indicate the stature of Stendhal to a public which was only allowed to read, say *Armance* and *La Vie De Henri Brulard?*) Miller's main line of development runs through *Tropic of Cancer, Black Spring, Tropic of Capricorn,* and *The Rosy Crucifixion* (the first volume of which, containing nearly a thousand pages of prose, is due to appear in Paris this spring). So far in England and the U.S.A. the public has had to remain content with a few collections of essays, short stories and excerpta—which give a more muddled impression of Miller's work than is really necessary. Much of the work in these collections is good, of course; but the best of it represents Miller's peripheral activities rather than his main task —which is a seven-volume autobiography. Inasmuch as his main task is only half-done, then, he is entitled to the suspended judgement of his critics—and of those who level against his work the charge of formlessness. The connecting line of development in Miller's work may not yet be clear—the line which is to link them into a single autobiographic whole. One thing is certain: he will not follow a line based upon times, events or characters. Organization of moods and ideas must be the key to his work. Yet already the span between *Tropic of Cancer* and *Tropic of Capricorn* covers a tremendous revolution in ideas. The fleshly struggle which rages in his first book, has been transferred to the metaphysical plane in his third; the battlefield is no longer the flesh but the spirit. Bergson and Spengler have given way to the Chinese and the Hindus, so to speak. Even his use of obscenity as a technique has radically altered.

It is difficult to deal with the question of obscenity in art partly because of the pusillanimity of the Anglo-Saxon reading public, and partly because of that queer deficit in personal experience which makes the Anglo-Saxon somehow emotionally stunted, however intellectually capable he may be. This quality makes him over-value obscenity. He cannot simply look it in the eye. He must be for or against it—and both points of view are wrong in the eyes of Miller. The truth is that one should not, in a civilized country, have to make a case for obscenity in literature at all, to treat it as Something Awfully Serious which can, however, be Intellectually Justified. The Anglo-Saxon would like someone, please, to Make A Case for the obscenity, so that he can enjoy it without feeling guilty. Lawrence supplied such a demand in *Lady Chatterly* by making out a romantic and puritanical case for obscenity; his public was able to agree that sex was really a Sacrament, and that his gamekeeper was somehow an Important Symbol. The moral justification simply had to be there. The distinction between *Tropic of Cancer* and *Lady Chatterly*, centres about this point—for Miller (who, unlike Lawrence, has thoroughly assimilated Freud) recognizes that sex is *both* a sacrament *and* also uproariously funny (not to mention silly, holy, and tiresome all in one); and that to tidy it into part of a moral scheme is simply to shackle the reader more and more firmly into his puritanism. He has mastered, in fact, the great discovery of the age—ambivalence in values—and that is what lifts most of his work above the ruck of ordinary writing.

"The most insistent question put to the writer of obscene literature is: why did you have to use such language? The implication is, of course, that with conventional terms or means, the same effect might have been obtained. Nothing . . . could be farther from the truth . . . Effects are bound up with intentions and these in turn are governed by laws of compulsion as rigid as nature's own. That is something which non-creative individuals seldom understand . . . There will always be a gulf between the creative artist and public because the latter is immune to the mystery inherent in and surrounding all creation. Putting to one side all questions of ego and temperament, and taking the broadest view of the creative process, which makes of the artist nothing more than an instrument, we are nevertheless forced to conclude that the spirit of the age is the crucible in which, through one means or another, certain vital and mysterious forces seek expression . . . When obscenity crops out in art, in literature more particularly, it usually functions as a technical device; the element of the deliberate which is there has nothing to do with sexual excitation, as in pornography. If there is an ulterior motive it is one that goes far beyond sex. Its purpose is to waken, to usher in a sense of reality . . ."

For those then, who are on the look-out for the moral justification behind this literary practice, these words should prove of interest. Miller would like morality to be, not simply a barren code of observance, of behaviour, but a genuine reflection of the human spirit.

And in a paradoxical sort of way his attack on the properties is an attack upon prudery, and as such an invitation to reconsider morality, to revalue it. It is no use just acting good, he says, in effect, that is too easy. The problem is how to *be* good. The use of obscenity, then, has something like a religious function for Miller—and indeed his attitude to the four-letter words reminds one of the "unpronounceable word" in the Jewish religion—the 'mikvah'—which is at one and the same time the worst obscenity, and the holiest of holy words.

"Once the artist has made use of his extraordinary powers, and I am thinking of the use of obscenity in just such magical terms, he is inevitably caught up in a stream of forces beyond him. He may have begun by assuming that he could awaken his readers, but in the end he himself passes into another dimension of reality wherein he no longer feels the need to force an awakening. His rebellion over the prevalent inertia about him becomes transmuted, as his vision increases, into an acceptance and understanding of an order and harmony which is beyond man's conception and approachable only through faith . . . Ultimately, then, he stands among his own obscene objurgations, like the conqueror amidst the ruins of a davastated city . . . He knocked to awaken, but it was himself he awakened. And once awake he is no longer concerned with the world of sleep; he walks in the light, and, like a mirror, reflects his illumination in every act."

The statement is a challenging one, and one which removes Miller at a distance from Lawrence—whose ambition was simply to restore some of the flowering warmth of happy and candid sexual relations to the stunted Anglo-Saxon publics; yet both saw very clearly that the death of our world is bound up very tightly with the dying sexuality, the dying ego of Western man. "Once the obscene is accepted," writes Miller, "whether as a figment of the imagination or as an integral part of human reality, it inspires no more dread or revulsion than could be ascribed to the flowering lotus which sends its roots down into the mud of the stream on which it is borne."

"*A well read man,*" writes Proust, "*will at once begin to yawn with boredom when anyone speaks to him of a new 'good book,' because he imagines a sort of composite of all the good books that he has read and knows already, whereas a good book is something special, something incalculable, and is not made up of the sum of all previous masterpieces but of something which the most thorough assimilation of every one of them would not enable him to discover . . .*"

Alas! The proposition is all too true. The middle talent is not so difficult to assess. It is the outsize writer, the phenomenon, who is a difficult fish to hook! And in the case of Miller it is doubly difficult because he himself, splashing and floundering in the mystical menstrum of sensation and memory, does very little to help the critic or the public. Here and there he writes very badly; and being deficient in critical sense he often publishes pieces of work which are below his highest level simply in order to get them off his chest. Nearly everything written in dispraise of him is true—though unfortunately he has nearly always fallen upon critics with axes to grind. Mr. Orwell, for example, whose fluent and delightful prose has won him a deservedly wide public, has outlined a number of serious holes in the Miller chain-mail; he has a perfect right to the defects, but one must insist on a more balanced picture of Miller the artist. It is possible after all to have serious religious or moral intentions and not be a political man. And Miller's refusal to interest himself in the betterment of the world by planned economy and legislation may come from a perfectly serious conviction that the world cannot be improved that way; that it can best be improved by the self-improvement of the individual. It must be admitted, however, that Miller rather enjoys giving a picture of himself which suggests something between a crook, a cowboy and a clown; it is really his own fault if the critic takes fright at the picture he presents of a ruthless, antisocial and unmoral desperado. This Faustian vein in Miller is, however, a source of considerable amusement to his friends who know him to be the most gentle, most considerate and honourable of men. Indeed his fundamental generosity and warmheartedness make him appear very ill-equipped to play Mephistopheles; and while he is an enchanter, to be sure, his true pedigree stretches back through Prospero to Merlin. But the vein of irresponsible naïveté in his nature makes him easy enough game on occasion.

Some account of his life, and his writings in relation to it, deserves a place in this study.

He was born in New York City on 26 December 1891 of poor parents. He was transplanted to Brooklyn at the age of one, and spent his early life in the streets of this poor quarter of New York. He has re-created the scene magnificently in several places, but best of all in *Black Spring:*

"To be born in the street means to wander all your life, to be free. It means accident and incident, drama, movement. It means, above all, *dream*. A harmony of irrelevant facts which gives your wanderings a metaphysical certitude. In the street you learn what human beings really are; otherwise, or afterwards, you invent them. What is not in the open street is false, derived, that is to say, *literature* . . .

"In my dreams I come back to the 14th Ward as a paranoiac returns to his obsessions. When I think of those steel-grey battleships in the Navy Yard, I see them lying there in some astrologic dimension in which I am the gunnersmith, the chemist, the dealer in high explosives, the undertaker, the coroner, the cuckold, the sadist, the lawyer and contender, the scholar, the restless one, the jolt-head and the brazen-faced.

"Where others remember of their youth a beautiful garden, a fond mother, a sojourn at the seashore, I remember, with a vividness as if it were etched in acid, the grim soot-covered walls and chimneys of the tin-factory opposite us, and the bright circular pieces of tin that were strewn in the street, some bright and gleaming, others rusted, dull, copperish, leaving a stain on the fingers; I remember the iron-works where the red furnace glowed and men walked towards the glowing pit with huge shovels in their hands, while outside were the shallow wooden forms like coffins with rods through them on which you scraped your shins or broke your neck. I remember the black hands of the iron-moulders, the grit that had sunk so deep in the skin that nothing could remove it—not soap nor elbow grease nor money nor love nor death. Like a black mark on them! Walking into the furnace like devils with black hands—and later, with flowers over them, cool and rigid in their Sunday suits, not even the rains can wash away the grit. All these beautiful gorillas going up to God with swollen muscles and lumbago and black hands . . .

"One passes imperceptibly from one scene, one age, one life to another. Suddenly, walking down a street, be it real or be it a dream, one realizes for the first time that the years have flown, that all this has passed forever and will live on only in memory; and then the memory turns inward with a strange clutching brilliance and one goes over these scenes and incidents perpetually, in dream and reverie, while walking a street, while lying with a woman, while reading a book, while talking to a stranger . . . Henceforward we walk split into a myriad fragments, like an insect with a hundred feet, a centipede with soft-stirring feet that drinks in the atmosphere; we walk with sensitive filaments that drink avidly of past and future, and all things melt into music and sorrow; we walk against a united world asserting our dividedness. All things, as we walk, splitting with us into a myriad iridescent fragments. The great fragmentation of maturity. The great change. In youth we were whole and the terror and pain of the world penetrated us through and through . . . And then comes a time when suddenly all seems to be reversed. We live in the mind, in ideas, in fragments. We no longer drink in the wild outer music of the streets—we *remember* only. Like a monomaniac we relive the drama of our youth. Like a spider that picks up the thread over and over and spews it out according to some obsessive logarithmic pattern . . . If we are stirred by the reflection on a wet pavement it is because at the age of seven we were suddenly speared by a premonition of the life to come as we stared unthinkingly into that bright liquid mirror of the street. If the sight of swinging door intrigues us it is the memory of a summer's evening when all the doors were swinging softly and where the light bent down to caress the shadow there were golden calves and lace and glittering parasols and through the chinks in the swinging door, like fine sand sifting through a bed of rubies, there drifted the music and the incense of gorgeous unknown bodies. Perhaps when the doors parted to give us a choking glimpse of the world, perhaps then we had the first intimation of the impact of sin, the first intimation that here over little round tables, spinning in the light, our feet idly scraping the sawdust, our hands touching the cold stem of a glass, that here over these little round tables which later we are to look at with such yearning and reverence, that here, I say, we are to feel in the years to come the first iron of love, the first stains of rust, the first black, clawing hands of the pit . . ." Extensive quotation is the only way to trying to indicate the sweep and volume of Miller's prose, the powerful swell and cadence of its music. Its rough masculinity is very removed from "toughness" in the Hemingway sense; it has a rampaging Elizabethan quality, a rare tonic vitality which comes from the savage health of its creator. Taken in bulk, with all its prodigious tracts of roughage, its plateaux covered in uncut gems, its weird tracts of half-explored vegetation running along the snow-lines of metaphysics—one is reminded of the stutterings and stammering of a Whitman or a Melville. Like them, Miller belongs in the direct line of American genius—a genius which is essentially formless. They are portmanteau writers, discursive, rambling and prolix: vulnerable only because they do not bother to hide the fact that they are still growing. They may be tiresome but they are never bleak; and in Miller's case at any rate almost everything he writes is rewarding, even the nonsense and the light comedy. Writers of this *genre* have a very poor literary sense. They seem to need an impresario, a resident critic to plead with them against the publication of inferior work; they need, in a sense, to be saved from their own volcanic gifts. They lack the gifts of mendacity, temperance and cunning which alone can shape a literary career. They have, however, more important things to do with their time than to spend it worrying about a "literary career." This at any rate is true of Miller, who began *Tropic of Cancer* after a long period of actual starvation in Paris, knowing perfectly well that no publisher in the world would print it . . .

The road from Brooklyn Bridge to the Pont Neuf was a long and bitter one, packed with human experiences and a great deal of suffering. His early manhood, with its anxieties, revolts and despairs, has already been marvellously described in *Black Spring* and in *Tropic of Capricorn*. It is saturated in the sweat and violence of the open street. "There are huge blocks of my life," he writes, "which are gone forever. Huge blocks gone, scattered, wasted in talk, action, reminiscence, dream. There never was any time when I was living *one* life, the life of a husband, a lover, a friend. Whatever I was, whatever I was engaged in, I was leading multiple lives." And this sense of multiple meaning is admirably conveyed by his writing which follows ideas and memories down long labyrinths of images, long *couloirs*. of darkness, corridors full of shattered prisms. Miller's world is a world seen through a prism. It glitters indeed with a wild prismatic beauty. It is not a world described, contained, *edited* as the world of Proust or Joyce is: his method is the method of poetic documentary—the lens traversing the whole field from left to right, picking out dissimilar objects of scrutiny and marrying them up to the image which contains them both. Between story, poem and essay there is no dividing line. Sometimes the author uses them as separate medía, sometimes he jumbles them up together. And sometimes, it must be admitted, he falls asleep in the centre of his own canvas . . . out of the sheer spirit of mischief. Miller would have made a splendid Lord of Misrule. "I can think of no lovelier day than this in the full bloom of the xxth century, with the sun rotting away and a man on a little sledge blowing the *Song of Love* through his piccolo. This day shines in my heart with such a ghastly brilliance that even if I were the saddest man in the world I should not want to leave the earth . . . Imagine having nothing on your hands but your destiny. You sit on the doorstep of your mother's womb and you kill time—or time kills you. You sit there chanting the doxology of things beyond your grasp. Outside. Forever Outside."

Tropic of Cancer was begun in Paris in 1931 while the author was tramping the streets all day and sleeping wherever possible during the night—sometimes in the open. It was not published until 1934. It is difficult to describe the merits of this book simply because it is the expression of an entirely new personality in literature. While it is lacking entirely in the imposed form or proportions that one has been taught to expect in novels, the whole canvas is held together simply by the appetite and force of the personality behind the prose. This is how it begins:

"I am living at the Villa Borghese. There is not a crumb of dirt anywhere, nor a chair misplaced. We are all alone here and we are dead.

"Last night Boris discovered he was lousy. I had to shave his armpits and even then the itching did not stop. How can one get lousy in a beautiful place like this? But no matter. We might never have known each other so intimately, Boris and I, had it not been for the lice.

"Boris has given me a summary of his views. He is a weather prophet. The weather will continue bad, he says. There will be more calamities, more death, more despair. Not the slightest indication of a change anywhere. The cancer of time is eating us away. Our heroes have killed themselves or are killing themselves. The hero, then, is not Time but Timelessness. We must get in step, a lock-step, towards the prison of death. There is no escape. The weather will not change.

"It is now the fall of my second year in Paris. I was sent here for a reason I have not yet been able to fathom.

"I have no money, no resources, no hopes. I am the happiest man alive. A year ago, six months ago, I thought I was an artist. I no longer think about it. *I am.* Everything that was literature has fallen from me. There are no more books to be written, thank God. This then? This is not a book. This is a libel, slander, defamation of character. This is not a book in the ordinary sense of the word . . ."

Reveries, ideas, short stories, flights of images: the book contains them all. Yet its wholeness as a work of art is quite independent of the form. The triumph is one of an individuality which, by its sheer force, has tapped the well-springs of creative prose and turned them to its own uses. The tide of lyrical emotion carries one onwards through the savagery, the obscenity, the raw humour and the marvellous descriptive poetry of the book.

"Twilight hour. Indian blue, water of glass, trees glistening and liquescent. The rails fall away into the canal at Jaurés. The long caterpillar with lacquered sides dips like a roller-coaster. It is not Paris. It is not Coney Island. It is a crepuscular melange of all the cities of Europe and Central America. The railroad yards below me, the tracks black, webby, not ordered by engineers but cataclysmic in design like those gaunt fissures in the polar ice which the camera registers in degrees of black."

Tropic of Cancer might be called a description of Paris life from the viewpoint of a literary *clochard;* yet this is not all, for though Paris is reflected marvellously in these pages, the book is also a sort of swan-song for city man—a swan-song which is to end in a death-rattle! "The wallpaper with which the men of science have covered the world of reality is falling to tatters. The grand whorehouse they have made of life requires no decoration; it is essential only that the drains function adequately. Beauty, that feline beauty which has us by the balls in America, is finished. To fathom the new reality it is first necessary to dismantle the drains, to lay open the gangrened ducts which compose the genitourinary system that supplies the excreta of art . . . The age demands violence but we are getting only abortive explosions . . ."

The justification for the violence, for the obscenity, lies in the fact that such writing is fecundating; it bursts the barriers of all self-confession. Yet at every point it was healthy, vital, alive.

The publication of this book earned Miller a few admirers and the good opinion of several discerning and influential critics; it reached a second edition in its first year. After so many years of frustration, of working at jobs which he hated (the list is incredible and includes everything between a grave-digger and a concert pianist) he at last felt he had found his own voice. To be sure, it was not his first. He had begun his writing career in earnest in 1925 and had completed two long and unremarkable novels—novels which show no trace of his subsequent talents. He had also, like Whitman before him, peddled poems from door to door in the poorer quarters of New York. All this was behind him, and the publication of *Tropic of Cancer* marked a real turning point in his career.

Black Spring and *Tropic of Capricorn* were soon to follow, but their production was sporadically interrupted by other literary activities. An enormous volume on the world of D. H. Lawrence, which had been gathering chapters like a snowball over the previous decade, began to assume its final form. I do not know whether it was ever actually completed. Like all Miller's books it was, when I last saw it, in its thousand-page state, waiting to be pruned. *Tropic of Cancer* itself was distilled out of a colossal MS. which I was lucky enough to read, and which could not have been less than fifteen hundred pages long. It seemed to me that there was enough material to make three or four *Tropic of Cancers* from it. The same sort of prolixity was evident in the books to follow. Miller's production has always been a phenomenon to his friends—not to mention the speed at which he writes. Among the other activities of this joyous period was *The Hamlet Letters*—another book which is exasperatingly good in some parts, exasperatingly bad in others; while the editing of a small magazine in Paris kept Miller too busy for a major effort, but not busy enough to interrupt a steady flow of long critical essays, pen-portraits of intimate friends he admired, and short stories.

Public interest in his work was, and still is, sluggish, but the feeling that responsible critics in several countries admired his writing, and that at last reputable literary journals were open to him and eager to print it, acted as a tonic.

Tropic of Capricorn appeared in February 1939, and with its appearance Miller decided to take a holiday away from France. The curious reader will find an account of his Greek holiday in *The Colossus of Maroussi*, published in England. Early in 1940 he sailed for America where a further period of vicissitude and poverty awaited him—a period which ended some time in 1944 with his third marriage, and his establishment in a little house of his own situated in the Big Sur region of California. At the time of writing he is addressing himself to the fifth volume of his autobiography. I have already stressed his refusal to create a mould of form in which to cast his work—as Joyce did by borrowing a form from Homer, as Proust did by repetition and restatement and regrouping. Miller's work has no "characters," there are only savage charcoal cartoons of human beings: it has no time-springing—it is written in a perpetual historic present: it has no sequence, location, process . . . Its triumphs are the triumphs of all documents of the heart, and the appeal it makes to those of us who recognize his greatness, is the appeal of what is living, flowering, and indulging a boundless appetite for life. A friendly critic writes: "Miller demands rather a special recipe. Take Rousseau. Let him be psycho-analysed by Freud. Add Sennett's *Esoteric Buddhism* to Spengler. Mix this with a prose-gift as large as Lawrence and serve in Paris. I think him a bold mystic to mix piety and sensuality—the two hungers —so well. And to show us how to be happy men as well."

There is much that is below his highest standard, to be sure, much that is careless, ill-judged, rash, splenetic, shapeless, overstated . . . These defects are the peculiar defects of his particular type of genius. But they should not blind us to his positive qualities.

Judged by his best work he is already among the greatest contemporary writers. The completion of his seven-volume autobiography, if it fulfils the promise of what he has already given us, will put his name amongst the three or four great figures of the age. It only remains for me to add that this is a considered opinion.

from *TROPIC OF CANCER*

There is only one thing which interests me vitally now, and that is the recording of all that which is omitted in books. Nobody, so far as I can see, is making use of those elements in the air which give direction and motivation to our lives. Only the killers seem to be extracting from life some satisfactory measure of what they are putting into it. The age demands violence, but we are getting only abortive explosions. Revolutions are nipped in the bud, or else succeed too quickly. Passion is quickly exhausted. Men fall back on ideas, *comme d'habitude*. Nothing is proposed that can last more than twenty-four hours. We are living a million lives in the space of a generation. In the study of entomology, or of deep sea life, or cellular activity, we derive more. . . .

The telephone interrupts this thought which I should never have been able to complete. Some one is coming to rent the apartment. . . .

It looks as though it were finished, my life at the Villa Borghese. Well, I'll take up these pages and move on. Things will happen elsewhere. Things are always happening. It seems wherever I go there is drama. People are like lice—they get under your skin and bury themselves there. You scratch and scratch until the blood comes, but you can't get permanently deloused. Everywhere I go people are making a mess of their lives. Everyone has his private tragedy. It's in the blood now—misfortune, ennui, grief, suicide. The atmosphere is saturated with disaster, frustration, futility. Scratch and scratch—until there's no skin left. However, the effect upon me is exhilarating. Instead of being discouraged, or depressed, I enjoy it. I am crying for more and more disasters, for bigger calamities, for grander failures. I want the whole world to be out of whack, I want everyone to scratch himself to death.

So fast and furiously am I compelled to live now that there is scarcely time to record even these fragmentary notes. After the telephone call, a gentleman and his wife arrived. I went upstairs to lie down during the transaction. Lay there wondering what my next move would be. Surely not to go back to the fairy's bed and toss about all night flicking bread crumbs with my toes. That puking little bastard! If there's anything worse than being a fairy it's being a miser. A timid, quaking little bugger who lived in constant fear of going broke some day—the 18th of March perhaps, or the 25th of May precisely. Coffee without milk or sugar. Bread without butter. Meat without gravy, or no meat at all. Without this and without that! That dirty little miser! Open the bureau drawer one day and find money hidden away in a sock. Over two thousand francs—and checks that he hadn't even cashed. Even that I wouldn't have minded so much if there weren't always coffee grounds in my beret and garbage on the floor, to say nothing of the cold cream jars and the greasy towels and the sink always stopped up. I tell you, the little bastard he smelled bad—except when he doused himself with cologne. His ears were dirty, his eyes were dirty, his ass was dirty. He was double-jointed, asthmatic, lousy, picayune, morbid. I could have forgiven him everything if only he had handed me a decent breakfast! But a man who has two thousand francs hidden away in a dirty sock and refuses to wear a clean shirt or smear a little butter over his bread, such a man is not just a fairy, nor even just a miser—he's an imbecile!

But that's neither here nor there, about the fairy. I'm keeping an ear open as to what's going on downstairs. It's a Mr. Wren and his wife who have called to look at the apartment. They're talking about taking it. Only *talking* about it, thank God. Mrs. Wren has a loose laugh—complications ahead. Now *Mister* Wren is talking. His voice is raucous, scraping, booming, a heavy blunt weapon that wedges its way through flesh and bone and cartilage.

Boris calls me down to be introduced. He is rubbing his hands, like a pawnbroker. They are talking about a story Mr. Wren wrote, a story about a spavined horse.

"But I thought Mr. Wren was a painter?"

"To be sure," says Boris, with a twinkle in his eye, "but in the wintertime he writes. And he writes well . . . remarkably well."

I try to induce Mr. Wren to talk, to say something, anything, to talk about the spavined horse, if necessary. But Mr. Wren is almost inarticulate. When he essays to speak of those dreary months with the pen he becomes unintelligible. Months and months he spends before setting a word to paper. (And there are only three months of winter!) What does he cogitate all those months and months of winter? So help me God, I can't see this guy as a writer. Yet Mrs. Wren says that when he sits down to it the stuff *just pours out.*

The talk drifts. It is difficult to follow Mr. Wren's mind because he says nothing. *He thinks as he goes along*—so Mrs. Wren puts it. Mrs. Wren puts everything about Mr. Wren in the loveliest light. "He thinks as he goes along"—very charming, charming indeed, as Borowski would say, but really very painful, particularly when the thinker is nothing but a spavined horse.

Boris hands me money to buy liquor. Going for the liquor I am already intoxicated. I know just how I'll begin when I get back to the house. Walking down the street it commences, the grand speech inside me that's gurgling like Mrs. Wren's loose laugh. Seems to me she had a slight edge on already. Listens beautifully when she's tight. Coming out of the wine shop I hear the urinal gurgling. Everything is loose and splashy. I want Mrs. Wren to listen . . . .

Boris is rubbing his hands again. Mr. Wren is still stuttering and spluttering. I have a bottle between my legs and I'm shoving the corkscrew in. Mrs. Wren has her mouth parted expectantly. The wine is splashing between my legs, the sun is splashing through the bay window, and inside my veins there is a bubble and splash of a thousand crazy things that commence to gush out of me now pell-mell. I'm telling them everything that comes to mind, everything that was bottled up inside me and which Mrs. Wren's loose laugh has somehow released. With that bottle between my legs and the sun splashing through the window I experience once again the splendor of those miserable days when I first arrived in Paris, a bewildered, poverty-stricken individual who haunted the streets like a ghost at a banquet. Everything comes back to me in a rush—the toilets that wouldn't work, the prince who shined my shoes, the Cinema Splendide where I slept on the patron's overcoat, the bars in the window, the feeling of suffocation, the fat cockroaches, the drinking and carousing that went on between times, Rose Cannaque and Naples dying in the sunlight. Dancing the streets on an empty belly and now and then calling on strange people—Madame Delorme, for instance. How I ever got to Madame Delorme's I can't imagine any more. But I got there, got inside somehow, past the butler, past the maid with her little white apron, got right inside the palace with my corduroy trousers and my hunting jacket—and not a button on my fly. Even now I can taste again the golden ambiance of that room where Madame Delorme sat upon a throne in her mannish rig, the goldfish in the bowls, the maps of the ancient world, the beautifully bound books; I can feel again her heavy hand resting upon my shoulder, frightening me a little with her heavy Lesbian air. More comfortable down below in that thick stew pouring into the Gare St. Lazare, the whores in the doorways, seltzer bottles on every table; a thick tide of semen flooding the gutters. Nothing better between five and seven than to be pushed around in that throng, to follow a leg or a beautiful bust, to move along with the tide and everything whirling in your brain. A weird sort of contentment in those days. No appointments, no invitations for dinner, no program, no dough. The golden period, when I had not a single friend. Each morning the dreary walk to the American Express, and each morning the inevitable answer from the clerk. Dashing here and there like a bedbug, gathering butts now and then, sometimes furtively, sometimes brazenly; sitting down on a bench and squeezing my guts to stop the gnawing, or walking through the Jardin des Tuileries and getting an erection looking at the dumb statues. Or wandering along the Seine at night, wandering and wandering, and going mad with the beauty of it, the trees leaning to, the broken images in the water, the rush of the current under the bloody lights of the bridges, the women sleeping in doorways, sleeping on newspapers, sleeping in the rain; everywhere the musty porches of the cathedrals and beggars and lice and old hags full of St. Vitus' dance; pushcarts stacked up like wine barrels in the side streets, the smell of berries in the marketplace and the old church surrounded with vegetables and blue arc lights, the gutters slippery with garbage and women in satin pumps staggering through the filth and vermin at the end of an all-night souse. The Place St. Sulpice, so quiet and deserted, where toward midnight there came every night the woman with the busted umbrella and the crazy veil; every night she slept there on a bench under her torn umbrella, the ribs hanging down, her dress turning green, her bony fingers and the odor of decay oozing from her body; and in the morning I'd be sitting there myself, taking a quiet snooze in the sunshine, cursing the goddamned pigeons gathering up the crumbs everywhere. St. Sulpice! The belfries, the garish posters over the door, the candles flaming inside. The Square

so beloved of Anatole France, with that drone and buzz from the
altar, the splash of the fountain, the pigeons cooing, the crumbs disappearing like magic and only a dull rumbling in the hollow of the
guts. Here I would sit day after day thinking of Germaine and that
dirty little street near the Bastille where she lived, and that buzz-buzz
going on behind the altar, the buses whizzing by, the sun beating
down into the asphalt and the asphalt working into me and Germaine,
into the asphalt and all Paris in the big fat belfries.

And it was down the Rue Bonaparte that only a year before Mona
and I used to walk every night, after we had taken leave of Borowski.
St. Sulpice not meaning much to me then, nor anything in Paris.
Washed out with talk. Sick of faces. Fed up with cathedrals and
squares and menageries and what not. Picking up a book in the red
bedroom and the cane chair uncomfortable: tired of sitting on my ass
all day long, tired of red wallpaper, tired of seeing so many people
jabbering away about nothing. The red bedroom and the trunk always
open; her gowns lying about in a delirium of disorder. The red bedroom with my goloshes and canes, the notebooks I never touched, the
manuscripts lying cold and dead. Paris! Meaning the Café Select, the
Dôme, the Flea Market, the American Express. Paris! Meaning Borowski's canes, Borowski's hats, Borowski's gouaches, Borowski's prehistoric fish—and prehistoric jokes. In that Paris of '28 only one night
stands out in my memory—the night before sailing for America. A rare
night, with Borowski slightly pickled and a little disgusted with me
because I'm dancing with every slut in the place. But we're leaving in
the morning! That's what I tell every cunt I grab hold of —*leaving in
the morning!* That's what I'm telling the blonde with agate-colored
eyes. And while I'm telling her she takes my hand and squeezes it
between her legs. In the lavatory I stand before the bowl with a tremendous erection; it seems light and heavy at the same time, like a
piece of lead with wings on it. And while I'm standing there like that
two cunts sail in—Americans. I greet them cordially, prick in hand.
They give me a wink and pass on. In the vestibule, as I'm buttoning my
fly, I notice one of them waiting for her friend to come out of the can.
The music is still playing and maybe Mona'll be coming to fetch me,
or Borowski with his gold-knobbed cane, but I'm in her arms now and
she has hold of me and I don't care who comes or what happens. We
wriggle into the cabinet and there I stand her up, slap up against the
wall, and I try to get it into her but it won't work and so we sit down
on the seat and try it that way but it won't work either. No matter how
we try it it won't work. And all the while she's got hold of my prick,

she's clutching it like a lifesaver, but it's no use, we're too hot, too eager. The music is still playing and so we waltz out of the cabinet into the vestibule again and as we're dancing there in the shithouse I come all over her beautiful gown and she's sore as hell about it. I stumble back to the table and there's Borowski with his ruddy face and Mona with her disapproving eye. And Borowski says "Let's all go to Brussels tomorrow," and we agree, and when we get back to the hotel I vomit all over the place, in the bed, in the washbowl, over the suits and gowns and the goloshes and canes and the notebooks I never touched and the manuscripts cold and dead.

A few months later. The same hotel, the same room. We look out on the courtyard where the bicycles are parked, and there is the little room up above, under the attic, where some smart young Alec played the phonograph all day long and repeated clever little things at the top of his voice. I say "we" but I'm getting ahead of myself, because Mona has been away a long time and it's just today that I'm meeting her at the Gare St. Lazare. Toward evening I'm standing there with my face squeezed between the bars, but there's no Mona, and I read the cable over again but it doesn't help any. I go back to the Quarter and just the same I put away a hearty meal. Strolling past the Dôme a little later suddenly I see a pale, heavy face and burning eyes—and the little velvet suit that I always adore because under the soft velvet there were always her warm breasts, the marble legs, cool, firm, muscular. She rises up out of a sea of faces and embraces me, embraces me passionately—a thousand eyes, noses, fingers, legs, bottles, windows, purses, saucers all glaring at us and we in each other's arms oblivious. I sit down beside her and she talks—a flood of talk. Wild consumptive notes of hysteria, perversion, leprosy. I hear not a word because she is beautiful and I love her and now I am happy and willing to die.

We walk down the Rue du Château, looking for Eugene. Walk over the railroad bridge where I used to watch the trains pulling out and feel all sick inside wondering where the hell she could be. Everything soft and enchanting as we walk over the bridge. Smoke coming up between our legs, the tracks creaking, semaphores in our blood. I feel her body close to mine—all mine now—and I stop to rub my hands over the warm velvet. Everything around us is crumbling, crumbling and the warm body under the warm velvet is aching for me. . . .

Back in the very same room and fifty francs to the good, thanks to Eugene. I look out on the court but the phonograph is silent. The trunk is open and her things are lying around everywhere just as before. She lies down on the bed with her clothes on. Once, twice, three times, four times . . . I'm afraid she'll go mad . . . in bed, under the blankets, how good to feel her body again! But for how long? Will it last this time? Already I have a presentiment that it won't.

She talks to me so feverishly—as if there will be no tomorrow. Be quiet, Mona! Just look at me . . . *don't talk!* Finally she drops off and I pull my arm from under her. My eyes close. Her body is there beside me . . . it will be there till morning surely. . . . It was in February I pulled out of the harbor in a blinding snowstorm. The last glimpse I had of her was in the window waving good-bye to me. A man standing on the other side of the street, at the corner, his hat pulled down over his eyes, his jowls resting on his lapels. A fetus watching me. A fetus with a cigar in its mouth. Mona at the window waving good-bye. White heavy face, hair streaming wild. And now it is a heavy bedroom, breathing regularly through the gills, sap still oozing from between her legs, a warm feline odor and her hair in my mouth. My eyes are closed. We breathe warmly into each other's mouth. Close together, America three thousand miles away. I never want to see it again. To have her here in bed with me, breathing on me, her hair in my mouth—I count that something of a miracle. Nothing can happen now till morning. . . .

I wake from a deep slumber to look at her. A pale light is trickling in. I look at her beautiful wild hair. I feel something crawling down my neck. I look at her again, closely. Her hair is alive. I pull back the sheet—more of them. They are swarming over the pillow.

It is a little after daybreak. We pack hurriedly and sneak out of the hotel. The cafés are still closed. We walk, and as we walk we scratch ourselves. The day opens in milky whiteness, streaks of salmon-pink sky, snails leaving their shells. Paris. Paris. Everything happens here. Old, crumbling walls and the pleasant sound of water running in the urinals. Men licking their mustaches at the bar. Shutters going up with a bang and little streams purling in the gutters. *Amer Picon* in huge scarlet letters. *Zigzag.* Which way will we go and why or where or what?

Mona is hungry, her dress is thin. Nothing but evening wraps, bottles of perfume, barbaric earrings, bracelets, depilatories. We sit down in a billiard parlor on the Avenue du Maine and order hot coffee. The toilet is out of order. We shall have to sit some time before we can go to another hotel. Meanwhile we pick bedbugs out of each other's hair. Nervous. Mona is losing her temper. Must have a bath. Must have this. Must have that. Must, must, must . . .

"How much money have you left?"

Money! Forgot all about that.

Hôtel des Etats-Unis. An *ascenseur*. We go to bed in broad daylight. When we get up it is dark and the first thing to do is to raise enough dough to send a cable to America. A cable to the fetus with the long juicy cigar in his mouth. Meanwhile there is the Spanish woman on the Boulevard Raspail—she's always good for a warm meal. By morning something will happen. At least we're going to bed together. No more bedbugs now. The rainy season has commenced. The sheets are immaculate. . . .

IRIS MURDOCH

from *SARTRE*   by Iris Murdoch

THE SICKNESS OF THE LANGUAGE

Sartre says: "The function of a writer is to call a spade a spade. If words are sick, it is up to us to cure them. . . . If one starts deploring the inadequacy of language to reality, like Brice Parain, one makes oneself an accomplice of the enemy, that is, of propaganda. . . . I distrust the incommunicable; it is the source of all violence."[1]

What is this sickness of the language? It is impossible to give a neat answer to the question. The fact is that our awareness of language has altered in the fairly recent past. We can no longer take language for granted as a medium of communication. Its transparency has gone. We are like people who for a long time looked out of a window without noticing the glass—and then one day began to notice this too. The beginnings of this new awareness lie far back (in England, one may find it in Hobbes and Locke) but it is only within the last century that it has taken the form of a blinding enlightenment or a devouring obsession. The more one looks at the phenomenon the more one has that feeling of a discovery which is made in all spheres simultaneously; the sort of feeling which tempts people to invoke the useless notion of the *Zeitgeist*. One suddenly begins to connect *The Concept of Mind* with the marble sugar lumps of surrealism (attacks on the notion of essence) and Hegel's *Logic* with *Finnegan's*

[1] *What is Literature?* pp. 210–211. Quotations from *What is Literature?* are taken from Bernard Frechtman's translation. All other translations quoted are my own.

Wake (attempts to present the universe concretely and non-discursively as one huge pulsating interpenetrating particular).

This age may or may not deserve to be called one of "existentialist" thinking, but it is certainly the ending of a period of "essentialist" thinking. In every sphere our simple "thingy" view of the world is being altered and often disintegrated at an unprecedented rate; and a crisis in our view of the operation of language is inevitable. This fragmentation may sometimes appear as the pure joy of a new discovery, a more exact observation. It was with no sense of loss that Monet declared that the principal person in a picture was the light. In the delighted vision of the impressionist painter the world of hard self-contained objects was transformed into a scintillating haze of "appearances," a dance of "sense data." This was done too in the name of a new realism, an observation which, set free from the stale domination of "essences" and general notions, could be faithful to the true momentary looks of the world. The writer, however, whose business was words, seemed to suffer a more distressing upheaval, and was less ready with new techniques. A sense of the desperate rapidity of change, the responsibility of speech in an incomprehensible situation, a feeling of being "left out," obscure guilt at the inhumanities of a materialistic society: all these may have contributed to his *malaise*. But whatever the "causes," it was the poet, whose relation to language is always more sensitive and more easily deranged than that of the prose writer, who first showed an extreme reaction. With the symbolists, poetry seemed to take a plunge into a perverse and deliberate obscurity.

The language of poetry is not in the ordinary sense "communicative"; but it has usually taken for granted the normal power of reference possessed by words and sentences, their power to point fairly unambiguously at items in the world. Precision of reference had been sometimes more, sometimes less, important to the poet; but now suddenly it seemed that the whole referential character of language had become for him a sort of irritant or stumbling block. It was as if the poet began to see the world with a dreadful particularity, as a great ineffable mass of inextricable processes. To lose the discursive "thingy" nature of one's vision and yet to feel the necessity of utterance is to experience a breakdown of language—which may be met in either of two extreme ways. The poet may accept and even intensify his sense of the chaotic interpenetration of reality, and attempt to make his language into the perfect expression of this overrich world. To do this is to weaken the referential character of language by overloading it. On the other hand, the poet may attempt to draw language out of the ineffable flux altogether, and to erect it into a pure and non-referential structure on its own. The former reaction was that of Rimbaud, the latter that of Mallarmé.[2]

Rimbaud seems to seek to achieve a dream-like plenitude wherein language disintegrates through an overdetermination of meaning; the thick accumulation of exact and highly sensory imagery produces a rich blending all-enveloping confusion in the mind of the reader. Mallarmé seeks rather to make language perform the impossible feat of simply *being* without referring at all. The reader is held by a pure incantation wherefrom the ordinary senses of the words have been systematically purged. Meaning has been destroyed in the one case by being crowded in, in the other by being charmed out. Characteristic of both poets is the way in which language appears to them like a metaphysical task, an angel to be wrestled with. Their attention is fixed upon language itself to the point of obsession, and their poems are thing-like, non-communicative, non-transparent to an unprecedented degree; they are independent structures, either outside the world or containing the world. Language loses its character of communicative speech. For both poets, the conclusion is silence: for Rimbaud a real silence, for Mallarmé the self-contradictory ideal silence of a totally pure poetry. Both enterprises have, too, a touch of madness about them. If a certain magical effect can be produced by conjuring with words it is as if some cosmic problem will have been solved, or some cosmic event induced. One is reminded of Kirillov in *The Possessed*, who felt that if *one* free act could be performed the bonds would fall from the whole human race; or else of that imagined splitting of the atom which would dissolve the universe.

Does the world change first and pull language after it, or does a new awareness of language suddenly make us see the world differently? In the various fields where our experience of language was undergoing change, the new thing had the air of being a pure discovery, something which burst unexpectedly upon us, and which was unique, peculiar to the field in question. The philosopher's new self-consciousness about language seemed to him more like an enlightenment than a sickness. "No one of our recent revolutions in thought is more important than this progressive rediscovery of what we are talking

---

[2] I owe the neat model offered by this contrast to Miss Elizabeth Sewell's book *The Structure of Poetry*. See too Jean Paulhan's *Les Fleurs de Tarbes*, which also analyses two extreme tactics in the warfare with language.

about," wrote I. A. Richards in 1924, in *Principles of Literary Criticism.* It was science, not poetry, however, which revolutionized the philosopher's consciousness of language. The nineteenth-century efflorescence of scientific methods, and the mathematical symbolisms which accompanied them, made the philosopher see the relation of symbols, including words, to reality in a new light. Language was suddenly construed on the model of the scientific definition: the meaning of a sentence being exactly determined by an explanation of the particular sensible observations which would decide its truth. Language was no longer thought of as naming things, even empirical things; it was seen as a way of delimiting, interpreting and predicting sense experience. Metaphysical objects were eliminated and physical objects disintegrated into the appearances, or sensa, which justified statements about them. "The limits of my language are the limits of my world," Wittgenstein said. With a new sense of power, the philosopher, his attention fixed upon language, began to see words as the determining framework of reality.

With criteria of meaning drawn from the sciences, however, this framework was as yet an extremely restricted one. The meaning of poetry, of religious and theological statements, and of statements in morals and political theory remained problematic. The search, in any case a vain one, for strange objects named by such propositions was gladly discontinued; but it was some time before a patient study was made of their more complex functioning (or "logic"). Boldly, the language was divided between descriptive (empirical) uses, and emotive uses; and the propositions in question were then said to have "emotive meaning," to be expressions of feeling without external reference. Even the meaning of poetry became a subject for psychological measurement rather than logical investigation. The immediate result of this move was a loss of confidence in the communicative power of language in these spheres. Language as exact communication seems possible only against the background of a common world, to whose reliable features the uses of words can be related by firm conventions. In the realm of morals and theology, and even political philosophy, a greater sophistication about the function of words seemed to lead to a weakening of that sense of a common world. "Good" was no longer thought to name an objective quality, nor "democracy" an identifiable form of government; and the alternative appeared to be to regard such words as the recommendatory cries of beings who, after all, turned out to be a blend of neat reason and neat passion. It was this aspect of the enlightenment, obscurely grasped by lay critics, which occasioned the intermittent storming against "logical positivism" as a breeder of cynicism and underminer of belief in the young. The possibility of honest affirmation seemed to have been taken away. On the other side, however, of this counsel of "despair" lay a more patient and self-aware return to the complexities of "human life." Gradually the philosopher came to see language not as a structural mirror, or even as a categorical frame, of experience of the sensible world, but as one human activity among others. Language and the world no longer stood apart; language now fell into focus as a part of the world, and with this came a readiness to study, on their own merits, the complex ways in which ethical, political, and religious propositions operated.

Yet the powerful fascination of the emotive-descriptive distinction still lingers. It appeals, of course, not purely on account of its dubious philosophical merits. It also gives an intellectual expression and "justification" to a real sense of loss: the loss of a world of ideas and values assumed to be common to all thinking beings. The view that political and ethical remarks are simply expressions of emotion might well occur to any critical reader of the daily press. (Just as the view that poetry is sheer disorder might well occur to a reader of Rimbaud!) This weakening and obscuring of the sense of moral and political terms is not an accident, however, or even a plot. The smaller, expanding world of the nineteenth century, where the disruptive forces were not only dispossessed and weak, but incoherent, disunited, and speechless, could think itself a single world wherein rational communication on every topic was a possibility. This assumption can no longer be made. The breakdown of the notion of meaning in certain spheres, which might appear to be an achievement of the linguistic philosophers working in isolation, or as the handmaids of science, may also be seen as the consequence of a tragic discovery: the discovery that rational men can have different "natures" and see the world with a radical difference. So perhaps it was the loss of an actual common background, after all, which occasioned the linguistic sophistication, and not the latter which exposed the former as an illusion. Whatever the reason, we can no longer even imagine that all reflective men have common purposes and common values. In such circumstances, it might be comforting to be able to attribute the resultant difficulties of communication, not to the amendable world or to our corrigible selves, but to an innate peculiarity of the relevant terms. This, in its way, was a surrender to "the incommunicable," which is said to be "the source of all violence."

Poetry was affected first by the linguistic disturbance; prose literature in general, and the novel in particular, were drawn later into the storm area. This was not surprising. The novel, traditionally, is a story, and the telling of a story seems to demand a discursive referential use of language to describe one event after another. The novelist seemed to be, by profession, more deeply rooted in the ordinary world where things were things and words were still their names. Yet, in time, a deep change came about both in the structural technique of the novel and its page-to-page use of language. The novelist, too, seemed now to turn to literature as to a metaphysical task whereon the sense of the universe was at stake. Compare the attitude of Proust to his work with that of Tolstoy or even Conrad. The writings of the two latter show forth, are nourished by, their answers to life's questions; Proust's work *is* his answer to life's questions. The human task has become a literary task, and literature a total enterprise, wherein what is attempted might be called reconciliation by appropriation.

Many obvious factors combined to unnerve the writer: the rapid change of the social and moral world which formed his subject-matter, war and ideology and new elements of violence and extremity in daily life, the advent of psychoanalysis. And it was within the ranks of literary people that there then developed the most deliberate and savage attack which had yet been made upon language: Surrealism. Surrealism was born after the 1914 war, under the godmotherly influence of Tristan Tzara's Dadaism, a destructive hate movement, anti-social, anti-literary, anarchical. It developed, under the leadership of André Breton, into a curious revolutionary enterprise. Literature had begun to encroach upon life. The Surrealists set to work to reverse the process. They professed themselves indifferent to art and morality; they were animated by a profound hatred of their society, and an abounding belief in the liberating value of an untrammelled exploration of the unconscious. Poetry was a voyage into dream, language itself simply a medium for automatic utterance, a net for trawling in the depths of the mind, and so extending the bounds of the real; an end which could equally well be reached by other means: *collages,* the fabrication of unnerving objects, or the impact of shocking or pointless acts. For what was sought was not the here today, gone tomorrow, value of "truth," but the undiscriminated richness and particularity of "reality."

The Surrealists proclaimed themselves followers of Rimbaud, opponents of Mallarmé. They rejected the intellectual fight with language, the attempt to outwit it and withdraw it from life, or to batter the sense out of it; they were rather for the swooning surrender to words which would carry them to subterranean caverns of encrusted opulence. Rimbaud, moreover, was idolized for another reason; because he had passed through art into life, because in the end he had rejected speech, because he had lived his destiny intensely. That *long, immense et raisonné déreglement de tous les sens* which Rimbaud had said to be the poet's task—a discipline which was to make of him *le grand malade, le grand criminel, le grand maudit—et le suprême savant*—was embraced by the Surrealists as a universal programme of action. This revolutionary activity could not, however, remain easily upon the plane of personal salvation. The Surrealists soon found that they were fellow-travellers, and ready to assimilate the more romantic aspect of Marxism.[3] The Moroccan war of 1925 even precipitated many of them into the Party.

The animating spirit of Surrealism, however, did not bend easily to Party discipline. Much as the Surrealists professed to despise literature, they still wished to regard it as a liberating force in its own right, and not as a tool of opportunist Party tactics. Much as they hated bourgeois society, the revolution for which they yearned was a revolution of the spirit. The question could not long be delayed: is there such a thing as Surrealist literature? And though for a long time the official answer was negative, yet in fact Surrealist writers could not but become absorbed by the literary techniques which their head-on clash with language had suggested to them. The movement gradually disintegrated into two halves, one part moving on toward direct action by way of the Communist Party, the other part slipping back into literature. Language had won that particular battle; but it had been severely mauled in the process.

The impact of Surrealism upon the themes, technique, and language of the novel in France was immediate, and its effect lasting. Meanwhile, and independently, an impressionist technique had made its appearance in England. Confronted with the chaotic process of the modern world, incomprehensible and gathering speed, and if one can find no place in this process for oneself as actor, or for one's language as instrument, one is after all at liberty to stand back and simply record the particulars as they swirl by, making out of them what wistful personal beauty one can. "Life is a luminous halo, a semi-transparent envelope surrounding us from the beginning of consciousness to the end," wrote Virginia Woolf. "Is it not the task of the

[3] *"Transformer le monde," a dit Marx, "changer la vie," a dit Rimbaud, ces deux mots d'ordre pour nous n'en font qu'un*—Bréton.

novelist to convey this varying, this unknown and uncircumscribed spirit, whatever aberration or complexity it may display, with as little mixture of the alien and external as possible?" The flux whose grey undulations afflicted the hero of *La Nausée* with metaphysical torment is rose-coloured in Mrs. Woolf's work, and her characters take to it as to a natural medium. The logical conclusion of this method is reached in the writings of James Joyce, where (Rimbaud's form of the sickness) the referential nature of language almost gives way under the pressure of the flood of undiscriminated "reality" demanding expression.

When they wearied of automatic writing the Surrealists went back, though with new skills, to firmer literary forms and steadier uses of language. *Finnegan's Wake* reached the extremity alone. The novel moved into what has been called its post-impressionist phase.[4] The impressionist painters tried to paint exactly what they saw, with very startling results. The post-impressionists, by dislocating the "appearances" ever so slightly, and colouring them with some special mood of their own, produced something even stranger. (The Surrealists had already discovered how little contriving is required to make some everyday object look grotesque, to turn the photograph into a nightmare.) The novelist went beyond the impressionistic "realism" of Mrs. Woolf toward a mood of intellectual play, manipulating ideas, spinning fantasies, and experimenting more light-heartedly with language. Cleverness, brilliance, were now the novelist's attributes. The traditional form of the novel was left, on the whole, to writers of lesser talent, who purveyed, in answer to public demand, easy literature of a faintly ideological kind.

This is the situation of language and literature which Sartre is not alone in deploring. An English critic, D. S. Savage,[5] sees it in terms of a moral failure and a crisis of value. "Art is speech, and speech is ultimately impossible where there is no absolute existential relation to truth." According to Savage, the novelists he studies deny this relation, in their various ways, and so move toward "the impossibility of speech." Of Huxley's early phase (the key to his later phase) Savage writes: "Unaware that meaning and purpose do not reside as objective facts in the world of things but are interior realities

---

[4] I owe this extension of the comparison with painting to Professor Bullough. I am not sure if I am making exactly the same use of it.

[5] *The Withered Branch,* a study of Hemingway, Forster, Woolf, Margiad Evans, Huxley and Joyce. See especially Savage's remarks on Joyce's "magical" use of language.

which wait for their realization upon interior dynamic movement, oblivious to the truth that personality is not a substance with which we are endowed by nature, but an inward integration which may be achieved only by the decisive choice of oneself, he arbitrarily attributes his own purposelessness to the universe as a whole" (p. 137). And in discussing Joyce: "Language is not isolate, is not magical. It is the vehicle of communication, and is related intrinsically to meaning, and through meaning to truth—which is a transcendent value. Language is healthy when it is related directly to meaning, and it can be so related only when the mind itself aspires vertically to truth as an absolute centre" (p. 193).

That meaning and purpose do not reside as objective facts in the world of things was something of which, in fact, people were becoming obscurely conscious. ("In the world everything is as it is and happens as it does happen. *In* it there is no value." Wittgenstein: *Tractatus* 6.41.) There were a variety of reactions, however, to this breaking of the social and moral fabric. When purposes and values are knit comfortably into the great and small practical activities of life, thought and emotion move together. When this is no longer so, when action involves choosing between worlds, not moving in a world, loving and valuing, which were once the rhythm of our lives, become problems. Emotions which were the aura of what we treasured, when what we treasured was what we unreflectively did, now glow feverishly like distant *feux follets*, or have the imminent glare of a volcanic threat. The attempt to go on making a total sense of the social and political world, as well as acting in it, demanded a new conception of value which connected it with the character and affirmation of the agent.

Those who were deeply concerned with practice on the scale and in the kind which demanded such an interpretation, those thinkers who were committed in a political or religious sense, made the search for truth in action the reconciling and central feature of their philosophies. Such were thinkers of a Marxist or existentialist type. Those who were less concerned, for one reason or another, with ideological activity, with reflexion upon the choice between different worlds, were readier to accept the divided scene at its face value and to take a more dualistic view. Phenomena were divided into the real and the unreal; it was the task of thought to express or mirror the real, and in this passive mirroring or spontaneous expression truth consisted; not in the dynamic picking and choosing, discriminating and evaluating of practical life.

The linguistic philosophers (in their early phase) took as real the facts of science and everyday life; they regarded as unreal the world of art, politics and religion, emotion, fantasy and dream. Value, failing to be *in* the world, was a sort of exclamation. Truth was correspondence with fact, was the sensibly verifiable. Interpretation of human conduct was left to behaviouristic psychologists. This was followed by a more sophisticated and self-consciously anti-dualistic phase, wherein language came to be viewed, no longer as the mirror of the world, but as one human activity among others. Yet the dualism which this philosophy opposed was still a crude version of the mind-body dualism: the Cartesian dualism (thinking and extended substance) and not the Kantian dualism (empirical world and creative spirit). In spite of a more patient treatment of the logic of ethical statements the serious study of the latter dualism was left to the "committed" philosophies of the continent.

The Surrealists went the other way; they took as real the passions and desires, the destructive rage of emotion that no longer lived with everyday values and purposes, the lurid figures of the unconscious. To the undiscriminated and unevaluated world of sense they preferred the equally undiscriminated and unevaluated world of dream. This was the "reality" that concerned the writer, and not the ephemeral value of a "truth" that was thought out in terms of historical action. The Surrealists were not really concerned with working out the details of a practical programme. They never came to terms with the world sufficiently to do so. Their revolution was the perpetual revolution of romanticism, the violent juxtaposition of the hated bourgeois "everyday life" and the life of desire; a sounding clash rather than a serious struggle.

Characteristic of both the Surrealists and the linguistic philosophers was the readiness to resolve what seemed a harsh and hopeless dualism into a simple and static monism. This could be done by taking one aspect of life as its total and allowing the other aspects to appear simply as peripheral clouds. For both parties, then, mental activity lost its complexity and depth and appeared as a simple unitary operation: the everyday wielding of tool-like symbols, or the unreflective expression of the contents of the consciousness (it was not Professor Ayer but Tristan Tzara who first said: *la pensée se fait dans la bouche*), while the same rather despairing monistic attitude appears in literature as a readiness simply to record the flux of reality, or to become absorbed in sporting with language itself.

Sartre grew up under the shadow of Surrealism. It was probably in connexion with the Surrealist-Communist struggle that he first encountered the problem of the "liberating" role of literature; can art liberate without being itself committed? Can it be committed without degenerating into propaganda? Sartre also inherits much of the spirit of Surrealism: he shares its "heroic" and exhibitionist temper, its fanatic hatred of bourgeois society, its cherishing of that flame of intense experience which was to be not exactly hard and gemlike, but vigorous, lurid and sweeping. Sartre is infected too with a certain Trotskyist romanticism, the nostalgia for the perpetual revolution. Yet he wears all these with a difference. He is more of a rationalistic intellectual than a poet by nature, and his experience has sobered him politically. The rich overabundance of reality, the phantasmagoria of "disordered" sensation, seem to the author of *La Nausée* a horrifying rather than a releasing spectacle, a threat to the possibility of meaning and truth. The more surprising contents of the consciousness are to be interpreted as distorted versions of our deep intentions and not as independent symbols, and certainly not as strays from a subterranean region of supreme value and power. Sartre fears, not loves, this notion of a volcanic otherness within the personality.

On the other hand, he is able to see a certain negative value in the destructive power of Surrealism and the literature of the breakdown of sense. False certainties must be seen through before true ones can be framed; as moral literature destroys itself, metaphysical literature imposes itself. "Human life begins on the other side of despair." The crude dualistic scepticism of *Principles of Literary Criticism* and *Language, Truth and Logic* taught philosophers something essential, effected the break with the past; they were then able to move on from seeing language as mirror or exclamation to seeing it as an activity in the world among other activities in the world. But the scene of this activity is for the modern British empiricist an everyday one from which certain conflicts are excluded. The "world" of *The Concept of Mind* is the world in which people play cricket, cook cakes, make simple decisions, remember their childhood and go to the circus; not the world in which they commit sins, fall in love, say prayers or join the Communist Party.

Sartre too wishes to conceive language neither as a vehicle for realistic reporting nor as an expression of the unsorted totality of the unconscious. Literature is not to be a reconciliation through appropriation, it is to be an activity going forward in a world where certain reconciliations are impossible and certain conflicts inevitable. The world in which Sartre sees language as active is the world of ideological battles, where morality is a function of self-conscious political and religious allegiances and not of a simple and unreflective social round. Sartre wants to put language to work in the context of the great questions of faith; here it is not to be either despised or idolised but used. Sartre's observations are recommendations for the proper use of language rather than analyses of its actual use; and this differentiates him from the British linguistic philosophers. Yet he regards himself as nevertheless expressing an important truth about the human condition when he affirms that language is *properly* a medium of communication.

The hero of *La Nausée* saw language and the world as hopelessly divided from each other. "The word remains on my lips: it refuses to go and rest upon the thing." Language was an absurd structure of sounds and marks behind which lay an overflowing undiscriminated chaos: the word which pretended to classify the infinitely rich and unclassifiable existent, the political slogan or social label or moral tag which concealed the formless heaving mass of human consciousness and human history. Roquentin experiences in an intense and total form that vision of the world which makes men despair of language or else sport with it or even attempt to make it into a self-contained system and a stronghold against chaos. Roquentin himself inclines to a "literary" solution of his dilemma. But what he is concerned to appropriate and stabilize by these means is simply the shape of his own life. Roquentin is not Sartre, or is perhaps an aspect of an immature Sartre. Roquentin's political insight is of a destructive and negative kind. He is aware that words may conceal or justify violence and disorder; he seems unaware that despair of words or their too exclusive cultivation ("pure literature" as well as "the incommunicable") may do so equally. Or rather it is that while he sees the absurdity of certain attempts to dominate chaos, he has no real faith in any salvation other than the tenuous personal one which he envisages at the close. What is treated in *La Nausée* as a metaphysical discovery is conceived by Sartre elsewhere as a malady with political causes and political remedies. The problem is to find a middle way (a third force) between the ossification of language and its descent into the senseless, between the bad faith of *salauds* and spiritual chaos, between (to translate again) an acceptance of totalitarian standards (capitalist *or* communist) and political cynicism. Sartre, as we shall see, going beyond the situation of Roquentin and beyond his solution, wants to connect in a great equation literature, meaning, truth, and democracy.

GENET

from *SAINT GENET* by Jean-Paul Sartre

THE METAMORPHOSIS

Bandit, thief, hoodlum, scamp!
It's the pack of decent folk
A-hunting the child.
— Prévert

THE MELODIOUS CHILD DEAD IN ME LONG BEFORE THE AXE CHOPS OFF MY HEAD

Genet is related to that family of people who are nowadays referred to by the barbaric name of *passéistes*.[1] An accident riveted him
to a childhood memory, and this memory became sacred. In his early
childhood, a liturgical drama was performed, a drama of which he was
the officiant: he knew paradise and lost it, he was a child and was
driven from his childhood. No doubt this "break" is not easy to localize.
It shifts back and forth, at the dictate of his moods and myths, between
the ages of ten and fifteen. But that is unimportant. What matters is
that it exists and that he believes in it. His life is divided into two
heterogeneous parts: before and after the sacred drama. Indeed, it is

[1] *Passéiste:* one who is not adapted to the present age, who is not a
man of his time, who "lives in the past."—Translator's note.

166

not unusual that the memory condense into a single mythical moment the contingencies and perpetual re-beginning of an individual history. What matters is that Genet lives and continues to re-live this period of his life as if it had lasted only an instant.

To say "instant" is to say *fatal instant*. The instant is the reciprocal and contradictory envelopment of the before by the after. One is still what one is going to cease to be and already what one is going to become. One lives one's death, one dies one's life. One feels oneself to be one's own self and another; the eternal is present in an atom of duration. In the midst of the fullest life, one has a foreboding that one will merely survive, one is afraid of the future. It is the time of anguish and of heroism, of pleasure and of destruction. An instant is sufficient to destroy, to enjoy, to kill, to be killed, to make one's fortune at the turn of a card. Genet carries in his heart a bygone instant which has lost none of its virulence, an infinitesimal and sacred void which concludes a death and begins a horrible metamorphosis. The argument of this liturgical drama is as follows: a child dies of shame; a hoodlum rises up in his place; the hoodlum will be haunted by the child. One would have to speak of resurrection, to evoke the old initiatic rites of Shamanism and secret societies were it not that Genet refuses categorically to be a man who has been resuscitated.[2] There was a death, that is all. And Genet is nothing other than a dead man. If he appears to be still alive, it is with the larval existence which certain peoples ascribe to their defunct in the grave. All his heroes have died at least once in their life.

"After his first murder, Querelle experienced the feeling of being dead . . . His human form—what is called the envelope of flesh—continued nevertheless to move about on the surface of the earth."

His works are filled with meditations on death. The peculiarity of these spiritual exercises is that they almost never concern his future death, his being-to-die, but rather his being-dead, his death as past event.

This original crisis also appears to him as a metamorphosis. The well-behaved child is suddenly transformed into a hoodlum, as Gregor Samsa was changed into a bug. Genet's attitude toward this metamorphosis is ambivalent: he both loathes it and yearns for it.

He lives in terror lest the original crisis recur; he fears it as one

[2] The candidate for shamanic functions is killed by the spirits. His body is cut to pieces. Then he comes to life again. Only then is he a shaman. Almost all "rites of passage" center about death and rebirth. The theme of death and resurrection similarly governs all initiations.

fears an attack of epilepsy. "Querelle could not get used to the idea, an idea never formulated, of being a monster. He would consider, would regard his past with a smile that was ironic, frightened and tender at the same time, insofar as this past merged with himself. A young boy who has been metamorphosed into an alligator and whose soul appears in his eyes might in like manner—if he is not quite conscious of his maw, of his enormous jaw—consider his scaly body, his solemn tail that slaps the water or the beach or grazes other monsters . . . He knew the horror of being alone, stricken by an immortal enchantment in the midst of the living world."

The initial event determined Genet's inner climate, which will be horror.

"Few are the moments when I escape from horror, few the moments when I do not have a vision, or some horrifying perception of human beings and events."

This horror is both fear of past metamorphoses and terrified expectation of their repetition:

"A young Italian . . . was laughing and relating some trivial experiences . . . I took him for an animal that had been metamorphosed into a man. I felt that, in the presence of this privilege which I thought he possessed, he could, at any given moment, turn me, by his simple wish, even unexpressed, into a jackal, a fox, a guinea-fowl."

At every instant Genet fears "the miracle, that catastrophe of horror, horrifying as an angel . . . though radiant as the solution of a problem in mathematics, frighteningly exact." But the aim of these passages is to give poetic expression to his fear: it is not literally *true* that Genet is afraid of being changed into a jackal. In the following passage, however, he expresses himself almost without transposition. Genet, who is in the presence of a handsome young man, is afraid of dying:

"Which is to say that either I would become aware of being suddenly naked in a crowd which sees my nakedness; or that my hands would become overgrown with leaves and I would have to live with them, tie my shoelaces with them, hold my cigarette, scratch myself, open the door with them; or that he himself would know spontaneously what I am at bottom and would laugh at seeing me thus . . . or that I would see and feel my penis being eternally devoured by fish; or that a sudden friendship would permit me to caress toads and corpses to the point of orgasm, for when I evoke these—and other—torments, my death is in danger of being the knowledge of my shame which has appeared in the play of the manifestations most feared in the presence of the beloved being."

Note the connection between death and metamorphosis: "My death is in danger of being the knowledge of my shame." "The child who is transformed into an alligator fears lest some gleam from the interior of his body or from his own consciousness illuminate him, hook on to his scaly carapace the reflection of a form and make him visible to men."

When unmasked, he changes into himself. The metamorphosis that threatens him unceasingly is the constituent revelation that occurred one day through the mediation of others and that can recur any minute.

And no doubt this myth is fed by ordinary and quite real worries. Having reached manhood, Genet, who considers himself a coward, is afraid of revealing his cowardice to his young lovers: "In the presence of the person I adore and in whose eyes I seemed an angel, here am I being knocked down, biting the dust, turning inside out like a glove and showing exactly the opposite of what I was."

As a professional thief, he is quite simply afraid of being caught: "A little old woman said to him quietly, 'What have you stolen, young man?' . . . a new universe instantly presented itself to Darling: the universe of the irremediable. It is the same as the one we were in, with one peculiar difference: instead of acting and knowing we are acting, we know we are acted upon . . . the order of this world—seen inside out—appears so perfect in its inevitability that this world has only to disappear."

But the striking thing is that the erotic humiliations of a homosexual and the occupational risks of a thief are tinged with an aura of the sacred. Confronted with a trivial, everyday event, Genet is "turned inside out," "like a glove"; the whole world is involved, one touches the ineluctable. These erotic and occupational accidents have a meaning which transcends them, and, as has been said of love, "they are much more than what they are," because they manifest the "immortal enchantment" that begot a monster and killed a child.

These metamorphoses fascinate him. He fears them and lives only for them. Apart from these brusque changes of Being, nothing in the world interests him. Having died in boyhood, Genet contains within him the dizziness of the irremediable, he wants to die again. He abandons himself to the instant, to the cathartic crises that reproduce the first enchantment and carry it to the sublime: crime, capital punishment, poetry, orgasm, homosexuality. In each case we shall find the paradox of the before and after, a rise and fall, a life staked on a single card, the play of the eternal and the fleeting. The very images and the words that designate them are of the same nature: from the bright scaffold, spring roses, "lovely effect of death"; from the "ebony prick" spring white flowers, death and flowering of pleasure; a decapitated head falls from the guillotine, a black member shrivels and droops. If metamorphosis is a death, death and pleasure are metamorphoses.

Thus, Genet lives outside history, in parenthesis. He no more cares about his individual adventure—which he contemptuously calls the anecdote—than did an ancient Egyptian about his national history. He deigns to take notice of the circumstances of his life only insofar as they seem to repeat the original drama of the lost paradise. He is a man of repetition: the drab, slack time of his daily life—a *profane* life in which everything is permissible—is shot through with blazing hierophanies which restore to him his original passion, as Holy Week restores to us that of Christ. Just as Jesus does not cease to die, so Genet does not cease to be metamorphosed into a foul insect: the same archetypical event is reproduced in the same symbolic and ritual form through the same ceremonies of transfiguration. To Genet, as to the faithful of a religious community, sacred time is cyclical: it is the time of Eternal Recurrence. Genet *has been,* he *has lived.* As for the event that determined his fate, it has long since ceased to be a memory and has entered the category of myths, so that what has been written about the mentality of primitives might be applied to Genet word for word: "What we might call (his) 'history' is reduced exclusively to the mythical events which occurred *in illo tempore* and which have not ceased to repeat themselves from that time until ours."[3] Genet has no *profane history.* He has only a sacred history, or, if one prefers, like so-called "archaic" societies he is continually transforming history into mythical categories.

If we wish to understand this man, the only way to do so is to reconstruct carefully, through the mythical representations he has given us of his universe, the original event to which he constantly refers and which he reproduces in his secret ceremonies. By analysis of the myths we shall proceed to re-establish the facts in their true significance.

*

Genet is seven years old. The National Foundling Society has placed him in the care of Morvan peasants. Adrift in nature, he lives

[3] Cf. Mircéa-Eliade, *L'Eternal Retour.*

"in sweet confusion with the world." He fondles himself in the grass, in the water; he plays; the whole countryside passes through his vacant transparency. In short, he is innocent.

This innocence comes to him from others—everything comes to us from others, even innocence. Grown-ups never weary of taking stock of their belongings: this is called regarding. The child is in the assortment, between two stools or under the table. He comes to know himself through their regard, and his happiness lies in being part of the stock. To Be is to belong to someone. If property defines Being, the quiet, sober steadiness of earthly possessions defines the Good. Good as good soil, faithful as a spade, as a rake, pure as milk, Genet grows up piously. He is a good little boy, a respectful and gentle child, weaker and smaller than his playmates, but more intelligent. He is always at the head of his class. In addition, he is serious, thoughtful, not talkative, in short, as good as gold. This Good is simple: one has parents whom one worships, one does one's homework in their presence, and before going to bed one says one's prayers. Later, one likewise becomes an owner of things and one works hard and saves. Work, family, country, honesty, property: such is his conception of the Good. It is graven forever upon his heart. Later on, despite the fact that he steals, begs, lies, prostitutes himself, it will not change. The local priest says that his is a religious nature.

This child is the victim of a cruel hoax. If you say to adults that they *are* innocent, they get annoyed, but they like to have *been* innocent. It is an alibi, an occasion for sentiment, a pathway to resentment and all forms of *passéiste* thinking, a ready-made refuge for time of misfortune, a way of asserting or implying that one was better than one's life. The myth of childhood innocence is a bastardized, positive and convenient form of the myth of Paradise Lost. As saints, intercessors and vestals of this pocket religion, it is the function of children, from the age of one to ten, to represent for grown-ups the original state of grace. Many of them find it to their advantage to become these sacred vessels, in particular those who are very secure, for example, the eldest of large families. But there are some whose actual situation contradicts the mythical virtues with which they have been adorned. Genet is one of these. He was given to believe, as were all the other village youngsters, that his soul was white; he therefore sees himself as white. Or rather, he sees nothing at all, but takes the grown-ups' word for it: they are able to discern his secret snows. This modest pride is going to determine his destiny: it consecrates, without his suspecting it, the priority of the object over the subject, of what one is to others over what one is to oneself. Nevertheless, the fact is that he *lives* his innocence, that he enjoys it, that it makes him happy. It would be wrong to paint Genet's childhood in too-dark colors since he has been careful to inform us himself that it was the most beautiful period of his life.

And yet, from this moment on he lives in a state of uneasiness. The pious and lawful vocables which he has been made to learn are not very applicable to what he is and what he feels. But as he possesses no others, he can neither describe nor define his malaise. Unnamed, unnamable, marginal, unexpressed, this anxiety, which is faceless and without consistency, seems to him a negligible mood. Genet does *not perceive it.* Yet it expresses his deepest reality, which is contradictory, for his self-certainty contradicts the truth that he is for others. Innocent *in general,* he senses that he is suspect in particular. He is obliged, by error, to use a language which is not his own, which belongs only to legitimate children. Genet has neither mother nor heritage —how could he be innocent? By virtue of his mere existence he disturbs the natural order and the social order. A human institution with its birth-register and its bureaucracy has come between the species and himself. He is a fake child. No doubt he was born of a woman, but this origin has not been noted by the social memory. As far as everyone and, consequently, he himself are concerned, he appeared one fine day without having been carried in any known womb: he is a synthetic product. He is obscurely aware that he belongs legally to administrative bodies and laboratories, and so there is nothing surprising in the fact that he later feels elective affinities with reformatories and prisons. Being a fabricated creature, he will find his truth in sophism; being a child of miracle, he will be mineral or spirit; but he does not belong to the intermediate kingdom: to life. He will never care for sports or physical pleasure; he will never be gluttonous or sensual; he will never have confidence in his body. For want of having known the primordial relationship with naked flesh, with the swooning fertility of a woman, he will never have that tender familiarity with his own flesh, that abandon which makes it possible for others to reproduce within themselves and by themselves the indissoluble intimacy of mother and nursling. He is said to be "contrary to nature." But the reason is that, as far back as he can remember, nature has been against him. We others who issue from the species have a mandate to continue the species. Genet, who was born without parents, is preparing to die without descendants. His sexuality will be sterility and abstract tension.

How does the little boy foresee his destiny? I cannot say, but there is no doubt that he already lives it in advance. Since his earliest childhood, the unknown mother has been one of the chief figures of his mythology. He both worships and hates her, smothers her with kisses and seeks to debase her. He is still fairly young when he addresses the Mettray Reformatory as if it were his own mother; he imagines that it appears to him "with all that is peculiar to women"; tenderness, slightly nauseating stale smell emanating from the open mouth, deep heaving bosom, in short everything that makes the mother a mother. In short, the Mother-Goddess, fertile and bountiful; better still, nature personified. Later, in his books, woman will appear only as mother. Genet disregards girls, except to turn them over to his handsome murderers who casually slaughter them. In fact, he peoples his work with guilty women whose children are dead and who mourn triumphantly, and if at times we do encounter amorous females in their forties, they too are mothers, incestuous and sacrilegious mothers, for they are laid by young lovers who could be their sons. But the theme of the "guilty mother" seems to be of recent origin in Genet's work. When he referred to the Reformatory in the past, that big woman was simply severe. At the beginning, *he* was the guilty one. Whenever the child tries to reach beyond the bureaucracy of which he seems an emanation to his true origins, he finds that his birth coincides with a gesture of rejection. He was driven out the very moment he was brought into the world. Later, it is all of society that will cast him out, but this social rejection is latent in the maternal rejection. The child senses that a woman tore him from herself, alive, covered with blood, and sent him rolling outside the world, and he feels himself an outcast. Ever since his birth he has been the unloved one, the inopportune, the superfluous. Undesirable *to his very being*, he is not that woman's son but her excrement. And we shall see how insistently, with what masochistic pleasure Genet will later compare himself to filth, to a waste product. Psychoanalysts have observed that children often feel a parent's death to be a condemnation; the mother goes away so as no longer to see her unnatural son. The abandoning of a child signifies an even more radical condemnation! Is it a mysterious sentence that is punishing him for having committed the crime of being born? Is it a prophetic verdict that is making him pay in advance for future crimes? In any case, the judge is unknown, the child is ignorant of the charges and of the law, but the condemnation attacks his existence itself and eats away at it. Beneath the supposed innocence that adults have conferred upon him is hidden a sense of elusive guilt. Being nobody's son, he is nothing. As a result of his fault, disorder has wormed its way into the beautiful order of the world, a crack has appeared in the fullness of being.

Being nothing, he possesses nothing. Whether judged from the viewpoint of Having or that of Being, he is equally at fault. He knows that he does not quite belong to his foster parents, that the public authorities have loaned him to them and can take him back, and that consequently nothing his parents own belongs to him. For others, things are warm, alive, elastic, but if he takes them in his hands, they die. He can name them, count them, even try to use them, but their dense opacity becomes an absence; it is to the others that they address their homey smile. If, later on, in the presence of the handsome young men who fascinate him, he re-experiences that strange impression of being *kept at a distance*, it is because it has never left him: "Whenever I was close to an object he had touched, my hand would stop three inches from it, with the result that things, outlined by my gestures, seemed extraordinarily inflated, bristling with invisible rays or augmented by their metaphysical double, to my now sensitized fingers." It is the material possession of things that is forbidden him, and his life will be a long effort to dematerialize them, to construct with air their metaphysical double, which is all he can possess.

Of course, he is neither cold nor hungry. He is given board and lodging. But there's the rub—he is *given* them. This child has had more than enough of gifts. Everything is a gift, including the air he breathes. He has to say "thank you" for everything. Every minute a gift is put into his hands at the whim of a generosity that leaves its mark on him forever. Every minute Genet moves a little further away from his foster parents. All this bounty *obliges* him to recognize that they *were not obliged* to adopt him, to feed him, to take care of him, that they "owed him nothing," that he is *obliged* to them, that they were quite free not to give him what he was not free not to accept, in short, that he is not their son. A true son does not have to display his gratitude. He draws from the family purse, and it is his father's duty to bring him up. Deprived of everything through the kindness of others, Genet will later express his hatred of all generosity towards inferiors:

"Madame is kind! Madame adores us. She loves us the way she loves her armchair . . . like her bidet, rather. Like her pink enamel toilet seat. And we, we can't love each other. . . . Filth doesn't love filth. It's easy to be kind, and smiling, and sweet . . . when you're beautiful and rich. . . . But what if you're only a maid?"

A lady once said to him, "My maid must be pleased. I give her my dresses." "That's nice," he replied, "does she give you hers?"

Castoff of a society that defines being by having, the child Genet wants to have in order to be. However, the normal modes of appropriation and denied him. He will obtain nothing by purchase, nothing by heritage. The gift accords him a relative and provisional being but enslaves him forever to his benefactors. There remains work. But his work at school is also a gift: he *receives* general education just as later he will *receive* technical education: they want "to make a man of him." He helps in the fields, he helps at home. But this unproductive help confers no rights upon him. It will never pay for the care he is given; it is merely the expression of his gratitude.

A vicious circle. One might say about the little Genet what Rougemont has said about Don Juan: that he *is* not enough in order to have —and also the opposite: that he *has* not enough in order to be. Different circumstances might have broken the circle, might have dissociated being from having: had he been placed in a working-class home, had he lived in an industrial suburb of a big city, had he been accustomed, at an early age, to hearing the very right of ownership challenged, or had his foster father worked in a nationalized branch of industry, he might perhaps have learned that one *is* also what one *does*. But—height of misfortune—he had to be sent into the fields. Those who provided him with the first image of man were landowners. To that stern, that mineral race, the farmer and his land form an indissoluble couple: one *has* the property because one *is* the legitimate heir, and, vice versa, one *is* shaped by what one *has*. The peasant acquires the silent immobility of his field. Our future burglar starts by learning absolute respect for property.

*

How will this abstract child react to his double exile? By a miming of being and having, in short, by playing games, like all children. He will have two favorite ones, saintliness and pilfering. Insufficiency of being prompts him to play the former, and lack of having, the latter.

Saintliness first. He is already fascinated by this word, which he will later call the most beautiful in the French language. Though he does not yet dream clearly of becoming a saint, he feels that a man is not worth much if he does not live on grasshoppers, if he does not die at the stake with a smile on his lips. This exaltation betrays his secret disorder. It is not unusual for young boys to have extreme tastes, for them to want to be perfect, to be everything, to be first in everything, but if they want to become great captains or great doctors, it is in order to be great among men and of a greatness recognized by men. In Genet's mysticism, however, we discern a rejection of the human order. An abandoned child, he takes revenge by admiring the children who abandon father and mother to follow Christ. It pleases him that the saints are answerable only to God, that they long to wrest themselves from the species and that they go counter to their most legitimate desires in order to achieve within themselves an anti-nature. His contempt for his body makes asceticism easy for him. For the same reasons we shall later see him make of love a form of torture. But, above all, he asks God to give him the rightful existence that Men deny him. He derives at least one advantage from his orphan's solitude: his inner life is not socialized. No gaze disturbs his original privacy. A mother claims to know everything, she makes her child feel that she can read his mind, he thinks he is never alone. One evening, at dinner, it suddenly occurred to a little girl that her mother was silly. The child blushed to her ears and left the table, convinced that her parents had *heard* her inner voice. For a long time, our wicked thoughts will seem to us to be public knowledge; for a long time, we shall lie to others to the very depths of our being. But no family ceremony has consecrated Genet's union with his social image. Alone, without words, without a secret witness, he lives with himself in a state of concubinage. This solitude will later be mated; he will talk to *himself*, will worship *himself*, reinventing for his own use the archaic myths of the double and of the twins. For the time being, he takes it into his head to elect God witness to his secret life. God compensates for the absent mother, for indifferent Society. In becoming an object of concern to an infinite being, Genet will acquire the being which he lacks. He will be a saint, since he is not a son.

Another and even more amusing game: from time to time God turns his head away; whereupon soft, silent, unperceived acts flow from the child. Thefts. The budding saint robs his foster parents and sometimes their neighbors. He robs them in all innocence, without remorse and without shame, and without ceasing to want to be a saint. In his eyes this petty pilfering does not count. He is hardly aware of what he is doing; his hands simply wander. Moreover, his foster mother wasn't shy about filching. She was an "honest woman," of course, and remained honest while stealing. Honesty is an eternal essence which is not dimmed by accidental lapses.

Besides, it is unimportant who suggested to him his first thefts; it is unimportant whether he first stole alone or with playmates. The essential point is that he thinks less of stealing than of engaging in imaginary experiments in appropriation. He experiments, as scientists say, "just to see." He is feeling his way with the aim of establishing forthwith a possessive relationship with things. Since an owner is a man who can use a thing without having to say "thank you," Genet will lay hands, in secret, on personal effects, tools, trinkets—in secret, so as not to have to thank anyone. He will use them in solitude. But *using* is, in this situation, only a means of possessing. The aim is not merely to take the object but also to assume the familiar, expert, off-hand attitude which will indicate, to invisible witnesses, that he is its real owner. The servant girls Solange and Clair[4] do not rob Madame. They put on her dresses when she is out, they adjust them, drape them, they primp and preem; they admire themselves in the mirror, they receive the real caresses of the silk and satin as an investiture. Their sensations and gestures designate them, in their own sight, as Madame. It is Madame's reflection that they see in the mirror, and each in turn becomes more servant-like so that the other may feel more mistress-like. It is only a game. But should the dress be spotted, should it be burned by an ash, the imaginary using of it will end in real consumption: they will roll it up, carry it away and destroy it—and thus become thieves. Genet moves from game to theft with the same fatality. It is highly significant that his first acts of larceny did not spring from hunger and covetousness. These are needs that care not a rap about mine and thine, that demand simply to be satisfied. Under their pressure the hungry man challenges, provisionally or definitively, the right of others to possess. In the case of Genet, however, his thefts, far from challenging property, affirm it. This child who has enough to eat but whom society keeps at a distance wants, by means of a solitary act, to integrate himself into the community. He is aiming at the impossible. His austere and feverish quest for Being involves an imaginary satisfaction only. Thus is born that most peculiar nature which carries out a real operation whose aim and meaning lie in unreality.

The act is performed in two stages. The first does not count for anyone, not even for the one who commits it. The mind clouds over, everyone dies then and there, even the little thief. "The culprit is your hand."[5] In the absence of human creatures, a hand moves in the desert. When the people come to life again, nothing has changed, except that there is a hundred francs less in a purse and a hundred francs more

---

[4] In Genet's play *The Maids*.
[5] Cocteau, *Anna la Borme*.

in a pocket. The second moment, on the other hand, requires the most intense consciousness: Genet begins his spiritual exercises. Outcast of a consuming society, the rites which he celebrates in secret, reproduce the cardinal act of the society which excludes him: he sacrifices, he consumes, that is, he destroys. An object goes up in smoke, a piece of fruit melts to water in his mouth, his pleasure blossoms and fades, it is going to die. It is this process of dissolution that constitutes the entire ceremony. By a fictive communion he touches, on this stolen food, on this evanescent and stealthy pleasure, his imaginary being as fair-haired-boy-rightfully-possessing-the-fruits-of-his-earth; he eats it. Like "the youngster too vacillating to be included in the breed . . . who turned in on himself in the form of a slice of bread smeared with soft cheese, already the snow of peaks, the lily or other whiteness constitutive of inner wing,"[6] he turns in on himself, he regards himself. The pleasure is real. Real, too, the chewing and swallowing. But their reality is of no interest in itself; it is there only to lend a body to the desperate efforts of appropriation. The important thing is to use these real facts as symbols. The legitimate owner puts out his hand, picks a piece of fruit and eats it peacefully. Genet transfers to himself the owner's gestures and sensations so as to identify himself with the latter by an effort of mind. He takes in order to convince himself that he has the right to take; he eats as an actor eats on the stage; he is playing at possession; he embodies the owner as Barrault embodies Hamlet. However, he makes, at the same time, a considerable effort to be his own audience so as to catch himself in the act of possessing. Need I say that he is always about to succeed but never does? It doesn't matter. He already finds within himself what the Marquis de Sade calls the "Principle of delicacy," which makes him prefer nothingness to being, imagination to reality, tension to enjoyment. In short, his operation clearly falls into the category of poetic acts: it is the systematic pursuit of the impossible. No wonder that he wrote later that "the land of the Chimeras is the only one worth inhabiting" and that he quoted the following line from Pope: "Nothing is beautiful, save that which is not."[7] But what appears with the first thefts is not only that straining of the soul toward something beyond the true which will henceforth characterize Genet's inner tempo, but also the particular nature

[6] Mallarmé: Poèmes en prose. Réminiscence. *Oeuvres complètes.* (Pléiade), Paris, p. 278.

[7] This is not Pope's line but a translation of Genet's misquotation, from memory, of a French rendering.—Translator's note.

of his poetic procedure. He never dreams. He does not turn away from the world in order to invent better worlds, he does not abandon himself to images, to musings. His imagination is a corrosive operation that is practiced *on* the real, an operation aimed not at evading but at transcending reality, and, as we have seen, at de-materializing it. Other children would have played at ownership with imaginary belongings. A pebble would have been a gold piece. They would have made believe they were buying or eating. But our little thief wants to eat "for real," wants to have *real* pleasure in his mouth. Only, this real pleasure is neither wanted nor felt for its own sake; it is in the service of an impossible attempt to coincide, in the realm of the imaginary, with the essence of an owner of things. As a result, the whole system is de-realized, the very enjoyment becomes imaginary. The true pleasure of a thief becomes a fictive pleasure of a fake owner. Reality is worn so thin that one can see the light through it. To imagine is to give the imaginary a bit of the real to chew at. For this reason, Genet will be able to say of the chimerical Ernestine: "She never left reality." No imaginary without reality. It is in the real's movement to annihilate itself that the pale shadows of the imagination are embodied. And thereby, despite all the differences which we shall point out later, Genet's thefts are not so far removed from the object-poems produced by surrealism, the inner contradiction of which represents the pure instant of the falling-away to nothingness, through which can be perceived the eternal absence of another world.

The thefts spread and multiply. Genet now robs neighbors. There is no more effective defense against the temptation to have *everything* than to own something. If you have only a crumb that has fallen from the table, your life will be spent in defending that crumb, in convincing others and yourself that it is the best of crumbs and that, in the last analysis, it contains the universe. Genet has nothing, which amounts to saying that he has an eminent right over everything. At this point there begins the systematic turning of the positive into the negative and the negative into the positive which later, carried to an extreme, will lead Genet to "saintliness." In the "land of the Chimeras," a conversion of signs is sufficient to change penury into wealth. This pariah whom the world rejects is secretly pursuing the eminent possession of everything.

We have all known the kind of bright, healthy child with a "winning gaze" and "frank smile" whom everyone takes for a little angel. One day we realize that he steals things. At first we simply can't understand, he seemed so nice! And then we feel personally offended. He fooled us, he's a little hypocrite. We start regarding his virtues as crimes; he assumed the appearance of honesty the better to deceive us.

We do not perceive the air-tight partition that separates his virtues from his pilfering. We do not see that he lives on two levels at the same time. Of course Genet condemns theft! But in the furtive acts he commits when he is all alone he *does not recognize* the offense which he condemns. He, steal? When what he is trying to do is to win, in the teeth of destiny, a regular status, parents, property, when he is attempting to diminish his secret guilt and draw nearer to those whom he admires? What is he really seeking? To *be like others*, nothing more, and precisely because others are good and just, because they are right to be what they are. The truth is that he is impelled by anxiety. At times he feels obscurely within himself a kind of budding anguish, he feels that he is about to see clearly, that a veil is about to be torn and that he will know his destitution, his abandonment, his original offense. So he steals. He steals in order to ease the anguish that is coming on. When he has stolen the cakes and fruit, when he has eaten them in secret, his anxiety will disappear, he will once again find himself in the lawful and sun-lit world of honesty. His conduct is not to be regarded as sneaky. He is really and truly well-behaved and virtuous, and there is only one life that counts for him, the one he leads in the presence of adults. Outside that life there is only a bad dream, a kind of nameless nightmare in which he sometimes feels he is going to be unhappy and from which he awakes very quickly, an obscure menace against which he has invented two exorcisms, the game of saintliness and that of stealing. I would compare this childish magic, which operates at the frontiers of nothingness, of sleep, to the fantasies of onanism rather than to anything else. To the child who steals and the child who masturbates, to exist is *to be seen by adults,* and since these secret activities take place in solitude, they *do not exist.* The truth is that little Genet has been taught an ethic *that condemns him.* He believes in it with all his soul, but by the same token he destroys himself, for this ethic of ownership casts him doubly into nothingness, as ragamuffin and as bastard. This is the key to his conduct and state of disturbance. In broad daylight he is luminous, honest, happy, but the more he asserts his happiness in the light, the more he ruins and tortures himself in the darkness. He is going to reduce himself to despair. If he steals, if he dreams of saintliness, it is not in defiance of peasant ethics, but because of it. He has recourse to the double compensatory activity because he is unable to liquidate a system of values that denies him his place in the sun.

Shall I say he is unhappy? Not yet. In fact, one should emphasize the optimism and will to happiness that characterize this child in the depths of his heart. Not for a moment has he wanted to believe that there was no way out of the situation. Not for a moment does he imagine that he is condemned to poverty and bastardy—it would not be just, it would not be right. God will substitute for the absent mother, theft will substitute for property. A petty theft here, a slight ecstasy there, these are enough to maintain his inner balance. Quickly he returns to sweet, natural confusion. But while he is stealing in innocence, while he modestly covets the martyr's palm, he is unaware that he is forging his destiny.

Translated by BERNARD FRECHTMAN

from *OUR LADY OF THE FLOWERS*

At present, the image of fatality is, for me, the triangle formed by three men too ordinary-looking not to be dangerous. Imagine that I am walking up a street. All three of them are on the left-hand sidewalk, where I have not yet noticed them. But *they* have seen me. One of them crosses over to the right side of the street, the second stays on the left, and the last slackens his pace and forms the apex of the triangle in which I am about to be enclosed: it's the Police.

"Police."

They stepped into the ante-room. The whole floor was covered with a rug. Anyone who is willing to mix detective-story adventures into his daily life—a life of shoes to be laced, buttons to sew on, blackheads to remove—has to be a bit fay himself. The detectives walked with one hand on the cocked revolvers in their jacket pockets. At the other end of the kid's studio apartment, the mantelpiece was topped by a huge mirror framed in rocaille crystal, with complicated facets; a few chairs upholstered in yellow silk were scattered about. The curtains were drawn. The artificial light came from a small chandelier; it was noon. The detectives smelled crime, and they were right, for the studio reproduced the stuffy atmosphere in which Our panting Lady, his gestures caught in a form stiff with courtesy and fear, had strangled the old man. There were roses and arum on the mantelpiece, in front of them. As in the old man's apartment, the varnished furniture was all curves, from which the light seemed to well

182

up rather than settle, as on the globes of grapes. The detectives moved forward, and Our Lady watched them move forward in a silence as fearful as the eternal silence of unknown space. They were moving forward, as was he himself then, in eternity.

They came at just the right moment. In the middle of the studio, on a big table, a big naked body lay flat on the red velvet cover. Our Lady of the Flowers, who was standing attentively beside the table, watched the detectives approach. At the same time that the ominous idea of a murder occurred to them, the idea that this murder was sham destroyed the murder; the awkwardness of such a proposition, the awkwardness of its being both absurd and possible, of its being a sham murder, made the detectives feel uneasy. It was quite obvious that they could not have been in the presence of the cutting to pieces of a murdered man or woman. The detectives were wearing signet rings of real gold, and their neckties had genuine knots. As soon as— and before—they got to the edge of the table, they saw clearly that the corpse was a tailor's wax dummy. Nevertheless, the idea of murder clouded the simple data of the problem. "You there, I don't like your looks." The elder of the detectives said this to Our Lady because the face of Our Lady of the Flowers is so radiantly pure that immediately, and to anyone, the idea occurred that it was false, that this angel must have been two-faced, with flames and smoke, for everyone has had occasion to say at least once in his life, "You'd have thought he was a true saint," and wants, at any price, to be more crafty than destiny.

So a sham murder dominated the scene. The two detectives were merely after the cocaine that one of their stool-pigeons had tracked down to the kid's place.

"Hand over the coke, and make it snappy."

"We don't have any coke, chief."

"Come on, kids, make it snappy. Otherwise, we'll take you away and make a search. That won't help you any."

The kid hesitated a second, three seconds. He knew the ways of detectives and he knew he was caught. He made up his mind. "Here, that's all we have."

He held out a tiny little packet, folded like a packet of pharmaceutical powder, which he removed from the case of his wristwatch. The detective pocketed it (his vest pocket).

"What about him?"

"He don't have any. Honest, chief, you can search."

"And what about that? Where does it come from?"

The dummy. Here we must perhaps recognize Divine's influence.

She is present wherever the inexplicable arises. She, the Giddy One, strews traps in her wake, artful pitfalls, deep dungeon cells, even at the risk of being caught in them herself if she makes an about-face, and because of her the minds of Darling, Our Lady and their cronies bristle with ridiculous gestures. With their heads high, they take falls that doom them to the worst of fates. Our Lady's young friend was also a crook, and one night he and Our Lady of the Flowers stole a cardboard box from a parked car. When they opened it, they found it full of the frightful pieces of a wax dummy that had been dis-assembled.

The cops were putting on their overcoats. They didn't answer. The roses on the mantelpiece were lovely, heavy and excessively fragrant. This further unsteadied the detectives. The murder was fake or un-finished. They had come looking for dope. Dope . . . laboratories set up in garret rooms . . . which explode . . . wreckage . . . Does that mean cocaine is dangerous? They took the two young men to the Vice Squad, and that same evening they went back with the Com-missioner to make a search that yielded three hundred grams of cocaine. The kid and Our Lady were not thereby left in peace. The detectives did all they could to get as much information out of them as possible. They fired questions at them, searched through the dark-ness to unravel a few threads that might lead to other seizures. They subjected them to modern torture: kicks in the belly, slaps, rulers in the ribs, and various other games, first one and then the other.

"Confess!" they screamed.

Finally, Our Lady rolled under a table. Wild with rage, a detective dashed at him, but a second detective held him back by the arm, mumbled something to him, and then said aloud, "Let him go, come on, Gaubert. After all, he hasn't committed a crime."

"Him, with that baby-doll mug of his? He's capable of it, all right."

Trembling with fear, Our Lady came out from under the table. They made him sit down on a chair. After all, it was only a cocaine offense, and in the adjoining room the other kid was being treated less roughly. The officer who had stopped the game of massacre re-mained alone with Our Lady. He sat down and offered him a cigarette.

"Tell me what you know. No great harm done. Just a couple of grams of dope. You're not going to get the guillotine."

It will be very difficult for me to explain precisely and describe minutely what took place inside Our Lady of the Flowers. It is hardly possible to speak in this connection of gratitude toward the more soft-spoken of the detectives. The easing of the strain that Our Lady felt as a result of the phrase "There's not much harm done"—no, it's not quite that. The detective said:

"The thing that got him sore was your dummy."

He laughed and inhaled a mouthful of smoke. Gargled it. Did Our Lady *fear* a lesser punishment? First, there came from his liver, right up against his teeth, the confession of the old man's murder. He didn't make the confession. But the confession was rising, rising. If he opens his mouth, he'll blurt it all out. He felt he was lost. Suddenly he gets dizzy. He sees himself on the pediment of a not very high temple. "I'm eighteen. I can be sentenced to death," he thinks very quickly. If he loosens his fingers, he falls. Come, he pulls himself together. No, he won't say anything. It would be magnificent to say it, it would be glorious. No, no, no! Lord, no! Ah! he's saved. The confession withdraws, withdraws without having crossed.

"I killed an old man."

Our Lady has fallen from the pediment of the temple, and instantly slack despair lulls him to sleep. He is rested. The detective has hardly moved.

"Who, what old man?"

Our Lady comes back to life. He laughs. "No, I'm kidding. I was joking."

With dizzying speed he concocts the following alibi: a murderer confesses spontaneously and in an idiotic way, with impossible details, to a murder so that they'll think he's crazy and stop suspecting him. Wasted effort. They start torturing him again. There's no use screaming that he was only joking. The detectives want to know. Our Lady knows that they will know, and because he's young, he thrashes about. He is a drowning man who is struggling against his gestures and upon whom, nevertheless, peace—you know, the peace of the drowned—slowly descends. The detectives are now mentioning the names of all men murdered during the last five or ten years whose murderers have not been caught. The list lengthens. Our Lady has the needless revelation of the extraordinary ignorance of the police. The violent deaths unroll before his eyes. The detectives mention names, more names, and whack him. They're on the verge of saying to Our Lady, "Maybe you don't know his name?" Not yet. They mention names and stare at the child's red face. It's a game. The guessing-game. Am I getting warm? Ragon? . . . His face is too upset to be able to express anything comprehensible. It's all in disorder. Our Lady screams, "Yes, yes, it's him. Leave me alone."

His hair is in his eyes. He tosses it back with a jerk of his head, and this simple gesture, which was his rarest preciosity, signifies to him the vanity of the world. He wipes away some of the drool that flows from his mouth. Everything grows so calm that no one knows what to do.

Overnight, the name of Our Lady of the Flowers was known throughout France, and France is used to confusion. Those who merely skim the newspapers did not linger over Our Lady of the Flowers. Those who go all the way to the end of the articles, scenting the unusual and tracking it down there every time, brought to light a miraculous haul; these readers were schoolchildren and the little old women who, out in the provinces, have remained like Ernestine, who was born old, like Jewish children who at the age of four have the faces and gestures they will have at fifty. It was indeed for her, to enchant her twilight, that Our Lady had killed an old man. Ever since she had started making up fatal tales, or stories that seemed flat and trivial, but in which certain explosive words ripped the canvas, showing, through these gashes, a bit of what went on, as it were, behind the scenes, people were staggered when they realized why she had talked that way. Her mouth was full of stories, and people wondered how they could be born of her, who every evening read only a dull newspaper: the stories were born of the newspaper, as mine are born of cheap novels. She used to stand behind the window, waiting for the postman. As the time for the mail approached, her anguish would heighten, and when finally she touched the gray, porous pages that oozed with the blood of tragedies (the blood whose smell she confused with the smell of the ink and paper), when she unfolded them on her knees like a napkin, she would sink back utterly, utterly exhausted, in an old red armchair.

A village priest, hearing the name of Our Lady of the Flowers float about him, without having received a pastoral letter concerning the matter, one Sunday, from the pulpit, ordered prayers and recommended this new cult to the particular devotion of the faithful. The faithful, sitting in their pews, quite startled, said not a word, thought not a thought.

In a hamlet, the name of the flower known as "queen of the fields" made a little girl, who was thinking of Our Lady of the Flowers, ask, "Mommy, is she someone who had a miracle?"

There were other miracles that I haven't time to report.

The taciturn and feverish traveler who arrives in a city does not fail to go straight to the dives, the red-light districts, the brothels.

He is guided by a mysterious sense that alerts him to the call of hidden love, or perhaps by the bearing of, the direction taken by certain habitués, whom he recognizes by sympathetic signs, by passwords exchanged between their subconscious minds, and whom he follows on trust. In like manner, Ernestine went straight to the tiny lines of the short crime items, which are—the murders, robberies, rapes, armed aggressions—the "Barrios Chinos" of the newspapers. She dreamed about them. Their concise violence, their precision left the dream with neither time nor space to filter in: they floored her. They broke upon her brutally, in vivid, resounding colors: red hands placed on a dancer's face, green faces, blue eyelids. When this tidal wave subsided, she would read all the titles of the musical selections listed in the radio column, but she would never have allowed a musical air to enter her room, for the slightest melody corrodes poetry. Thus, the newspapers were disturbing, as if they had been filled only with columns of crime news, columns as bloody and mutilated as torture stakes. And though the press has very parsimoniously given to the trial, which we shall read about tomorrow, only ten lines, widely enough spaced to let the air circulate between the overviolent words, these ten lines—more hypnotic than the fly of a hanged man, than the words "hempen collar," than the word "Zouave"—these ten lines quickened the hearts of the old women and jealous children. Paris did not sleep. She hoped that, the following day, Our Lady would be sentenced to death; she desired it.

In the morning, the sweepers, impervious to the sweet and sad absences of those sentenced to death, whether dead or not, to whom the Criminal Court gives asylum, stirred up acrid dust, watered the floor, spat, blasphemed, and joked with the court clerks who were setting out the files. The hearing was to begin at exactly twelve forty-five, and at noon the porter opened the doors wide.

The courtroom is not majestic, but it is very high, so that it gives a general impression of vertical lines, like lines of quiet rain. Upon entering, one sees on the wall a big painting with a figure of justice, who is a woman, wearing big red drapings. She is leaning with all her weight upon a saber, here called a "glaive," which does not bend. Below are the platform and table where the jurors and the presiding judge, in ermine and red robe, will come to sit in judgment on the child. The name of the presiding judge is "Mr. Presiding Judge Vase de Sainte-Marie." Once again, in order to attain its ends, destiny resorts to a low method. The twelve jurors are twelve decent men suddenly become sovereign judges. So, the courtroom had been filling up since noon. A banquet hall. A table was set. I should like to speak sympathetically about the courtroom crowd, not because it was not hostile to Our Lady of the Flowers—I don't mind that—but because it is sparkling with a thousand poetic gestures. It is as shuddering as taffeta. At the edge of a gulf bristling with bayonets, Our Lady is dancing a perilous dance. The crowd is not gay; its soul is sad unto death. It huddled together on the benches, drew its knees and buttocks together, wiped its collective nose, and attended to the hundred needs of a courtroom crowd that is going to be weighed down by much majesty. The public comes here only in so far as a word may result in a beheading and as it may return, like Saint Denis, carrying its severed head in its hands. It is sometimes said that death hovers over a people. Do you remember the skinny, consumptive Italian woman that it was for Culafroy, and what it will later be for Divine? Here death is only a black wing without a body, a wing made with some remnants of black bunting and supported by a thin framework of umbrella ribs, a pirate banner without a staff. This wing of bunting floated over the Court, which you are not to confuse with any other, for it is the Court of Law. The wing enveloped it in its folds and had detailed a green crêpe-de-Chine tie to represent it in the courtroom. The tie, which lay on the Judge's table, was the only piece of evidence. The Death visible here was a tie, and that's how I like it to be: it was a light Death.

The crowd was ashamed of not being the murderer. The robed lawyers were carrying briefs under their arms and smiled as they greeted each other. They occasionally approached the Little Death quite closely and most pluckily.

The newspapermen were with the lawyers. The delegates of the Church Youth Clubs were speaking in whispers among themselves. They were disputing a soul. Was it necessary to throw dice for it in order to send it to the Vosges? The lawyers, who, despite their long silken robes, do not have the gentle and death-driven bearing of ecclesiastics, kept coming together in little groups and then breaking up. They were very near the platform, and the crowd could hear them tuning up their instruments for the funeral march. The crowd was ashamed of not dying. The religion of the hour was to await and envy a young murderer. The murderer entered. All one could see was strapping Republican Guards. The child emerged from the flanks of one of them, and the other unchained his wrists. Reporters have described the movements of the crowd when a famous criminal enters. I therefore refer the reader, if I may, to their articles, as my role and my art do not lie in describing mob behavior. Nevertheless, I shall make so bold as to say that all eyes could read, graven in the aura of Our Lady of the Flowers, the following words: "I am the Immaculate Conception." The lack of light and air in his cell had made him neither too pale nor too puffy; the lines of his closed lips were the lines of a sober smile; his clear eyes knew nothing of Hell; his entire face (but perhaps he stood before you like the prison, which, as that woman walked by singing in the darkness, remained for her an evil wall, whereas all the cells were secretly taking flight, flown by the hands, which were beating like wings, of the convicts who were electrified by the singing), his image and his gestures released captive demons or, with several turns of a key, locked in angels of light. He was wearing a very youthful, gray flannel suit, and the collar of his blue shirt was open. His blond hair kept falling over his eyes, and you know about the jerk of the head with which he drove it back. Thus, when he had everyone in front of him, Our Lady, the murderer, who in a little while would be dead, murdered in turn, jerked his head slightly, while blinking his eyes, which made his curly lock, that fell close to his nose, bound back to his head. This simple scene transports us, that is, it raises up the moment, as the fakir's oblivion to the world raises him up and holds him suspended. The moment was no longer of the earth, but of the sky. Everything gave grounds for fear that the hearing might be chopped up into those cruel moments that would pull away trap-doors from under the feet of the judges, lawyers, Our Lady and the guards, and, for an eternity, would leave them lifted up as fakirs, until the moment when slightly too deep a breath would restore the suspended life.

The guard of honor (members of the colonial troops) entered noisily with their hob-nailed boots and rattling bayonets. Our Lady thought it was the firing-squad.

Have I mentioned the fact that the audience was made up mostly of men? But all of them, darkly dressed, with umbrellas on their arms and newspapers in their pockets, were shakier than a bower of wistaria, than the lace curtain of a crib. Our Lady of the Flowers was the reason why the courtroom, all invaded by a grotesque and dressed-up crowd, was a May hedgerow. The murderer was sitting on the criminal's bench. The removal of chains enabled him to put his hands deep into his pockets. Thus he seemed to be anywhere, that is, rather in the waiting-room of an employment bureau, or on a park bench, watching from afar a Punch and Judy show in a kiosk, or perhaps even in church, at Thursday catechism. I swear he was waiting for anything. At a certain moment, he took one hand out of his pocket and, as a while before, flicked back, with, at the same time, a toss of his pretty little head, the blond curly lock. The crowd stopped breathing. He completed his gesture by smoothing back his hair, down to the nape of the neck, and I am thereby reminded of a strange impression: when, in a person who has been dehumanized by glory we discern a familiar gesture, a vulgar feature (there you have it: tossing back a lock of hair with a jerk of the head) that breaks the hardened crust, and through the crevice, which is as lovely as a smile or an error, we glimpse a patch of sky. I had once noted this in the case of one of Our Lady's thousand forerunners, an annunciatory angel of this virgin, a blond young boy ("Girls blond as boys . . ." I shall, indeed, never weary of this phrase, which has the charm of the expression: "a French guardswoman") whom I used to watch in gymnasium groups. He depended upon the figures that he helped to form and, thus, was only a sign. But whenever he had to place one knee on the floor and, like a knight at a coronation, extend his arms at the word of command, his hair would fall over his eyes and he would break the harmony of the gymnastic figure by pushing it back, against his temples, and then behind his ears, which were small, with a gesture that described a curve with both his hands, which, for an instant, enclosed, and pressed like a diadem, his oblong skull. It would have been the gesture of a nun pushing aside her veil, if at the same time he had not shaken his head like a bird preening itself after drinking.

It was also this discovery of the man in the god that once made Culafroy love Alberto for his cowardice. Alberto's left eye had been knocked out. In a village, an event of this kind is no small matter. After the poem (or fable) that was born of it (recurring miracle of Anne Boleyn: from the steaming blood sprang a bush of roses, that might have been white, but were certainly fragrant), the necessary sifting was done in order to disengage the truth scattered beneath the marble. It then became apparent that Alberto had been unable to avoid a quarrel with his rival over his girl friend. He had been cowardly, as always, as the whole village knew him to be, and this had given victorious promptness to his opponent. With a stab of his knife, he had put out Alberto's eye. All Culafroy's love swelled up, as it were, when he learned of the accident. It swelled with grief, with heroism, and with maternal tenderness. He loved Alberto for his cowardice. Compared to this monstrous vice, the others were pale and inoffensive and could be counterbalanced by any other virtue, particularly by the most beautiful. I use the popular word in the popular sense, which is so becoming to it and which implies the fullest recognition of the bodily powers: guts. For we may say of a man who is full of vices: All is not lost so long as he doesn't have "that one." But Alberto did have *that* one. So it made no difference whether he had all the others; the infamy would have been none the greater. All is not lost so long as valor remains, and it was valor that Alberto had just lacked. As for suppressing this vice—for example, by pure and simple negation—that was out of the question, but it was easy to destroy its belittling effect by loving Alberto for his cowardice. Though his downfall, which was certain, did not embellish him, it poetized him. Perhaps Culafroy drew closer to him because of it. Alberto's courage would not have surprised him, nor left him indifferent, but now, instead, he was discovering another Alberto, one who was more man than god. He was discovering the flesh. The statue was crying. Here, the word "cowardice" cannot have the moral—or immoral—sense usually ascribed to it, and Culafroy's taste for a handsome, strong and cowardly young man is not a fault or aberration. Culafroy now saw Alberto prostrate, with a dagger stuck into his eye. Would he die of the wound? This idea made him think of the decorative role of widows, who wear long crepe trains and dab their eyes with little white handkerchiefs rolled up as tight as snowballs. He no longer thought of anything but observing the external signs of his grief, but as he could not make it visible to people's eyes, he had to transport it into himself, as Saint Catherine of Siena transported her cell. The country folk were confronted with the spectacle of a child who dragged behind him the train of ceremonial widow's weeds; they did not recognize it. They did not understand the meaning of the slowness of his walk, the bowing of his forehead and the emptiness of his gaze. To them it was all simply a matter of poses dictated by the pride of being the child of the slate house.

Alberto was taken to the hospital, where he died; the village was exorcised.

Our Lady of the Flowers. His mouth was slightly open. Occasionally he would shift his eyes to his feet, which the crowd hoped were wearing selvage slippers. At the drop of a hat they expected to see him make a dance movement. The court clerks were still fussing with the records. On the table, the lithe little Death lay inert and looked quite dead. The bayonets and the heels were sparkling.

"The Court!"

The Court entered by a jib-door that was cut out of the wall-paper behind the jurors' table. Our Lady, however, having heard in prison of the ceremoniousness of the Court, imagined that today, by a kind of grandiose error, it would enter by the great public door which opened in the middle, just as, on Palm Sunday, the clergy, who usually leave the sacristy by a side door near the choir, surprise the faithful by appearing from behind them. The Court entered, with the familiar majesty of princes, by a service door. Our Lady had a foreboding that the whole session would be faked and that at the end of the performance his head would be cut off by means of a mirror trick. One of the guards shook his arm and said, "Stand up." He had wanted to say "Please, stand up," but he didn't dare. The audience was standing in silence. It sat down again noisily. M. Vase de Sainte-Marie was wearing a monocle. He looked shiftily at the tie and, with both hands, fumbled about in the file. The file was as crammed with details as the chamber of the examining-magistrate was crammed with files. Facing Our Lady, the district attorney did not let out a peep. He felt that a word from him, a too commonplace gesture, would transform him into the devil's advocate and would justify canonization of the murderer. It was a difficult moment to endure; he was risking his reputation. Our Lady was seated. A slight movement of M. Vase de Sainte-Marie's fine hand brought him to his feet.

The questioning began:

"Your name is Adrien Baillon?"

"Yes, sir."

"You were born on December 19, 1920?"

"Yes, sir."

"In . . . ?"

"In Paris."

"Very well. Which district?"

"The eighteenth, sir."

"Very well. Your . . . er-acquaintances gave you a nick-name . . . (He hesitated; then:) Would you mind telling it to the Court?"

The murderer made no answer, but the name, without being uttered, emerged by the forehead, all winged, from the crowd's brain. It floated over the courtroom, invisible, fragrant, secret, mysterious.

The judge replied aloud:

"Yes, that's right. And you are the son of . . . ?"

"Lucie Baillon."

"And an unknown father. Yes. The accusation . . ." (Here the jurors—there were twelve of them—took a comfortable position, which, though suiting each of them individually because it favored a certain propensity, was consistent with each one's dignity. Our Lady was still standing, with his arms dangling at his sides, like those of that bored and delighted little king who from the stairway of the royal palace witnesses a military parade.)

The judge continued:

". . . on the night of July 7 to 8, 1937, entered, and no trace has been found of forced entry, into the apartment situated on the fifth floor of the building located at number 12 Rue de Vaugirard and occupied by M. Paul Ragon, sixty-seven years of age."

He raised his head and looked at Our Lady:

"Do you acknowledge the facts?"

"Yes, sir."

"The investigation specifies that it was M. Ragon himself who opened the door for you. At least, that is what you have stated without being able to prove it. Do you still maintain it?"

"Yes, sir."

"Then, it appears that M. Ragon, who knew you, seemed delighted with your visit and offered you liquor. Then, without his expecting it, with the help . . . (he hesitated) . . . of this tie, you strangled him."

The judge took the tie. "Do you recognize this tie as belonging to you and as being the instrument of the crime?"

"Yes, sir."

The judge had the soft tie in his fingers, a tie like a piece of ectoplasm, a tie that had to be looked at while there was still time, for it might disappear at any moment or stiffen in the dry hand of the judge, who felt that if it did actually become erect or disappear, he would be covered with ridicule. He therefore hastened to pass the instrument of the crime to the first juror, who passed it to his neighbor, and so on, without anyone's daring to linger over recognizing it, for each of them seemed to be running the risk of being metamorphosed under his own eyes into a Spanish dancer. But the precautions of these gentlemen were futile, and though they were not aware of it, they were thoroughly changed. The guilty gestures of the jurors, seemingly in connivance with the destiny that governed the murder of the old man, and the murderer, who was as motionless as a mediumistic subject who is being questioned, and who, by virtue of such immobility, is absent, and the place of this absence, all these darkened the courtroom where the crowd wanted to see clearly. The judge droned on and on. He had reached the following point:

"And who gave you the idea of this method of committing murder?"

"Him."

The entire world understood that Him was the dead man, who was now replaying a role, he who had been buried and devoured by worms and larvae.

"The victim?"

The judge started shouting frightfully: "It was the victim himself who showed you how you were to go about getting rid of him? Look here, explain what you mean."

Our Lady seemed embarrassed. A gentle modesty prevented him from speaking. Shyness too.

"Yes. You see, M. Ragon was wearing a tie that was too tight. He was all red. So he took it off."

And the murderer very gently, as if he were consenting to an infamous real or a charitable action, admitted: "So I thought that if I tightened it, it'd be worse."

And a little lower still, barely loud enough for the guards and the judge (but it was lost on the crowd): " 'Cause I got good arms."

The judge, overwhelmed, lowered his head:

"You wretch!" he cried. "Why?"

"I was fabulously broke."

Since the word "fabulous" is used to qualify a fortune, it did not seem impossible to apply it to destitution. And this fabulous impecuniousness made for Our Lady a pedestal of cloud; he was as prodigiously glorious as the body of Christ rising aloft, to dwell there alone and fixed, in the sunny noonday sky. The judge was twisting his beautiful hands. The crowd was twisting its faces. The clerks were crumpling sheets of carbon paper. The eyes of the lawyers suddenly looked like those of extra-lucid chickens. The guards were officiating. Poetry was kneading its matter. Alone, Our Lady was alone and kept his dignity, that is, he still belonged to a primitive mythology and was unaware of his divinity and his divinization. The rest of the world knew not what to think and made superhuman efforts not to be carried off from the shore. Their hands, the nails of which had been ripped away, clung to any safety plank: crossing and uncrossing their legs, staring at stains on their jackets, thinking of the family of the strangled man, picking their teeth.

"Now explain to the court how you proceeded."

It was awful. Our Lady had to explain. The police had demanded details, so had the examining-magistrate, and now it was the court's turn. Our Lady was ashamed, not of his deed (that was impossible), but of continually repeating the same old story. He was so tired of ending his account with the words "Until he was done for," that he boldly thought of giving a new version. He decided to relate something else. Yet, at the same time, he related exactly the story he had told in the very same words to the detectives, the judge, the lawyer and the psychiatrists. For, to Our Lady, a gesture is a poem and can be expressed only with the help of a symbol which is always, always the same. And all that remained with him of his two-year-old act was the bare expression. He was re-reading his crime as a chronicle is re-read, but it was no longer really about the crime that he was talking. Meanwhile, the clock on the wall opposite him was behaving in orderly fashion, but time was out of order, with the result that, every second, the clock ticked off long periods and short ones.

Of the twelve good old men and true of the jury, four were wearing spectacles. These four were cut off from communion with the courtroom, glass being a bad conductor—it insulates—and they followed, elsewhere, other adventures. In fact, none of them seemed interested in this murder case. One of the old men kept sleeking his beard; he was the only one who appeared to be attentive, but, looking at him more closely, we see that his eyes are hollow, like those of statues. Another was made of cloth. Another was drawing circles and stars on the green table-cover; in daily life he was a painter, and his sense of humor led him at times to color pert little sparrows perched on a garden scarecrow. Another was spitting all his teeth into his pale blue—France blue—handkerchief. They stood up and followed the judge through the small hidden door. The deliberations are as secret as the election of a chief of masked bandits, as the execution of a traitor within a confraternity. The crowd relieved itself by yawning, stretching and belching. Our Lady's lawyer left his bench and walked over to his client. "Keep your chin up, my boy," he said, squeezing Our Lady's hands. "You answered very well. You were frank. I think the jury is with us."

As he spoke, he squeezed Our Lady's hands, supported him or clung to him. Our Lady smiled. It was a smile that was enough to damn his judges, a smile so azure that the guards themselves had an intuition of the existence of God and of the great principles of geometry. Think of the moonlight tinkling of the toad; at night it is so pure that the vagabond on the highway stops and does not go on until he has heard it again.

"They putting up a fight?" he asked, winking.

"Yes, yes, it's all right," said the lawyer.

The guard of honor presented arms, and the unhooded Court emerged from the wall. M. Vase de Sainte-Marie sat down in silence; then everyone sat down very noisily. The judge placed his head between his beautiful white hands and said, "We shall now hear the witnesses. Oh! first let's look at the police report. Are the inspectors here?"

It is extraordinary that a presiding judge should be so absent-minded as to forget so serious a thing. Our Lady was shocked by his mistake, just as he would have been shocked by a spelling mistake (had he known how to spell) in the prison regulations. A clerk ushered in the two detectives who had arrested Our Lady. The one who had formerly carried on the now two-year-old investigation was dead. They therefore gave a succinct report of the facts: an astounding story in which a fake murder led to the discovery of a real one. This discovery is impossible, I'm dreaming. "All because of a trifle!" But, after all, I admit this amusing discovery, which leads to death, a little more readily ever since the guard took away the manuscript I had in my pocket during recreation. I have a feeling of catastrophe; then I dare not believe that a catastrophe of this kind can be the logical outcome of such slight carelessness. Then I think of the fact that criminals lose their heads because of such slight carelessness, so slight that one should have the right to repair it by backing up, that it's so trifling that if one asked the judge, he would consent, and that one cannot. Despite their training, which they say is Cartesian, the members of the jury will be unable, when, in a few hours, they condemn Our Lady to death, to figure out whether they did so because he strangled a doll or because he cut up a little old man into pieces. The detectives, instigators of anarchism, withdrew with a pretty kowtow to the judge. Outside, snow was falling. This could be guessed from the movement of the hands in the courtroom which were turning up coat collars. The weather was overcast. Death was advancing stealthily over the snow. A clerk called the witnesses. They were waiting in a little side-room, the door of which opened opposite the prisoner's box. The door opened, each time, just enough to let them edge through sideways, and one by one, drop by drop, they were infused into the trial. They went straight to the bar, where each raised his right hand and replied "I so swear" to a question no one asked. Our Lady saw Mimosa II enter. The clerk, however, had called out, "René Hirsch." When he called "Antoine Berthollet," First Communion appeared; at "Eugène Marceau" Lady-apple appeared. Thus, in the eyes of Our bewildered Lady, the little faggots from Pigalle to Place Blanche lost their loveliest adornment, their names, lost their corolla, like the paper flower that the dancer holds at his fingertips and which, when the ballet is over, is a mere wire stem. Would it not have been better to have danced the entire dance with a simple wire? The question is worth examining. The faggots showed the framework that Darling discerned behind the silk and velvet of every armchair. They were reduced to nothing, and that's the best thing that's been done so far. They entered aggressively or shyly, perfumed, made up, expressed themselves with studied care. They were no longer the grove of crinkly paper that flowered on the terraces of cafés. They were misery in motley. (Where do the faggots get their *noms de guerre?* But first it should be noted that none of them were chosen by those who bore them. This, however, does not hold for me. I can hardly give the exact reasons why I chose such and such a name. Divine, First Communion, Mimosa, Our Lady of the Flowers and Milord the Prince did not occur to me by chance. There is a kinship among them, an odor of incense and melting taper, and I sometimes feel as if I had gathered them among the artificial or natural flowers in the chapel of the Virgin Mary, in the month of May, under and about the greedy plaster statue that Alberto was in love with and behind which, as a child, I used to hide the phial containing my spunk.) Some of them uttered a few words that were terrifyingly precise, such as: "He lived at 8 Rue Berthe," or "I met him for the first time on October 17. It was at Graff's Café." A raised pinky, lifted as if the thumb and forefinger were holding a teacup, disturbed the gravity of the session, and by means of this stray straw could be sensed the tragic nature of its mass. The clerk called out, "M. Louis Culafroy." Supported by Ernestine, who was wearing black and stood bolt upright, the only real woman to be seen at the trial, Divine entered. What remained of her beauty fled in confusion. The lines and shadows deserted their posts; it was a débâcle. Her lovely face was uttering heartrending appeals, howls as tragic as the cries of a dying woman. Divine was wearing a brown, silky camel-hair coat. She too said, "I so swear."

"What do you know about the accused?" asked the judge.

"I've known him for a long time, your Honor, but nevertheless

I can say that I think he's very naïve, very childlike. I've always regarded him as being very sweet. He could be my son."

She went on to tell, with a great deal of tact, how they had lived
together for a long time. There was no mention of Darling. Divine
was at last the grown-up she had not been allowed to be anywhere
else. By God! here he is again, the witness, who has finally emerged
from the child Culafroy whom he had never ceased to be. If he
never performs any simple act, it is because only a few old men
may be simple, that is, pure, purged, simplified as a diagram, which
is perhaps the state of being of which Jesus said: ". . . like unto little
children" (though no child is ever like that), which a life-long wither-
ing labor does not always achieve. Nothing about him was simple,
not even his smile, which he liked to draw out with the right corner
of his mouth or spread across his face, with his teeth clenched.

The greatness of a man is not only a function of his faculties, of
his intelligence, of whatever gifts he may have; it is also made up
of the circumstances that have elected him to serve them as support.
A man is great if he has a great destiny; but this greatness is of the
order of visible, measurable greatness. It is magnificence seen from
without. Though it may be wretched when seen from within, it is
then poetic, if you are willing to agree that poetry is the breaking
apart (or rather the meeting at the breaking-point) of the visible
and the invisible. Culafroy had a wretched destiny, and it is because
of this that his life was composed of those secret acts, each of which
is in essence a poem, as the infinitesimal movement of the finger of
a Balinese dancer is a sign that can set a world in motion because
it issues from a world whose multifarious meaning is unavowable.
Culafroy became Divine; he was thus a poem written only for himself, hermetic to whoever did not have the key to it. In short, this
is his secret glory, like the one I have decreed upon myself so as
to obtain peace at last. And I have it, for a fortune-teller in a fair-
booth assured me that some day I would be famous. With what sort
of fame? I tremble at the thought. But this prophecy is enough to
calm my old need for thinking I have genius. I carry within me,
preciously, the words of the augury: "Some day you will be famous."
I live with it in secret, like families, in the evening, by the lamp,
and always, if they have one, with the shining memory of their kinsman who was sentenced to death. It illuminates and horrifies me. This
quite virtual fame ennobles me, like a parchment that no one can
decipher, an illustrious birth kept secret, a royal bar sinister, a mask
or perhaps a divine filiation, the kind of thing Josephine must have

felt, she who never forgot that she had given birth to the child who was to become the prettiest woman in the village, Marie, the mother of Solange—the goddess born in a hovel who had more blazons on her body than Mimosa had on her buttocks and in her gestures, and more nobility than a Chambure. This kind of consecration had kept the other women of her age (the others, mothers of men) away from Josephine. In the village, her situation was akin to that of the Mother of Jesus among the women of the Galilean village. Marie's beauty made the town illustrious. To be the human mother of a divinity is a more disturbing state than that of divinity. The Mother of Jesus must have had incomparable emotions while carrying her son, and later, while living and sleeping side by side with a son who was God —that is, everything and herself as well—who could make the world not be, His Mother, Himself not be, a God for whom she had to prepare, as Josephine did for Marie, the yellow corn-mush.

Moreover, it was not that Culafroy, as child and Divine, was of exceptional finesse. But exceptionally strange circumstances had chosen him as their place of election, without informing him, had adorned him with a mysterious text. He served a poem in accordance with the whims of a rhyme without rhyme or reason. It was later, at the hour of his death, that, in a single wonder-struck glance, he was able to reread, with his eyes closed, the life he had written upon his flesh. And now Divine emerges from her inner drama, from that core of the tragic which she bears within her, and for the first time in her life is taken seriously in the parade of humans. The district attorney stopped the parade. The witnesses had left by the open door. Each having appeared for but a second, they burned up as they passed; the unknown whisked them away. The true centers of life were the witness-room—a Court of Miracles—and the chamber of the jury. It was there that the room of the foul crime, with all its accessories, was reconstructed. The amazing thing was that the necktie was still there, crouching on the green table, paler than usual, soft, but ready to dart forth, as a slouching hoodlum on the bench in a police station might dart forth. The crowd was as restless as a dog. Someone announced that Death had been delayed by a derailment. It grew dark all at once. Finally, the judge called upon the expert alienist. It was he who, really and truly, sprang up through an invisible trap-door of an invisible box. He had been sitting among the audience, which had not suspected him. He stood up and walked to the bar. He read his report to the members of the jury. From the winged report dropped such words as the following: "unbalanced . . .

psychopathy . . . interrelation . . . splanchnic system . . . schizophrenia
. . . unbalanced, unbalanced, unbalanced, unbalanced . . . equilibrist,"
and all at once, poignant, bleeding, "the sympathetic nerve." He did
not pause: ". . . unbalanced . . . semi-responsibility . . . secretion . . .
Freud . . . Jung . . . Adler . . . secretion . . ." But the perfidious voice
was caressing certain syllables, and the man's gestures were struggling
against enemies: "Father, watch out on the left, on the right." Certain words finally ricochetted on the perfidious voice (as in pig-
latin words where you have to unscramble other words that may be
naïve or nasty: edbay, oorday). One understood the following:
"What is a malefactor? A tie dancing in the moonlight, an epileptic
rug, a stairway going up flat on its belly, a dagger on the march
since the beginning of the world, a panicky phial of poison, gloved
hands in the darkness, a sailor's blue collar, an open succession, a
series of benign and simple gestures, a silent hasp." The great psy-
chiatrist finally read his conclusions: "That he (Our Lady) is psy-
chically unbalanced, non-affective, amoral. Yet, that in any criminal
act, as in any act, there is an element of volition which is not due to
the irritating complicity of things. In short, Baillon is partly responsible
for the murder."

Snow was falling. About the courtroom, all was silence. The
Criminal Court was abandoned in infinite space, all alone. It had
already ceased to obey the laws of the earth. Swiftly it flew across
stars and planets. It was, in the air, the stone house of the Holy
Virgin. The passengers no longer expected help from the outside
world. The moorings had been cut. It was at that moment that the
frightened part of the courtroom (the crowd, the jurymen, the lawyers,
the guards) should have dropped to their knees and broken out into
hymns of praise, when the other part (Our Lady), freed from the
weight of carnal labors (to put someone to death is a carnal labor),
had organized itself as a couple and sung: "Life is a dream . . . a
charming dream . . ." But the crowd does not have the sense of
grandeur. It does not obey this dramatic injunction, and nothing was
less serious than what followed. Our Lady himself felt his pride softening. He looked at Judge Vase de Sainte-Marie for the first time
with the eyes of a man. It is so sweet to love that he could not keep
from dissolving into a feeling of sweet, trusting tenderness for the
judge. "Maybe he ain't a louse!" he thought, and at once his sweet
insensitivity collapsed, and the relief it afforded him was like the
release of urine from the penis after a night of continence. Remember
that when Darling used to wake up, he would find himself on earth

after he had pissed. Our Lady loved his executioner, his first executioner. He was already granting a kind of wavering, premature pardon to the icy monocle, the metallic hair, the earthly mouth, the future sentence delivered according to frightful Scriptures. Exactly what is an executioner? A child dressed as a Fatal Sister, an innocent isolated by the splendor of his purple rags, a poor, a humble fellow. Someone lit the chandeliers and wall-lights. The public prosecutor took the floor. Against the adolescent murderer, who had been cut out of a block of clear water, he said only things that were very fair, within the scope of the judge and jurors. That is, it was necessary to protect rentiers, who sometimes live all the way upstairs, beneath the roof, and to put to death children who slaughter them. . . . It was all very reasonable, spoken in a very sagacious and at times noble tone. With an accompaniment of his head: ". . . It is regrettable (in a minor key; then, continuing in the major) . . . it is regrettable . . ."

His arm, pointing at the murderer, was obscene. "Strike hard!" he cried. "Strike hard!"

The prisoners referred to him as "The Blowhard." At that formal session, he illustrated very accurately a poster that was nailed to a huge door. An old marquise, lost in the darkness of the crowd, thought to herself, "The Republic has already guillotined five of us . . . ," but her thought went no deeper. The tie was still on the table. The jurors still had not got over their fear. It was just about then that the clock struck five. During the indictment, Our Lady had sat down. The courthouse seemed to him to be situated between apartment buildings, at the rear of the kind of well-shaped inner courtyard on which all the kitchen and toilet windows look out, where uncombed housemaids lean forward and, with their hands cupped over their ears, listen and try to miss nothing of the proceedings. Five stories and four faces. The maids are toothless and spy on each other behind them. Through the gloom of the kitchen, one can make out the gold or plush spangles in the mystery of the opulent apartments where ivory-headed old gentlemen watch with tranquil eyes the approach of murderers in slippers. For Our Lady, the courthouse is at the bottom of this well. It is small and light: like the Greek temple that Minerva carries in her open hand. The guard at his left made him stand up, for the judge was questioning him: "What have you to say in your defense?" The old tramp who was his cell-mate at the Santé prison had prepared a few suitable words for him to say to the Court. He looked for them but was unable to find them. The phrase "I didn't do it on purpose" took shape on his lips. Had he said it, nobody would have

been surprised. Everyone expected the worst. All the answers that occurred to him came forward in slang, and a feeling for the proprieties
suggested to him that he speak French, but everyone knows that in
trying moments it is the mother tongue that prevails. He had to be
natural. To be natural, at that moment, was to be theatrical, but his
maladroitness saved him from ridicule and lopped off his head. He
was truly great. He said, "The old guy was washed up. He couldn't
even get a hard-on."

The last word did not pass his jaunty little lips. Nevertheless,
the twelve old men, all together, very quickly put their hands over
their ears to prevent the entry of the word that was as big as an
organ, which, finding no other orifice, entered all stiff and hot into
their gaping mouths. The maleness of the twelve old men and of
the judge was flouted by the youngster's glorious immodesty. Everything was changed. Those who were Spanish dancers, with castanets
on the fingers, became jurors again, the sensitive painter became a
juror again, the old man of cloth became a juror again, so did the
old grouch, so did the one who was pope and the one who was Vestris.
Don't you believe me? The audience heaved a sigh of rage. With
his beautiful hands the judge made the gesture that tragic actresses
make with their lovely arms. Three subtle shudders ruffled his red
robe as if it were a theatre curtain, as if there clung to the flap, at
the calf, the desperate claws of a dying kitten, the muscles of whose
paws had been contracted by three little death throes. He nervously
ordered Our Lady to behave with decorum, and the lawyer for the
defense took the floor. With mincing little steps under his robe (which
were really like little farts), he came to the bar and addressed the
Court. The Court smiled, that is, with the smile imparted to the face
by the austere choice (already made) between the just and the unjust, the royal rigor of the brow that knows the dividing line—that
has seen clear and judged—and that condemns. The Court was smiling. The faces were relaxing from the tension; the flesh was softening
up again; little pouts were ventured, but, quickly startled, withdrew
into their shells. The Court was pleased, quite pleased. The lawyer
was doing his utmost. He spoke volubly, his sentences went on and
on. One felt that they had been born of lightning and would peter
out in tails of comets. He was mingling what he said were his childhood memories (of his own childhood, in which he himself had been
tempted by the Devil) with notions of pure law. Despite such contact, pure law remained pure and, in the gray drool, retained its hard,
crystal brilliance. The lawyer spoke first of being brought up in the

gutter, the example of the street, of hunger, of thirst (my God, who was he going to make of the child a Father de Foucauld or a Michel Vieuchange?); he spoke also of the almost carnal temptation of the neck, which is made the way it is in order to be squeezed. In short, he was off the track. Our Lady esteemed this eloquence. He did not yet believe what the lawyer was saying, but he was ready to undertake anything, to assume anything. Yes, a feeling of uneasiness, the meaning of which he understood only later, indicated to him, by obscure means, that the lawyer was undoing him. The Court was cursing so mediocre a lawyer who was not even according it the satisfaction of overcoming the pity it should normally have felt while following the speech for the defense. What game was this idiotic lawyer playing? If only he would say a word, a trifling or crude word, that would make the jurors, for at least the space and time of a murderous leer, be smitten with an adolescent corpse and, thus avenging the strangled old man, feel that they, in turn, had the soul of a murderer (sitting comfortably in the warm room, without any risks, except merely the little Eternal Damnation). Their pleasure was disappearing. Would they have to acquit because the lawyer was a blockhead? But did anyone think that this might have been the supreme foxiness of a poet-lawyer? Napoleon is said to have lost Waterloo because Wellington committed a blunder. The Court felt that it had to sanctify this young man. The lawyer was drooling. He was speaking, at the moment, of possible re-education—in their reserved stall, the four representatives of the Church Youth Clubs then played poker dice to settle the fate of the soul of Our Lady of the Flowers. The lawyer was asking for an acquittal. He was imploring. They no longer understood him. Finally, as with a promptness for sensing the one moment in a thousand for saying the crucial word, Our Lady gently, as always, screwed up his face and said, though without thinking it, "Ah no, not the corrida, it ain't worth it. I'd rather croak right away."

The lawyer stood there dumbfounded; then quickly, with a cluck of his tongue, he gathered his scattered wits and stammered, "Child, see here, child! Let me defend you."

"Gentlemen," he said to the Court (he might, without any harm, as to a queen, have said Madame), "he's a child."

At the same time, the judge was saying to Our Lady, "See here, see here, what are you saying? Let's not rush matters."

The cruelty of the word stripped the judges and left them with no other robe than their splendor. The crowd cleared its throat. The judge did not know that in slang the corrida is the reformatory. Sitting motionless on his wooden bench, squarely and solidly, between his guards in their yellow leather girths and their boots and helmets, Our Lady of the Flowers felt himself dancing a light jig. Despair had shot through him like an arrow, like a clown through the tissue-paper of a hoop; despair had gone beyond him, and all that remained was the laceration, which left him there in white rags. Though he was not intact, he held his ground. The world was no longer in the room. That's how it should be. It all has to end. The Court was re-entering. The rapping of the rifle-butts of the guard of honor gave the alarm. Standing bareheaded, the monocle read the verdict. It uttered for the first time, following the name Baillon, the words "known as Our Lady of the Flowers." Our Lady was given the death penalty. The jury was standing. It was the apotheosis. It's all over. When Our Lady of the Flowers was given back to the guards, he seemed to them invested with a sacred character, like the kind that expiatory victims, whether goat, ox, or child, had in olden times and which kings and Jews still have today. The guards spoke to him and served him as if, knowing he was laden with the weight of the sins of the world, they had wanted to bring down upon themselves the benediction of the Redeemer. Forty days later, on a spring evening, the machine was set up in the prison yard. At dawn, it was ready to cut. Our Lady of the Flowers had his head cut off by a real knife. And nothing happened. What would be the point? There is no need for the veil of the temple to be ripped from top to bottom because a god gives up the ghost. All that this can prove is the bad quality of the cloth and its rustiness. Though it behooves me to be indifferent, still I would not mind if an irreverent scapegrace kicked through it and ran off shouting, "A miracle!" It's flashy and would make a very good framework for the Legend.

Translated by BERNARD FRECHTMAN

CHAPMAN MORTIMER

Young Men Waiting is a novel set in Montparnasse in which there does not occur a single French word; nor is there reference to any street or café in that neighborhood. How is it then possible to convey so physical and deeply detailed an authenticity of the scene? The answer may be in the realization that the bulk of literature devoted to the expatriate is formulated on a false premise, i.e., the scene is treated from the subject's point of view as an exotic one, whereas the fact is that to a man living in the same street, in the same room, year after year, his surroundings are not exotic; they have ceased to be anything but ordinary. The entire imagery, standard to this sort of writing—the hawk-eyed concierges, lolling fat in doorways . . . the smock-clad schoolboy carrying a large bottle of wine . . . the young tubercular *poule*, smile frozen above her *apéritif* on the terrace of the Dôme—do not actually exist in the mind's eye of one to whom they are everyday sights. Through familiarity the exotic or literary aura they may once have held has been lost; the thought pattern has returned to elementals: "crossing the Boulevard Montparnasse" is not, in truth, "crossing the Boulevard Montparnasse," but, simply, "crossing the street."

This basic principle—of adherence to what is true, rather than to what is merely literary precedent—will also account for the remarkable authenticity of character in *Young Men Waiting*. The author, Chapman Mortimer, is English. It could be said that the characters in the book are English as well; yet, in Bull, Paco and O'Connell, we have portraits of *American* expatriates, drawn to a point of credibility unforeseen by either Hemingway or Henry Miller. Moreover, it is not improbable that the book in translation offers the reader of almost any Western culture an equally convincing image of the expatriate prototype of his culture. It is one of those extremely rare works then, which, in not depending on tricks of character portrayal or props of place, does not incur their limitations.

from *YOUNG MEN WAITING*

They did not know him. They did not know who he was, and for this reason, quite casually and almost as a matter of course, they felt antagonistic towards him when he began to frequent Lepape's restaurant.

"Papa's" was where they dined every night: Bull, Paco and O'Connell. Everyone knew that. It was they who had christened the place "Papa's" and Lepape's wife Eugenie was "Jennie" to them—to the regulars.

They were the regulars . . . but who was he?

In the quarter, of course, he was familiar enough, for like the nut-vendor or the men with oriental carpets who haunted the big café terraces, he and his dog were a normal part of the everyday scene; but if one day he had vanished altogether from the cafés, from Montparnasse, or from the earth, they would not have noticed his absence.

O'Connell had once seen him at the far end of the Rue des Plantes —and with a long loaf of bread in his hand; but that was all they knew about him: that he lived somewhere beyond the cemetery. Nevertheless, as he was, like themselves, a student—or at any rate a young man whose whole appearance asserted a claim of some sort—they resented his appearance in the restaurant as an intrusion.

Tonight in particular he seemed like an interloper, for tonight a casual visitor had taken a seat by the window—the seat where he generally sat with his dog—and Jennie had asked the stranger to move.

"This table's booked," she had said.

Tonight, in fact, Eugenie had accepted him. Since he arrived she had been attentive to him and aloof with them, and even Bull, who never said very much, had shaken his head. Ever since he had taken the seat she had kept for him Jennie had almost ignored them, and in revenge Paco and O'Connell had been talking about him, making a game of it.

They referred to him with every other breath, amusing themselves by discussing him in veiled terms, insulting him in oblique ones; approaching him, as it were, with the whole of a brazen sentence, dancing up to him, then, at the last moment, turning aside from the final word that might have given the game away. They were rather like blackbirds mobbing an owl—Bull thought—trying to see how near they could get without actually touching him; only in their case the owl had no idea that he was being mobbed.

They knew he was listening and that he was unaware they were talking about him, and they were gambling on the results of their skirmishes.

They were bringing Jennie into it too, coupling her with the young man neither she nor they knew; doing their best to embarrass her and doing it in terms they hoped she would understand. They thought she did understand, for she was walking about between the tables and the kitchen, pretending to be deaf but wearing an expression of slightly ominous, persevering calm that seemed to show that she was not so deaf as she wished to appear.

Bull, of course, took no part. Bull never took part. He was, in O'Connell's opinion, preoccupied as usual with his own thoughts and quite happy. Paco, however, believing that he knew what his friend's thoughts were, had said to himself: "So you're taking Jennie's part, are you?" and he had behaved all evening as though Bull were not there. But both Paco and O'Connell noticed that when the man at the window stood up to go, Bull turned round in his seat to watch him, and they noticed that Jennie stopped what she was doing behind the bar and with her eyes fixed on the departing guest with a kind of sullen attentiveness followed every movement till he was out of the door.

"It's as though she expected something," O'Connell thought—more or less in passing, for they were all watching now, and they saw him open the door for his dog and go out without a nod or a greeting, as composed as though the dining-room were his own; as though he were alone in it.

He hesitated for an instant outside the glass door, then turned left, and as he passed along the length of the window that was the whole front wall of the restaurant they saw the dog's tail wave once, then once again, just above the frame, seeming to show how glad it was to leave them all behind.

O'Connell sighed regretfully, glanced at Jennie, at Paco, at Bull. . . .

The dog and its master had disappeared and Jennie was coming to the table.

The faces of all three young men were turned towards her approach, waiting for her, and when she reached the table she leaned across it, her hand whipped up unexpectedly from her side, and her hand and Paco's brown cheek met with a loud, characteristic smack.

"You took the words out of my mouth, Jennie," said Bull's voice deliberately, and O'Connell, who had begun a laugh, ended it.

His red, good-natured face beamed briefly, a boisterous sound started to come out of his throat then died abruptly away, and though he continued to grin because he had the kind of features that appear always to be grinning it was obvious that he was shocked.

He had observed privately that Jennie had not said anything at all, but it was not her silence that had shocked him; nor was it her action.

Given time he would have completed his laugh. He would have admitted that in some respects they had gone too far and he would probably have regretted that his face had not been slapped too. Jennie, he was well aware, had every right to be offended—though he had not expected her to be so squeamish—but still less had he expected Bull to take her part . . . and that was what Bull had done.

Bull who was so slow had suddenly become prompt. Bull who had seemed not to be listening to a word they said had suddenly spoken up in a tone no one had ever heard from him before. He had spoken as though he were emptying a bucket into a gutter. . . .

". . . and," O'Connell thought, "it wasn't water in that bucket either."

Once again he looked from one to another of his companions, waiting to see what would happen. He noticed that Eugenie was waiting too . . . that she wore a dull, almost sightless expression . . . but that didn't matter, he told himself hurriedly. Jennie could do what she liked. . . .

What did matter was that his friends were still gazing steadily at one another across the table; and that Paco quite plainly had his ears laid back.

Neither of them seemed to have anything to say. So far as O'Connell could see Paco did not notice Jennie. So far as he could see Bull had grown roots.

And nothing happened.

Jennie went away without a word, joining her husband in the kitchen, but nobody seemed to notice and O'Connell thought it was up to him to find a distraction.

"Well," he said, standing up awkwardly and trying to sound more buoyant than he felt, "that seems to be that. Let's go." And a little to his surprise the other two stood up at once and they all went out together.

The bell over the door rang shrilly as they opened it; rang again when Paco pulled it shut and paused for a moment looking up at the top of the door-frame. Bull, a pace or two ahead, stood waiting for him, and O'Connell, feeling that he was doing his best to keep the party united, halted waveringly between them.

"Papa ought to get rid of that damned bell," said Paco, then he moved away from the door, gathering up the other two as he advanced, and they walked on in silence till they reached the corner.

There it was Bull who stopped without warning, and taken by surprise his companions had gone on a couple of steps before they realised it.

Once more they faced each other, but this time Paco and O'Connell waited side by side and Bull stood alone.

"I'm going home," he said briefly, and turning his back on them he walked off.

They watched him for a moment, trying to make up their minds, then Paco said:

"Do you see what I see?"

"You mean Bull?"

"Yes. I mean Bull. But that's the least of it . . . that's not what you're supposed to see at all. You're supposed to be looking at Bull turning his back. It's a gesture—capital letters and all that. The Back, in fact. There it is. Tap on that and it won't be poor old Bull who'll turn round. It will be something to make you tremble—something apocalytic. That's the idea, anyhow."

"But what's the matter? What's on his mind?"

"Nothing," explained Paco, "but you don't know Bull. His mind's biblical. It's like the world in the early stages of creation. Nothing's settled yet; but stir it up a bit . . . "

"What do you mean—biblical?" O'Connell interrupted impatiently, then dismissing both his question and the possible answer he said again:

"What's going on? What's the matter?"

"What's going on is going on there." Paco pointed after Bull. "Look. You can almost see it. Some prehistoric notion has come to the surface . . ." He broke off and with a swift movement of his hand that made the other duck he tapped on O'Connell's forehead with one aggravating finger.

"There's monsters there," he said. "Didn't you know?"

He was laughing, but O'Connell did not like it. He did not like being tapped on the head like that and he replied sourly. He thought that Paco was not really laughing at all, and it occurred to him suddenly that he understood Bull pretty well at the moment.

Paco had not been laughing in the restaurant either, he decided.

Paco had walked off much as Bull had done, leaving O'Connell standing by himself on the corner and looking disconsolately back along the deserted, darkened street at the light from Papa's window; thinking about what he had seen and heard . . . wondering about these evidences of a quarrel. . . .

And the following evening, an hour or two before it was time to go to the restaurant, he was still wondering; still thinking dismally about the halt on the corner and telling himself that although he had not seen either Bull or Paco since then he would see them presently at dinner. But in the back of his mind there was a suspicion.

He had often known them to quarrel before, but as a rule they quarrelled in silences—or Bull did—and last night for a moment at least Bull had forgotten to be silent.

"Last night," O'Connell thought, "it was a near thing."

O'Connell was an affectionate noisy young man, imaginative but rather thick-skulled. He counted a great deal on his friends, and of them all he counted most on Bull and Paco in whose company he spent as much of his time as possible. He liked to sit beside them, watching the other young men coming round; the other young men of their circle over whom his two friends together exercised a kind of authority. He would have liked to be sitting beside them now . . . beside Bull, who was as big as a house . . . and Paco. . . .

He would have liked to be sitting there on the terrace of the café, talking to them.

"If they were really to fall foul of each other . . ." he said for perhaps the twentieth time, and unable to imagine beyond that disagreeable point in his reflections he stared disconsolately at the traffic, at the trees, at the passers-by, at his irritatingly cheerful neighbours on the big terrace.

All round him people were talking, laughing, idling; leaning over tables at each other or spreading themselves and gazing about it. At the next table a couple were talking now and then in a language he could not recognise; a language that sounded to him like a soft, occasional grumbling; that might have interested him at any other time because the woman, whom he judged to be about thirty to fifty, had the most extraordinary eyes.

"If they really fall foul of one another . . ."

He told himself that he did not know what would happen, and it seemed to him that a bleak future resolved itself into the twin, dissimilar figures of his two friends; of Bull who was so large and who was loved; of Paco . . .

But what was Paco?

O'Connell did not feel he could pretend that Paco was loved, but he thought as rapidly as he was able and presently announced to himself with a kind of fierce loyalty that Paco was interesting.

Bull was believed to be immensely strong and he certainly looked it; but it was not for his strength that he was admired. It was for his ignorance. Bull, one said, knew nothing; by which one meant that he took no part in the intricate arguments that went on around him; that he used words with caution—almost with suspicion, as if they were explosives—and that if asked for an opinion on anything at all he was more likely to say "I don't know" than to give one.

Last night, O'Connell recalled, Paco had said he was a monster—like in the bible . . . and he thought that was probably true.

"Maybe," he reflected seriously, "maybe that's what he meant when he told me to tap on his back . . ." but the thought wandered too far out of his reach and he abandoned it.

It was certainly a fact that Bull's manner was usually one of apparently sullen preoccupation, and he could and often did sit for hours, never saying a word, never hearing a word; hardly moving: a ponderous shadow of a man with irritated eyes.

You often heard people saying: "Bull wouldn't hurt a fly." But why say so if that's what they thought? Besides, just as often someone else would say: "You never know—with a man like Bull."

"Last night . . ." began O'Connell, then shrugged his shoulders and thought about Paco.

Paco, he told himself, was quite different.

He was not often silent, but he was secretive . . . and the greatest liar imaginable. That had to be admitted. Disrespect was to him more or less a religion, and he had none of his friend's massive simplicity. He had a dark, rather fleshy, expressionless face that gave one a curious impression of melancholy. A rather square face. He very rarely smiled—except at women, when he showed his teeth—and he had exceptionally fine teeth, so his smiles were usually welcome.

He was blasphemous: O'Connell continued his catalogue soberly and without remarking that he was himself a great deal more blasphemous than Paco. He was blasphemous, yet everything he did had a ritualistic turn to it; and he was superstitious too. He had a song he sang on occasion—or whistled or hummed—a song he said he had written, for he said he was a poet. But O'Connell knew the song, which was an old one about a sailor, and while he kept his knowledge to himself he was nevertheless annoyed by it, and by the fact that no one else shared it.

No one had ever seen a line Paco had written, no one seemed to know the song . . . and that, O'Connell thought, was just like Paco.

It was like his name. No one knew that either, and he called himself Barcelona.

He was arrogant, restless . . . he would go a hundred yards out of his way rather than miss a stranger, yet although he treated every casual passer-by to the same brief, hostile scrutiny, one glance at a new face was generally enough for him.

"He's like a dog, isn't he?" Bull had once said of him. "He's like a dog—looking for its master."

"But," O'Connell muttered, "he only said that to me," and he was more astonished by the length of his list than by any of the items on it.

"It's funny," he thought. "It's funny they should make such remarks about each other . . . such close friends." Then it occurred to him that there was in any case something out of the ordinary about the friendship, for people were curious about it . . . talked about it . . . treated it with a kind of respect. They even showed respect to him because he was so much with them.

Some said they were lovers—Bull and Paco—and though he knew they were not O'Connell admitted that "lovers" described them pretty well.

They always seemed to have one another under observation . . . to be keeping an eye on each other . . . and that was strange too.

He never looked at his friends that way. In fact, until this moment he had never looked at Bull and Paco . . . till last night he had never even thought about them . . . and impressed by this reflection he was beginning his researches all over again when he caught sight of Mario making his way towards him; sidling towards him between the tables.

"What's he coming here for?" he asked himself, then guessed the answer.

"He's not coming to sit beside me. It's the woman with the eyes . . ." and he noticed that as Mario sat down the woman dropped her strange language.

He did not like Mario. Mario did not like him. But they talked in a desultory fashion for a few minutes, and observing that on a nearer view his acquaintance was disappointed by the eyes, O'Connell was pleased.

"Bastard!" he said to himself, and he was repeating it as he liked to do with words that gave him any satisfaction, when suddenly, unintentionally, surprised by a new sight, he said it aloud.

"Bastard!"

He even sounded surprised, and Mario laughed.

"Oh," he asked politely. "Where?"

O'Connell did not reply, for among the crowds moving aimlessly back and forth before the terrace he had seen the young man from Papa's restaurant: the man for whom Jennie had reserved a place.

"Just look at him," he said, and the man whose name he did not know walked slowly past.

Mario looked, then seeing O'Connell distracted he took this opportunity of making up his mind about the woman sitting beside him.

"He looks like a girl," said O'Connell, and after a moment's reflection he repeated:

"Like a girl . . . like a girl . . ."

Then it seemed that visions of real skirts came into his head, for he became wistful and began to fidget; but still he watched the young man who was walking farther and farther away along the broad pavement, and presently, rather pointlessly, he said:

"I think I'm going to die."

"He's always by himself, I notice." Mario's tone was faintly contemptuous, as if he meant to suggest that being by onself was in some way suspect, but he too watched the young man and wondered what had provoked O'Connell's remarks.

Before he reached any conclusion, however, a new voice joined in the conversation as the woman at his elbow asked:

"What's happened to the dog? I always think of him as the young man with the dog."

"It's probably been run over," replied her companion without interest. "You can't keep a dog in town." But O'Connell had a better explanation.

"He's on his way to the Colarossi," he said. "If he hasn't got the dog—that's where he's going."

"You see!" The woman sounded triumphant. "He can." She stressed the "he" impressively, then she added:

"So he's an artist."

Mario was amused by the way the two conversations fitted together, for neither O'Connell nor the couple at the next table appeared to be aware of their duet. The woman had picked up O'Connell's explanation without any acknowledgement; so far as he could judge, quite unconsciously; and when O'Connell came in again it was evident that he had noticed nothing.

"You haven't been in Papa's lately, have you?"

"No," said Mario, a little sorry that the duet was over, and once more he stared after the now distant figure retreating from one green tree to the next.

The Young Man with the Dog . . .

The young man who, in the streets and the academies, was always alone, and who was, he now discovered to his surprise, unexpectedly familiar.

Had anyone said to him: "Do you know the young man with the dog?" he would have been obliged to answer that he did not, but he would have known whom they meant, and he began to wonder how many of the people sitting about had been watching the same stranger . . . possibly even talking about him. . . .

How many of them had said the same things that had been said at their two tables? How many had asked the same questions?

Then, thinking about O'Connell's remarks he remembered the last one, and belatedly detecting the hint concealed in it he abandoned his speculations abruptly.

"Don't tell me he's turned up there!" he said.

"In Papa's? He turns up nearly every night—dog and all. And he brings his solitude with him, what's more. He makes the place feel like an undertaker's parlour—sitting the way he does—as far away as he can get, and all up and down . . . and he listens to every damn word you say."

O'Connell paused to glance appraisingly at the elegant young man to whom he was speaking, and he thought:

"Better not. Better not tell Mario about last night." Then, aloud, he went on:

"You know what he reminds me of?"

"What?"

"Of someone in a ballad. Of one of those maids who wander on the shores of duckponds and plait their hair—and then sing. One day he'll start to sing."

"Treble, no doubt?" suggested Mario, and the other replied dryly:

"No. Not treble . . ." he hesitated for a moment, thinking how little he liked Mario; glad he had decided not to tell what had happened in Papa's restaurant; but he could not resist adding:

"Not treble—just shrill. Ask Jennie. She began to itch the minute she saw him—over a week ago. And now—whenever he turns up—she's like a furnace. You can't touch her."

He broke off, aware that he had said more than he meant to, for everyone knew—or thought he knew—that Paco was Jennie's lover. Then he decided that he had not given anything away . . . he had told Mario nothing . . . and for a moment or two they sat in silence at the little round table, ignoring one another, absent-mindedly antagonistic.

"He blushes," said O'Connell presently. "You can make him blush whenever you want. We were doing it last night . . ."

Again he stopped, but he thought there could be no harm in telling that, so he laughed and went on:

". . . and Paco, of course, was winning."

"Winning?" Mario sounded only faintly curious.

"Yes. We were scoring . . . betting on it."

"And how is that done?" asked Mario.

"Oh—quite easily. When you thought you could make it you said 'Fanny' and laid out your money."

"Fanny?"

"Yes. That's Paco's name for him," explained O'Connell. "Anyone could raise you before you began, but if you were interrupted you got the kitty."

"Anyone? Who else was there?"

"Well . . . Paco. Bull wouldn't play."

"Wouldn't he?" said Mario, doing his best to sound encouraging, but O'Connell had heard the note of awakened curiosity in his voice and was on his guard.

"It was a damn silly game, really," he said, and stretching himself and yawning he tried to show that there was no more to tell. Then he thought that it would be as well to turn Mario's attention away from Papa's restaurant.

"Fanny!" he said suddenly, expelling the word and his breath on the same relieved gust. "Fanny! It suits him too, doesn't it?"

"Fanny," echoed Mario after a moment's consideration, "you mean Lord Fanny. He's an Englishman. He won't speak to anyone but waiters and dogs." And feeling that he was leaving on a rather successful note Mario got up and went away.

Lord Fanny!

Delighted to be alone again O'Connell thought "Lord Fanny" was excellent, and he repeated the nickname to himself once or twice.

"I must tell Paco," he said, but the grin that began to spread across his face was soon replaced by a more serious expression.

"I must tell Paco" did not have the same sound today that it would have had yesterday, and while he still felt better he supposed that was only the result of Mario's departure. On the other hand Paco would admit that Lord Fanny was better than Fanny—and surely Bull could not persist in quarrelling over a name when it fitted as well as that.

At this point O'Connell had to argue with himself for a moment or two, but soon he was saying that he could not understand Bull's objection anyway—for what did Bull care about Fanny? Yet that's what he had made all the fuss about . . . it must have been. . . . Bull was quarrelling about nothing but a name . . . or about someone he didn't know at all, which was as bad . . . and glad to have found an explanation, to be relieved of responsibility—and to him it seemed like a responsibility—O'Connell felt refreshed.

Presently he would be meeting Bull and Paco and telling them what Mario had said, and he was relishing this prospect in advance, pretending to himself that his earlier anxieties had been groundless, when he suddenly conceived a better idea.

"Why not?" he thought, and his face lit up as he began to see how simple his idea was.

He could follow Fanny—Lord Fanny. Talk to him. Take him round to Papa's . . .

That might make Bull look pretty foolish, but it would put an end to the row if they all sat down to dinner together.

"Dear God!" he said joyfully. "Why? Why couldn't I have thought of that before?" and a moment later he was walking rapidly away from the terrace, following the route taken by the young man with the dog.

As he had expected, Lord Fanny was there . . . working away . . . but for the time being he was out of reach and O'Connell was obliged to wait.

He was quite content to do this, and leaning his back against the wall, standing just inside the door, he stared about the big, ugly barn of a studio, feeling pleased with himself, with his clever idea, and with life.

The studio was like a theatre, and not much smaller; but in spite of the work for which it was designed it had an appearance of being dimly lit.

The model posed on a small platform set against one wall while the students sat in rows on benches arranged in a half-circle round the throne, and the benches were so steeply tiered one behind the other that the knees of the people on one row were higher than the heads of those on the next row down. In front of the seat at each level, running the full length of the crescent, there was a wooden rail on which drawing-boards could be rested, and because this was the only support possible, because the benches were packed from wall to wall, because everyone was obliged to crouch forward in the same way one got an odd impression of uniformity, of earnestness; almost of piety.

"They look," O'Connell thought, "like convicts," and he noted that Fanny was sitting about the centre of the third row from the front.

The model sat on a box, motionless and lazy. Only her eyes moved from time to time as her glance travelled attentively over the surrounding crowd. Above her head a number of bulbs had been drawn together, their flexes tied with string, and in their light she shone with a faintly rosy, incandescent brightness.

One of her legs was bent so that her long thigh sloped downward to the knee. The lower part of her leg led symmetrically back to her raised heel and only her toes touched the boards of the platform. The farther leg was bent too, the knee raised, the foot flat on a wooden block. One hand gripped a corner of the box and her weight rested on the arm above it. Her head rolled idly across one shoulder.

Although it was a pose from which it is impossible to escape in life-classes, O'Connell thought, and he was about to turn his attention to some other quarter when a voice said: "Rest."

This was what he was waiting for, and he watched alertly as all over the steep galleries heads were raised, boards were pushed forward to balance on the rail while their owners stood up, or stretched, or turned one way or another to start conversations.

Everywhere there was stirring and movement, and taking advantage of this temporary confusion O'Connell pushed quickly along the row immediately behind that on which Fanny was seated; and making room for himself where there was no room he sat down as near to the centre as possibly.

Lord Fanny was now just in front of him—a little to one side—but unlike his neighbours he had not relaxed.

He still bent over his drawing-board; still worked.

In one hand he gripped a bottle of ink. In the other hand he gripped his pen; and he held the pen so tightly that O'Connell could see his knuckles white with effort.

Under the board his legs were twisted like rope.

His head bobbed up and down in quick jerks, the pen hand moved nervously here and there, hovering sometimes, or scratching in little spasms of energy at one spot, or sweeping about in large, intelligent gestures from corner to corner of his drawing while he considered where next to apply himself.

"He'll burst into flames in a minute," O'Connell was thinking when he heard the same voice repeating, but in a louder tone:

"Rest!"

Then glancing at the model he saw that she too had ignored the first order, and he saw a little comedy that caused him to look at Fanny with new respect.

He saw that the model's eyes no longer strayed, and that they were half-closed; but underneath their heavy lids he saw two deep, intelligent pupils fixed on the young man with the dog. He saw Fanny, startled by the sharp voice, look first in the direction from which it came, then in confusion at the model; and he saw the model smile.

She smiled slowly, as if to show her independence before she showed her teeth, and she smiled at Lord Fanny.

"You and I," she seemed to say. "What do we care?"

O'Connell imagined he could almost hear it.

He imagined a coarse, lazily comfortable voice, and delighted by this fancy he was leaning forward to speak when someone laughed.

He could see why, for now he could see the colour of Fanny's cheeks; but he knew it was a mistake to laugh; and as if to confirm him in this view the voice cried again, angrily this time:

"Pose!"

To O'Connell the sequence of these events was perfectly clear and he did not question them.

"She's got herself to blame," he thought as he watched the model sulkily resume the pose from which she had scarcely had time to relax. "Whoever laughed was a fool . . . but Fanny really blushes like a rose!"

Then for a while he was too busy to make any further observations, for as everyone resumed their former devoted attitudes he found he was too tightly wedged between his neighbours and he had to make himself more comfortable.

He had to counter muttered protests and to explain by signs that were quickly understood that he was an old hand at this business, and when next he looked round at the dusty, colourless gloom that was so much like darkness and yet was not, everything had settled down as before. Everywhere the same crouching shapes stirred slightly but continuously, heads were raised and lowered in silence, and white faces showed themselves for an instant, appearing and disappearing like pale, inconsequential bubbles.

So Fanny was a dark horse . . . Fanny, for all his detachment, had made a hit. . . .

O'Connell reflected that he had never seen a model so willing to work, and he was deeply interested.

It was very quiet now, and the air was close and too warm. The feeble sounds of pencils and rubbers, the thin scraping of a knife on lead, an occasional cough or the infrequent whisper of one student speaking to another . . . these were the only sounds. . . .

. . . and Lord Fanny—maybe—was not as pious as he looked?

With nothing to do O'Connell listened to the peculiar, dense hush that is the result of concentration in crowded places, and it seemed to him that all the concentration was his own for he was watching the model again, noticing that she still kept her eyes fixed steadily on Lord Fanny, while Fanny, back at work, apparently imagined himself as anonymously obscure as ever.

"What's he doing anyway?" O'Connell wondered, and he leaned forward over the rail to look.

He had it in mind to speak; to say something about the model . . . some whispered absurdity; but he said nothing.

He only nodded once or twice in silent astonishment as he stared at the sheet under Fanny's hand; then he sat up again, looking to right and left of him and opening and shutting his mouth as if he had something to say but could not get it out.

"I never thought he'd be any good," he whispered to himself at last, and completely forgetting what he was doing there he added presently:

"Just look at that!"

But he looked instead at Fanny, watching him lift his head to gaze for a moment at the model, then lower it again over the page where her white flesh, translated, reappeared under his hand as a black, confused mass of lines on paper; watching him probing and cutting with his pen like a butcher with a knife; dismembering, rearranging; unconscious of everything but of ink and paper, and of his skill.

Up and down went his head—then scratch scratch scratch. Up and down—then scratch again . . .

O'Connell rested his back against the feet of someone behind him and stared at the dark beams high up under the roof; at the naked electric bulbs hanging deeply down from them on long flexes like the lines of fishermen.

Once or twice he swore under his breath as briskly obscene words formed themselves naturally on his tongue.

He couldn't get over it, he said, and as he threatened himself or warned himself of various impossible misfortunes he noticed that one bulb was swinging for no apparent reason. It swung one way, and then it swung the other . . . back, and then forward with a slow, reluctant motion as though it really were under water; and he followed it with his eyes, swearing as pointlessly as it was swinging, wondering about the young man with the dog . . . and about drawing with ink which could, as it turned out, be such a fierce occupation. Then abruptly, as if some sudden doubt had entered his mind, he stiffened, craning forward once more to see round Fanny's shoulder.

He could see even better now, and he forgot to swear.

Fanny knew what he was doing . . . he could see that . . . his pen was throwing off comment in all directions . . .

The page seemed larger—roomier—and at the same time more crowded than any other sheet of paper in sight. The figure on it looked as big as life, and when you could see it . . . when you could find your way around . . . it was as solid as a house. Nothing was accidental or casual. Every shadow had become a kind of calligraphic ornament; and the figure itself, black, contained, its limits defined with uncompromising childishness, appeared on the white sheet as startling as a cockroach on a napkin. Best of all, perhaps, this over-large, over-solid, over-intricate object was perched on a line so fragile that it seemed to be drawn in pencil, for Fanny had thus indicated the box on which the model sat; outlining it in quite a modest, formal manner, as if to re-assure; to make it clear that his drawing was only a drawing after all, and that no deception was intended.

In all this O'Connell thought there was something marvellous. In this pink young man and that black ink. In yesterday's rashes of blush-ing . . . and tonight's . . . and in that trick way of using a pen . . .

"And look at the model!"

It seemed to him that for all their overhanging lids the model's eyes were like the windows of a house on fire, and they never wavered. Fixed on the young man with the dog they never moved at all.

"What's she looking at?" he wondered. "What's going on in her head . . . or in Fanny's?"

He was becoming a little bewildered, for his own head was filling up with all sorts of difficult notions that had very little to do with Lord Fanny and nothing whatever to do with Bull or Paco or quarrels.

His imagination had somehow been touched, and though he sup-posed it was by the drawing—for he believed he knew something about that at least—it was just as likely that the mixture of lucidity and confusion of which he was conscious had some quite different cause.

Fanny's air of remoteness may have been to blame; or the model herself; or even the swinging bulb. There may have been other rea-sons of a kind of which O'Connell was totally unaware, for O'Connell, a thinking animal, was unsystematic and much more hairy than thoughtful; but the saddest brute has his moments of revelation and that was his case now.

He felt he understood, but he did not know what. Enlightenment was as fresh and vivid in his mind as when one is dreaming and the best he could make of it was to mutter under his breath for the second time:

"Maybe he's a dark horse?"

Maybe he was, but when "Rest" was called again the dark horse jumped as though someone had touched him with a pin, and after a tentative half-turn or two of his head he took a deep breath—held it, as far as one could see—and sinking his chin on his breast, stretching his arms across his board in such a way as to conceal what was on it, he gave himself up to self-conscious meditation.

Puzzled as much by one thing as by another now, O'Connell got up. He no longer thought of speaking to Fanny. He did not feel com-petent to approach him by himself, and bemused and even a little shocked, he shuffled as unobtrusively as he could towards the door.

"I must tell Bull," he thought, forgetting that earlier he had made up his mind in the same terms to "tell Paco."

"Bull will be interested."

He noticed that the model had left her perch and was sitting on the edge of the throne, a coat hung across her shoulders, a cigarette between her lips.

She was not looking at anyone now.

"Now," he thought, "she's waiting."

She was waiting exactly as Fanny himself did in Papa's restaurant: "warming her seat and waiting for someone to make advances."

"That was how Paco put it," O'Connell recalled, and briefly he wondered if that was what had annoyed Jennie.

But the model was waiting for Fanny, and thinking of his own description of the young man with the dog O'Connell felt sorry for her.

"No duckponds for her," he thought. "She's wasting her time."

Her legs were crossed and she slouched forward, resting her elbows on her knees, clasping her hands, and disclosing in the shadow of her coat the alarmingly animal nakedness of which she had long since ceased to be anything but careless.

His view of her—Fanny's remotenesses—the renewed bustle in the crowded studio—his own shuffling progress towards the door . . . all these seemed to add to his enlightenment and he felt hot, lonely, elated, all at the same time; and he had no sooner pushed out of the door than he saw the model's sad pose again, or a very similar one; but multiplied—two, three—four—six times; for sitting in a row on a bench and filling the narrow passage that was the entrance to the academy, six young women were waiting for employment.

He had often seen the same spectacle before without stopping to consider it, but now, with his thoughts alight and totally unexplained, this commonplace sight struck him as extraordinary and he halted and stared.

The models stared back.

They were quiet, patient, all young; all rather boldly shabby.

Under a solitary, economical light their ranged figures emerged indistinctly from the shadows they cast, and as the door swung behind him they all looked round together.

They sat listlessly, irritated by their idleness but so deep in it that they seemed entranced. Unconsciously they had adopted the same pose and all looked alike. The calf of each right leg hung over the knee of each left leg. . . .

On each dark lap lay a white hand.

They appeared to be dozing; lost in a bored, identical dream; but as he passed them their dangled legs swung sideways or were drawn back so that the two locked knees rose up at him a little, and in one blank face after another their eyes lifted more than lids to him speechlessly.

There was no one else in the passage. None of the young women said a word. But it did not occur to O'Connell that this might be because they had nothing to say to him.

The real reason for their silence he felt he knew. It added itself unhelpfully to the other matters around which his thoughts were already turning like moths about a lamp, and he came out into the open air feeling tongue-tied but prophetic.

The swollen-lidded woman on the throne . . . her dazed companions in the passage . . . Lord Fanny working away in there . . . the startling drawing . . .

Looking around in the street O'Connell made an effort to arrange these items in such a way that they would make sense; in such a way that they would account for his luminous but incomprehensible sensations of intelligence. He observed a house, and through an open window a man sitting at a table eating greedily. There was a lamp on the table and the rays from it reflected on a profusion of silver knives and forks, for though the man was alone the table had been set for a crowd—or so it seemed; and it seemed to O'Connell that he was standing in the dark, repeating "house" and "reflection" and other simple and unconnected words without the slightest chance of ever understanding one of them.

It seemed to him that he was surrounded by significant things . . . if only he could get the hang of them.

"What's house anyhow?" he asked himself. "What are reflections? What's the sense in drawing?"

Was he such a perfect fool that he had to stand there—and sure enough—he had stopped. He hadn't moved more than two or three paces from the entrance to the schools. . . .

He was standing there like a crazy man, staring into somebody's home. . . .

He hadn't even spoken to Fanny.

"Well," he said suddenly and loudly, "that's that." Then seized with the notion that now he knew exactly what he was doing he started off, and as he directed his hurrying steps towards Papa's restaurant he muttered once more:

"I must tell Bull."

WILLIAM GADDIS

In 1955, with the appearance of William Gaddis' 1000 page novel, *The Recognitions,* it was demonstrated once and for all that a general literary system which is based upon the strict interdependence of (1) non-writers reviewing books for money, against a deadline, and (2) the publishers' use of these reviews in advertising and distribution, is an abysmal failure.

The book, and it is doubtless a great one, was almost completely ignored. Reviewers who treated it at all did so vicariously; they did not become engaged by the work itself—they simply did not have the time. They disposed of it by category, label, pigeonhole—the most facile and common being to compare it, with great disfavor, to *Ulysses.* The author, it was said, was obviously trying to create a "work of art" or a "masterpiece"—this put them off. What they really said was that the author was trying to give the *impression* of having created a work of art or a masterpiece. This is because American "literary criticism" is not equipped to deal with work on any other level than that of the author's intentions. American critics—and this is true of no other contemporary culture—are themselves so far removed from the creative process, and from all imaginative thought, that their response to a work can never be on the basis of what the work is, but on what it seems to represent. It is psychologically untenable for such a person to admit the possibility of direct contact, or experience with a "work of art" or a "masterpiece"—other, of course, than those so certified and still smelling of the grave.

The Recognitions does not need praise; it needs to be read.

from *THE RECOGNITIONS*

> First of all, then, he is evil, in the judgment
> of God, who will not inquire what is ad-
> vantageous to himself. For how can anyone
> love another, if he does not love himself? . . .
> In order, therefore, that there might be a dis-
> tinction between those who choose good and
> those who choose evil, God has concealed that
> which is profitable to men.
> —Peter, in the Clementine *Recognitions*

—Wyatt . . . let's get married before we know too much about
each other.

That was unlike Esther.

She liked to get things out in the open, find why they *happened*.
Still, like other women in love, salvation was her original purpose,
redemption her eventual privilege; and, like most women, she could
not wait to see him thoroughly damned first, before she stepped in,
believing, perhaps as they do, that if he were saved now he would
never need to be redeemed. There was a historical genuineness about
Esther, which somehow persisted in spite of her conscious use of it.
In her large bones there was implicit the temporal history of a past,

226

and a future very much like it. There was size to her. She had the power of making her own mistakes appear as the work of some supramundane agency, possibly one of those often vulgarly confused with fate, which had here elected her capable of bringing forth some example which the world awaited. Principal among these (and no less a mistake, somewhere, which she must live out as though it were her own) was being a woman. She worked very hard to understand all this; and having come to be severely intellectual, probing the past with masculine ruthlessness, she became an accomplice of those very circumstances which Reason later accused of being unnecessary, and in the name of free will, by which she meant conscious desire, managed to prolong a past built upon them, refurbished, renewed, and repeated. With great diligence, and that talent of single purpose with which her sex pursue something unattainable in the same fashion they pursue something which is, her search for Reason was always interrupted by reasons. Things happened for reasons; and so, in her proposal it may have been simply her feminine logic insuring a succession of happenings which reasonably might never have happened at all. Or being a woman, and the woman she was, her proposal may have been an infinite moment of that femininity which is one of humanity's few approximations to beauty, asking no justification and needing none to act in a moment of certainty with nothing to fear, one day to be recalled in a fearful moment threatened by certainty.

Left hand; right hand: they moved over her with equal assurance. Undistinguished here they raised her flesh, and Esther rose to reconcile them, to provide common ground where each might know what the other was doing.

A year later, they had been married for almost a year; which was unlike Wyatt. He had become increasingly reluctant wherever decisions were concerned; and the more he knew, the less inclined to commit himself. Not that this was an exceptional state: whole systems of philosophy have been erected upon it. On the other hand, the more he refused to commit himself, the more submerged, and the more insistent from those depths, became the necessity to do so: a plight which has formed the cornerstone for whole schools of psychology. So it may be that his decision to marry simply made one decision the less that he must eventually face; or it is equally possible that his decision to marry was indecision crystallized, insofar as he was not deciding against it.

Knowing that extraordinary capacity for jealous hatred which men so often have for a woman's past, Esther was in a way grateful that he never asked her about hers. Still, she did not disown it, though much as she wanted to go everywhere she had never been, she as fervently never wanted to revisit any scene in that past, a frantic concatenation whose victim she remained, projecting her future upon it in all the defiant resentment of free will, in a world where she had been victimized by every turn of the die since her father had first cast it. Where Esther's mind had gone since, her thighs had followed with errant and back-breaking sincerity, in civilized correspondence to that primordial cannibal rite performed by sober comrades who eat their victims in order to impart to themselves the powers with which those victims had, as enemies, threatened to overcome them. (It is not simply hunger: those driven by hunger alone have been heard to remark afterward, —I should have preferred pork.)

Not hunger? One of the more fastidious comments risen in her past had sported the phrase *vagina dentata*. Still it was not hunger, but an insatiability which took this hunger as its course, seeking, in its clear demand, to absorb the properties which had been withheld from her; and finding, in its temporary satisfaction, and the subsequent pain of withdrawal, insatiability. Year after year the emancipated animus of free will labored its spinneret, spun out this viscous fluid of causality which had rapidly hardened into strands fatal as those of the tarantula's silk-lined burrow here in the sandy soil of native hope. She did not question it; no more than the trap door which the tarantula leaves open at the top, or the victims who tumble in, affirming her woman's part in deep despair over their common lot, expressed in a resentment of men for the success of their casual fortunes where her devourings continued, but not for love.

At no time was Esther unprepared for those attempts which the lives around her made to rise to tragedy; though by the time they managed it, they had escaped it, and through their ascendance she had come rather to see herself as the conglomerate tragic figure, since it was she who was always left. It confirmed something. Esther had spent little time with women. She seemed to find in their problems only weak and distorted plagiarisms of the monstrous image of her own. Thus it seemed very odd to many who knew her that she should choose a woman analyst. It became a very deep attachment, so long before any completion of her analysis that it was evident to both of them who had the upper hand. When Esther met Wyatt, she asked if she should marry, and was forbidden. She de-

manded, and was pled with. She married, and her analyst was a
suicide. It was a way things had of working out for Esther. It confirmed something.

Call him louder! Call him louder! Trumpets sounded, and the
roll of drums.

—And why you like Handel, Esther said quietly after their argument, or to continue it. She had a cold, which broke her voice low
with apparent emotion.

—Handel?

Is not His voice like a hammer . . . ?

—Mozart . . . She coughed.

Like a hammer that breaketh the stone

She swallowed. There was a magazine open in her hands, as there
was a book in his; but she was watching him, to see if the intent
strain in his face were for his reading, or tense suspension waiting,
borne upon the chords of music, for the next sound of constriction
and release in her throat. He did not move. Her throat drew tighter,
its strictures embraced, and she swallowed with difficulty. At that,
as though it were a signal of release from restraint, a hand rose to
hide the intent corner of his profile. —And *Tosca!* . . . she murmured,
as her throat bound up again, and she swallowed quickly. He did
not move. The book was a large one, but she could not make out
its title. It might have been anything; just as his tension must be
for her presence, since he appeared to read everything with the
same casual concentration. When she interrupted, there was no way
of knowing whether he was looking up from Diogenes Laërtius or
No Orchids for Miss Blandish. She might be breaking a thread in
Berkeley's *New Theory of Vision,* joining a rain of falling objects
from the supercelestial geography of Charles Fort, or only echoing
a voice in some cheap paper novel like *Les Damnés de la Terre.*
Mendelssohn's *Elijah* continued from the radio. She swallowed. Immediately, he cleared his throat, a vicarious measure which left her un-
relieved. If she asked, he might look up with, —Fort says, "By the
damned, I mean the excluded" . . . but she would have to ask, —Excluded from what? —"By prostitution, I seem to mean usefulness . . ."

She studied him now as though he might not be reading at all,
but peeping at her through fingers of the hand shielding his eye. She
cleared her throat. There was no way, as *Elijah* came to a close, to
reopen their discussion: unless the next composition should be something by Beethoven or Mozart. If the radio voice should announce,
Mozart's Symphony Number 37, Köchel Listing 444 . . . He turned

a page. Since their discussions seldom lasted long, she often carried them on in her own mind, reconsidering now (and certain she saw the glint of his eye between his fingers) her thralldom to the perfection of Mozart, work of genius without an instant of hesitation or struggle, genius to which argument opposed the heroic struggle constantly rending the music of Beethoven, struggle never resolved and triumphed until the end. —Genius in itself is essentially uninteresting. —But the work of genius . . . —It's difficult to share in perfection. —You, to share? she'd commenced; but that was all. He was reading. She swallowed, and caught the glitter of an eye. *Elijah* was finished. Still in her mind, "By prostitution, I seem to mean usefulness," Esther said:

—What are you reading?

—Eh? His surprise was a look (she would think of it one day, remembering, or trying to remember) indigenous to his face, either that immediate anticipatory surprise, reflecting sudden foretaste of something past (as when she asked him when he'd been in Spain: —I? I've never been in Spain); or it was this look he had now, the surprise of one intruded upon. And year after year as their marriage went on, the first came less and the other more often, until one day, remembering him, or trying to remember, it would be this one which would come to her, this face of confusion, of one intruded upon, an anxious look. He said, —Nothing.

—Nothing? You can't read nothing.

—It's a book on mummies.

—Mummies?

—Egyptian mummies.

—Why are you reading a book on Egyptian mummies?

He cleared his throat, but said nothing.

—But what I gave you of mine, the story I'm writing, you haven't read that yet.

—Yes, I did read it.

—And . . . well? What did you think?

—It was . . . you seemed quite partial to the word atavistic.

—Well that, is that all?

—Well Esther, the um, and double adjectives, cruel, red anger; hard, thin lips; dark, secret pain . . .

—But . . .

—But women's writing seems to get sort of . . . Sharp, eager faces; acid, unpleasant odor . . . listen. He turned toward the radio, where a poet whose work they both enjoyed was about to read. She looked at him a moment longer, and the book which had gone closed in his hand the instant she'd spoken to him. It had happened as directly as when once she had said, —You have wonderful eyes, and he turned them from her. What was it? As though to protect whatever lay beyond them until he could solve it himself, betraying the fear that in one lax moment his eyes might serve her as entrances. Even taking up a book she had read (Esther admired Henry James, but she trusted D. H. Lawrence), he did so anxiously, as though he might find the pages blank, the words eaten away by that hunger.

—Do you want to follow it? she asked, coming toward him with the *Collected Poems* opened in her hand. He shook his head, but did not look up, listening; and she sat down nearer him.

The poet read, in modulated tones given a hollow resonance by the radio. Esther's thumb was drawn down the page, following one line to the next, bent over the book, and her lips moved, forming around the poet's words as he spoke them, clear separate syllables which her lips, meeting and parting, moistened by her tongue, allowing exhalations in vowels, wet clicks from the roof of the mouth on *d*, brought into viscous consonance with her absorbedness, unrestrained by those lips clamped tight beside her until he cleared his throat and suddenly got to his feet. Before she could speak he had reached a door.

—But what? . . .

—I have some work, he said quickly, and left her there sitting, hunched over the pages, staring after him, while the poet read on in clear separate syllables. She blew her nose, and returned to the page before her, but her lips did not move, for she did not hear another word of the reading. Neither did her eyes, for she was gazing at the backs of her hands.

The room Wyatt had entered was as large as the bedroom, but had only one window which would have opened on an airshaft if anyone had bothered opening it. During the first year or so, the room served various vague purposes. Though between them they hadn't a great number of books, not great enough, that is, to warrant a library (for a library, to Esther, was a roomful of books), it served as that for awhile. However, this was not practical, for reasons of which each privately accused the other in refusing to admit his own. Esther liked books out where everyone could see them, a sort of graphic index to the intricate labyrinth of her mind arrayed to impress the most casual guest, a system of immediate introduction which she had found to obtain in a number of grimy intellectual households in Greenwich

Village. Her husband, on the other hand, did not seem to care where his books were, so long as they were where he put them. That is to say, separate. No doubt Boyle's *Skeptical Chemist,* Jallard's *The Church and the Papacy,* Cennino Cennini's *Libro dell' Arte,* or *La Chimie au Moyen Age* would have dressed up Esther's shelves; no doubt the *Grimorium Verum* and the *Turba Philosophorum* would have been dusted down their spines regularly. No doubt these were among the reasons he kept them on his own, or strewn among the litter which had gradually filled the undetermined room until it belonged to him. Things were tacked on the walls there haphazard, an arm in dissection from a woodcut in the *Fabrica* of Vesalius, and another sixteenth-century illustration from the *Surgery* of Paré, a first-aid chart called "the wound man"; a photograph of an Italian cemetery flooded by the Po; a calendar good for every day from 1753 to 2059; a print of a drawing of the head of Christ by Melozzo da Forlí; a ground plan of the Roman city of Leptis Magna; a mirror; and rolls of paper and canvases on stretchers leaning in the corners.

When he started to work at restoring paintings, in addition to his regular job, the littered room changed only slightly. There had always been piles of drawing paper, and canvases on frames, prepared and clean or the composition begun in black unfinished lines, most prominent, or most familiar among these the initiated portrait of Camilla. The gessoed surface had cracked here and there, and got unevenly soiled, but the composition was very clear in lines unaltered since he'd put them there some fifteen years before. Occasionally this was hung on one of the walls, as though being studied with an eye to completion. Other times it remained stacked with the other empty and besmirched canvases against a wall. There was a wide flat drafting table, and a heavy easel stood erect in the middle of the room under the bare electric bulb. But the most noticeable change was not to be seen: it lay heavily on the air, the smell of varnish, oils, and turpentine, quickened by the pervasive delicacy of lavender, oil of lavender which he used sometimes as a medium.

Esther had admired the drawing begun on that large soiled cracked surface, the fine-boned face (so unlike her own) whose flesh-less quality of hollows was elevated by heavy earrings, archaic hoops of gold she had seen in a leather box where her husband kept odds and ends; admired the drawing not for what it was but, as she said, for what it could be. He stood looking at it, and they were silent, for he knew she was looking at him. The only work he had ever finished, those paintings shown in Paris years before, had ended up in a ware-

house in New Jersey. Esther had never seen them. They seldom discussed painting, for like so many things upon which they might agree,
they never managed to agree at the same moment; and as the conversations of the early months of their marriage went on, their ideas
and opinions seemed to meet only in passing, each bound in an
opposite direction, neither stopping to do more than honor the polite
pause of recognition.

The poet's clear tones had given way to the ingratiating pillage
of the announcer, and she rose, the charm broken, with no word of
the poet in her head but, for no apparent reason, "By prostitution I
seem to mean usefulness." She picked up *The Royal Mummies* and
blew her nose as she crossed the room toward the half-open door,
where she put her head in, and the book, saying, —Do you want this
in there?

—What? Oh that, thank you.

—What are you doing?

—Nothing, just . . . this work. He motioned toward the plans
pinned on the drafting table.

—Don't they give you enough time down there, to do your work?
But he lowered his eyes from hers, shrugged and turned back to the
table. —If it were something real, but this, going to this silly job
every day, year after year.

—It's not a silly job, Esther, he answered soberly, without turning.

—Copying lines, copying plans, one bridge after another. Oh, all
right, it isn't silly but you could do better, you could do more.
Honestly Wyatt, the way you go day after day with your job and
your reading and your . . . fooling around, and you could do more.
It's not . . . you're not waiting to discover something, are you. Waiting to be discovered, aren't you? Oh I hate to go on like this, sounding like this . . . She paused, watching his narrow black-suited figure
bend as a vertical line came down the paper. —It's this . . . seeing
you like you are sometimes now, she went on slowly, —I see you
with your head down and, I don't know, but it upsets me, it makes
me unhappy to see you that way.

—Why? he asked in a voice near a whisper, his face close down
to the paper.

—Because you look so lonely and that's what I can't bear, she
brought out at his back. Then her eyes lowered to the floor when he
did not turn, and she brought the damp knot of the handkerchief to
her nose. —Don't you want anything . . . any of the things, that other
people want?

—Other people? he demanded, turning.

—Oh . . . , her throat caught. —Never mind. There. I'll leave you with company.

—That? the mirror?

—I love that, you having a mirror in here.

—But that . . . to correct bad drawing . . .

—Good night, I'm going to bed when I've done the dishes.

—I'll do them, if you're tired, he offered. —Your cold . . .

—Don't be silly. I'll do them. She left him there, knotting a piece of string in his hand. A few minutes later, when she'd turned out the lights in the living room, the light from the half-open door drew her eyes and she saw him standing, running the fingers of his right hand over his rough chin, up one cheek and then the other, as though to wake after the night needing a shave made sense, but finding his face rough with growth after a day's well-lighted consciousness a strange thing. Then he said aloud, —How safe from accident I am!

She had once heard him mentioned, with little more than curiosity, by people whom neither of them knew now. Then, when she came to asking more pointedly about him, there were anecdotes enough (someone she met at a party had heard he'd jumped off the Eiffel Tower, and with drunken persistence marveled at his survival). In and out dodged the vagrant specter, careering through conversations witness to that disinterested kindness which other people extend to one who does not threaten them with competition on any level they know. Costumed in the regalia of their weary imaginations, he appeared and vanished in a series of images which, compacted, might have formed a remarkable fellow indeed; but in that Diaspora of words which is the providential nature of conversation, the fugitive persisted, like those Jewish Christians who endured among the heathen, here in the figure of a man who, it appeared at last, had done many things to envy and nothing to admire.

—Wyatt, what is it? What's the matter?

—A dream? . . .

—Only a dream?

—But . . .

—It's all right, darling, whatever it was it's all right now.

—It was . . .

—What was it?

—At home, in bed, that parsonage was a big empty house and I know every step in it, I woke up and I could hear footsteps. I woke up there hearing very heavy footsteps in an even tread and I knew where they were going, I heard them down the stairs and through the front hallway and into the living room, across the living room and through the back hall past the dining room and toward the kitchen . . .

—But, was that all?

—But listen, what was terrible was that I know every step in that house, I know how many steps it takes to come down the stairs or to cross the living room, I can't tell you the number but I know, but these steps I heard in the darkness, they were regular and even, not in a hurry but what was terrible, they kept reaching places too soon. I know the sound, I know how the sounds change when you step from the front hall into the living room, or passing the dining room or off the last stair and . . . but these steps kept arriving too soon, not hesitating anywhere and not in a hurry, but if you take regular even steps, and there weren't enough of them.

—It is strange. And your voice, you sound like a child.

—It doesn't sound terrible does it, now.

—We'll talk about it in the morning, she whispered, and her hand moved down his body to find him and gently raise him into life.— There must be a reason . . .

—Reason! but, good God, haven't we had enough . . . reason.

Her hand twisted and her fingers, closed together, moved only enough to make themselves felt, to make their motion not an act but a sense, to arouse not simply the blood which rushed to meet them but, in a touch, something beyond it. —Why do you fight it all so hard, Wyatt?

—Women, he commenced, and then, —men rising to isolated challenges, he spends his life preparing to meet one, one single challenge, when he triumphs it's, they call it heroic, but you, I know how hard you try for me, women just go on, they just go on, and I . . .

—They have to, Esther said beside him, as he came over half upon her in the darkness. —If we could get away from here, you've been everywhere, you've studied in Germany and in Paris and I . . . Wyatt, if we could travel . . . She felt his leg relax on hers. —And you don't want to, you don't want to travel.

—To voyage . . .

—With me?

—Charles Fort says maybe we're fished for, by supercelestial beings . . .

—Yes, without me. Alone.

—My grandfather, he fell down a well once, did I tell you? He talks of voyages, he's oriented by the stars. Orientation sidérale, the man who experimented with ants in the desert in Morocco . . . Then he seemed to tighten and hold her off suddenly, and she asked:

—What is it?

—In that dream, I just remembered my . . . my hair was on fire.

She felt him run his hand over his hair, and down his rough cheek in the darkness. —We'll talk about it in the morning, she said, —not now.

—Not flames, he said holding her again.

—You, you'd go to Morocco . . .

—But just burning, he whispered, almost wondrously, as she rose to engage the incredulous tension of his right hand, still murmuring:

—And be more . . . Moroccan . . . than the Moors.

Next morning Esther woke alone, to realize that she had been alone most of the night. She swallowed, and found her cold better. She smelled coffee and went to the kitchen, where half a pot of it was boiling furiously on the stove. She started to call out, felt a wave of nausea, and sat down and decided to eat something. She got out bread and butter and looked for an egg, but could not find one. Then she poured some of the boiling coffee into a cold cup, and the cup cracked; nonetheless she poured until it was full and took it into the living room.

Light showed from the studio, and she heard sounds behind the half-closed door. Then:

—Damn you, damn you . . . damn you!

—What? she brought out, at the door. —What a smell.

—Nothing. He stood facing her under the bare brilliance of the bulb, as though stricken, in the midst of some criminal commission, as lightning freezes motion.

—What is it?

—Nothing, I'm . . . talking to myself.

—Are you working? still working?

—Yes, yes, working, he answered. His empty hands opened and closed at his sides, as though seeking something to occupy them. Then he caught up a knife in one, and with the other pointed to the straight easel, — on that.

—That? She looked at the familiar thing on the easel. It was a late eighteenth-century American painting in need of a good deal of work, the portrait of a woman with large bones in her face but an unprominent nose, a picture which looked very much like Esther. She found it so, at any rate; and even when he'd said, —As a painting, it isn't very good as a painting, is it? . . . she standing behind him could see no further than the portrait, held by the likeness as happened so often but seldom so clearly, finding resemblances to herself everywhere as though she set out from the start seeking identity with misfortune, recognition in disaster.

He had backed away from her, holding the knife, as though he were guarding something, or hiding it, and when she looked behind him on the wall she saw the black lines on the cracked soiled surface of the unfinished portrait. —That, she said, —that's what you were working on?

—That. He made a stab pointing behind her with the knife, and she moved to sink wearily against the door frame.

—A way to start the day, she said, looking at him. —I wish you'd stop waving that knife. Start the day? I feel like you've been in here all night, like you're always in here, and whoever it is that sleeps with me and talks to me in the dark is somebody else.

—I woke up, he said putting the knife down, —I wanted to work.

—But this . . . if you wanted to work on that, you can tell me, you don't have to pretend, . . . this secrecy . . .

—Aunt May, when she made things, even her baking, she kept the blinds closed in the butler's pantry when she frosted a cake, nobody ever saw anything of hers until it was done.

—Aunt May! I don't care about Aunt May, but you . . . I wish you would finish that thing, she went on, looking at the lines over his shoulder, —and get rid of her.

—Rid of her? he repeated. From somewhere he'd picked up an egg.

—Finish it. Then there might be room for me.

—You? to paint you?

—Yes, if you . . .

—But you're here, he brought out, cracking the egg over a cup, and he caught the yolk in his palm. —You're so much here. Esther . . . I'm sorry, he said with a step toward her, the egg yolk rolling from one palm to the other, threatening to escape. —I'm sorry, he said seeing the expression he'd brought to her face. —I'm tired.

—Even this, she said lowering her eyes, and bringing them round to the damaged likeness on the easel, —if you'd finish this.

—There's no hurry, he said quickly, —they've gone abroad, the people who own it, they may not be back for some time.

—If they were gone ten years you'd take ten years. You could do work like this in half the time you take, a tenth of the time, even if you won't paint yourself you could settle down to restoring work and make something of it. It's no wonder you don't sleep, that you're nervous and have bad dreams when you're not doing what you want to do.

He stood bent over a cup, where he held the egg yolk suspended between the squared fingertips of one hand, and a pin in the other, about to puncture it, and he looked up at her. —But I am, Esther.

—If you could finish something original, she said. —You look like an old man. Why are you laughing?

—Just then, he said straightening up, and the egg yolk still hanging from his fingers, —I felt like him, just for that instant as though I were old Herr Koppel, I've told you, the man I studied with in Munich. As though this were that studio he had over the slaughter-house, where we worked, he'd stand with an egg yolk like this and talk, "That romantic disease, originality, all around we see originality of incompetent idiots, they could draw nothing, paint nothing, just so the mess they make is original . . . Even two hundred years ago who wanted to be original, to be original was to admit that you could not do a thing the right way, so you could only do it your own way. When you paint you do not try to be original, only you think about your work, how to make it better, so you copy masters, only masters, for with each copy of a copy the form degenerates . . . you do not invent shapes, you know them, auswendig wissen Sie, by heart . . ." The egg yolk fell, most of it went into the cup. —Damn it, he said, looking at it, —but it doesn't matter, these stale eggs . . . "Country eggs you must have, with stale city eggs you cannot make good tempera . . ."

—I might have had it for breakfast.

—But, was it the last one? I didn't . . . I'm sorry, Esther, I . . . here . . . He poured the white from one stained cup into what yolk there was in the other. —Here, it just isn't . . . it's clean, there just isn't as much yolk . . .

—Aren't you going to your office? You'd better shave if you are, she said and left him offering the cup in the direction of the damaged likeness on the easel.

Her coffee was cold. She poured it into the sink, and went down to get the mail. She read one letter on the stairs, and called out before she'd closed the door behind her, —Wyatt, something awful's happened. Where are you? Then she almost screamed, seeing him standing in the door of the studio with blood all over one side of his face and his neck. —What happened?

—What is it? he asked. —What awful thing . . .

—What's happened to you? she cried running up to him.

—What? He stood there with a straight razor opened in his hand.

—What are you doing?

—Shaving . . .

—Did you do that . . . shaving? What are you doing in there, shaving.

—Oh, he said running his fingertips over his chin, and looking at the blood on them. —It's a mess, I'm sorry, Esther. The mirror, I was using this mirror in here, you have the one in the bathroom covered . . .

—Covered! she burst out impatiently, twisting the letter in her hand.

—It has a cloth over it, I thought for some reason you might . . .

—It's a handkerchief drying, why didn't you just pull it off. And that, she went on, getting breath, —that terrible thing, it's dangerous to shave with, look at it, just because your father . . . You're like a child about it, this image of his . . .

—What was the letter?

—The letter? This? Yes, that warehouse, the place in New Jersey where you had your things, it burned. And here, they send you a check for a hundred and thirty dollars.

—Really? That's fine.

—Fine? Aren't you upset? Things like those paintings, they can't be replaced.

—No, they can't, he said quickly, a hand to his chin where the blood had already begun to dry.

—Where are you going?

—To wash. I have to hurry, I . . . I have some plans to take in.

She caught him again at the front door, where he paused with a roll of papers under his arm. —No coffee? Nothing?

—I had some earlier. He pulled at the knob, but she had a hand on his arm.

—I wish you could rest, she said, and when he turned, looking at her as though he had suddenly been stopped in a crowded street: —Are you all right?

—I? Why yes, yes I'm all right, Esther, I . . . you mustn't . . . Goodbye, he broke and hurried toward the stairs.

A few minutes later, when she was standing pouring coffee into the cracked cup, the doorbell rang. It was a delivery boy with a dozen eggs. She put them on the kitchen table, and then took out a handkerchief and stood, steadying herself with a hand on the table, staring at the coffee, whose surface was broken with the regular beats of her heart.

It was dark afternoon when Esther came in, bearing in the forefront of her mind fragments of a conversation she had left a little earlier (on Rilke, not Rilke's poetry but Rilke the man, who refused to be psychoanalyzed for fear of purging his genius); but over this, and through the rest of her mind, skated an image far more familiar, plunging and surfacing, escaping under the applied hand of her memory, reappearing when she turned elsewhere, echoing, among faces and lanterns and the prows of boats, —Maybe we're fished for . . . , an image whose apparition she waited even now. Though it was dark in the studio, she opened the door and looked in there. Then she took off her coat, turned the radio on, and sat down, oblivious to the soprano singing nel massimo dolore, —Sempre con fè sincera la mia preghiera . . .

The door rattled, with muttering beyond it. She sat still. Finally he entered, in a state of some excitement. —I had trouble with the key, he said, and gave her a broken self-conscious laugh. She wanted time to study him before she spoke, but could not let him escape to the studio before she asked:

—Was it you I saw this afternoon? a little while ago?

—Me? Why? Where?

—Were you there, where they're showing Picasso's new . . .

—*Night Fishing in Antibes*, yes, yes . . .

—Why didn't you speak to us?

—Speak to who? You? Were you there?

—I was there, with a friend. You could have spoken to us, Wyatt, you didn't have to pretend that . . . I was out with someone who . . .

—Who? I didn't see them, I didn't see you, I mean.

—You looked right at us. I'd already said, There's my husband, we were near the door and you were bobbing . . .

—Listen . . .

—You went right past us going out.

—Look, I didn't see you. Listen, that painting, I was looking at the painting. Do you see what this was like, Esther? seeing it?

—I saw it.

—Yes but, when I saw it, it was one of those moments of reality, of near-recognition of reality. I'd been . . . I've been worn out in this piece of work, and when I finished it I was free, free all of a sudden out in the world. In the street everything was unfamiliar, everything and everyone I saw was unreal, I felt like I was going to lose my balance out there, this feeling was getting all knotted up inside me and I went in there just to stop for a minute. And then I saw this thing. When I saw it all of a sudden everything was freed into one recognition, really freed into reality that we never see, you never see it. You don't see it in paintings because most of the time you can't see beyond a painting. Most paintings, the instant you see them they become familiar, and then it's too late. Listen, do you see what I mean?

—As Don said about Picasso . . . she commenced.

—That's why people can't keep looking at Picasso and expect to get anything out of his paintings, and people, no wonder so many people laugh at him. You can't see them any time, just any time, because you can't see freely very often, hardly ever, maybe seven times in a life.

—I wish, she said, —I wish . . .

How real is any of the past, being every moment revalued to make the present possible: to come up one day saying, —You see? I was right all the time. Or, —Then I was wrong, all the time. The radio is still busy with Puccini, *Tosca* all the way through: from the jumble at the end of the second act, Wyatt rescues her words, repeats them, —Questo è il bacio di Tosca! That's reality, then. Tosca's kiss, reality?

—I wish . . . she repeats (preferring *Don Giovanni*).

—Maybe seven times in a life.

Magic number! but she sits looking at him, waiting in the space populated by memory. One night when she was doing her nails, he came in. —Wyatt, you've never had a manicure? Never? Let me give you a manicure . . . But he said something in a tone apologetic, alarmed, and took his hands away one clutched in the other.

—But it can't really be that simple . . . (a discussion: did the coming of the printing press corrupt? putting a price on authorship, originality). —Look at it this way, look at it as liberation, the first time in history that a writer was independent of patrons, the first time he could put a price on his work, make it a thing of material value, a vested interest in himself for the first time in history . . .

—And painters, and artists? Lithography, and color reproductions . . .

—Yes, I don't know, if one corrupts the artist and the other corrupts . . . that damned *Mona Lisa*, no one sees it, you can't see it with a thousand off-center reproductions between you and it.

—But how . . .

—I don't know, I've tried to understand it myself. Spinoza . . .

Mozart? The air is full of him, you've only got to have a radio receiving set to formulize the silence, give it shape and put it in motion: *Sleigh Ride* hurtles from the grid and strikes her. She suffers the impact without surprise. —I know you've never said you didn't want children, but whenever I've mentioned it you just look . . . you just get a look on your face. He puts his hand there, his right hand to his forehead and draws it down with feverish application, as though in this to pull away the features so long forming, revaluing for this moment; but above his hand, his face comes back into shape, the forehead quickly rises and recovers its lines, then the brows, and the eyes vividly devious permit nothing to enter. —I wish we were in the dark, you can talk to me in the dark, in the light you tell me things like . . . Zero doesn't exist.

—But you asked me . . .

—Or bad money drives out good.

Esther watched him now, standing in the middle of the room, drawing his hand down over his face as though, again, to wipe out some past, how long ago, or how recent, or all of it? She did not know, but sought one area among the German festivals, Handel at Breslau, Shakespeare at Stuttgart, Beethoven at Bonn, all in May; *Egmont* at Altenburg, *Der Fliegende Holländer* at Nürnberg in June; *Die Ägyptische Helena* at München . . .

—Munich, she said, —when you were in Munich?

—What?

—You never told me much about it.

—About Munich?

—And that boy you knew there that you spent so much time with.

—Han? I didn't spend a lot of time with him.

—You worked together, and drank together and traveled together.

—Traveled?

—That night you spent together at Interlaken, from what you've told me of that . . .

—We were there for almost a week, waiting for a look at the Jungfrau, it was hidden every day, I told you about that. And the day I left for Paris, early in the morning standing on the railway platform I looked up, and there it was as though it had come from nowhere, and at that instant the train came in right between us, good God I remember that well, that morning.

—But . . . But he had turned and gone into the studio, and she went to the kitchen, stopping only to change the station on the radio. They were silent through most of supper, as though in deference to a symphony of Sibelius which reached across the room to jar them into submission, for neither of them would have confessed, even privately, to liking it.

Sensing the thought, If he does not love me, then he is incapable of love, —I wish . . . she said. Moments like this (and they came more often) she had the sense that he did not exist; or, to re-examine him, sitting there looking in another direction, in terms of substance and accident, substance the imperceptible underlying reality, accident the properties inherent in the substance which are perceived by the senses: the substance is transformed by consecration, but the accidents remain what they were. The consecration has apparently taken place not, as she thought, through her, but somewhere beyond her; and here she sits attending the accidents.

Her lips did not move, neither did the words laid out there on the stillness of the white page: the faculty of reading suspended in her dull stare, the syllables remained exposed, hopelessly coexistent. Then one caught her eye, drew her on through another, and so through six, seven . . . When her wet tongue clicked *t, s*he looked up and the poem died on the page. —Did you know he was homosexual? she asked.

—Ummm.

—I didn't know it until Don told me today.

—Who?

—Don Bildow, he edits this little magazine, the . . .

—He's homosexual?

—Oh no, he isn't, Don isn't, don't you listen? He told me that this . . . this . . . She held up that *Collected Poems*, shunning to speak the poet's name. —Did you know it?

—What? Yes, I've heard something like that.

—Why didn't you tell me?

He looked up for the first time. —Tell you?

—You might have mentioned it, she said and put the book aside with its cover down.

—Might have . . . why would I mention it? What's that to do with . . .

—When we were sitting here listening to him read, it didn't occur to me, it's funny, it never occurred to me about him, pictures I've seen of him, and his poems, the things he says in his poems . . . and I'd wanted to meet him. Esther's eyes had come to rest on the floor, and the shadow thrown there from the chair, meaningless until it moved.

—And you're surprised? . . . upset over this?

—I'd wanted to meet him, she commenced, following the shadow's length back to its roots.

—Meet him? And now a thing like this . . . I don't understand, you Esther, you're the one who always knows these things about people, these personal things about writers and painters and all the . . .

—Yes but . . .

—Analyzing, dissecting, finding answers, and now . . . What did you want of him that you didn't get from his work?

Esther's eyes rose slowly from the floor the height of her husband's figure. —Why are you so upset all of a sudden? she asked him calmly. —Just because I'd mentioned Han . . .

—Han! he repeated, wresting the name from her. —Good God, is this what it is! That stupid . . . Han, why he . . . after all these years, a thing like this . . .

—And that painting you gave him, you've never given me . . .

—Gave him? It disappeared, that's what I told you. "You give it to me to remember you, because we are dear friends, this Memling you are making now . . ." He asked me for it, but it disappeared before it was even finished, when they arrested the old man, Koppel, that's what I told you. He subsided, muttering something, he'd picked up a piece of string and stood knotting it.

She murmured, her eyes back on the shadow's busy extremity, —You've told me . . .

—That stupid . . . Han, he went on, —in his uniform, pounding his finger with a beer stein, "You see? it couldn't hurt me . . ." At Interlaken, what else was there to do but drink? Snowed in, waiting, "There's something missing," he says, he hadn't shaved for three days, the blank look on his face, ". . . if I knew what it is then it wouldn't be so missing . . ." I've told you . . .

—Oh, you've told me, she said, impatient, looking up at him for a moment, then back at the shadow. —I don't know what all you've told me, what little . . . New England, all right, you're the Puritan, all this secrecy, this guilt, preaching to me out of Fichte about moral action, no wonder a thing like this upsets you, when I mention a poet I've wanted to meet and he turns out . . . you don't want to talk about it, do you! she pursued him, where he had got almost across the room, about to escape into the studio.

But he stopped in that doorway, reaching a hand inside he snapped on the bright light which flung a heavier shadow across the floor to her. —Listen, this guilt, this secrecy, he burst out, —it has nothing to do with this . . . this passion for wanting to meet the latest poet, shake hands with the latest novelist, get hold of the latest painter, devour . . . what is it? What is it they want from a man that they didn't get from his work? What do they expect? What is there left of him when he's done his work? What's any artist, but the dregs of his work? the human shambles that follows it around. What's left of the man when the work's done but a shambles of apology.

—Wyatt, these romantic . . .

—Yes, romantic, listen . . . Romantics! they marry cows and all kinds of comfort, soon enough their antics betray them to what would have been fatal in the work, I mean being obvious. No, here, it's competence right here in the world that's rewarded with romantic ends, and the romantics battling for competence, something to eat and carfare home . . . Look at the dentist's wife, she's a beauty. Who's the intimate of a saint, it's her Jesuit confessor, and the romantics end up anchorites in the desert.

Esther stood up, turning her back as she spoke to him so that he could not evade her question with a look, or by turning away himself, but was left with, —Then tell me, what are you trying to do? And she picked up a magazine, and came back to a chair with it, not looking up to where he took a step toward her from the brightly lighted doorway.

—There's only one thing, somehow, he commenced, faltering, —that . . . one dilemma, proving one's own existence, it . . . there's no ruse people will disdain for it, and . . . or Descartes "retiring to prove his own existence," his "cogito ergo sum," why . . . no wonder he advanced masked. Kept a salamander, no wonder. Something snaps, and . . . when every solution becomes an evasion, . . . it's frightening, trying to stay awake.

Though his voice had risen, still Esther did not look up, but sat quietly turning the pages of the magazine, and when she spoke did so quietly and evenly. —You've told me, all your reasons for letting year after year go by this way while you . . . work? And even this, look. This magazine your company puts out, look at this picture, this bridge, it's something your company did, designed by Ben somebody, I can't pronounce it, the road bridge at Fallen Ark Gap.

—Do you like it? he asked, suddenly standing beside her, anxiety still in his face and sounding in his voice, but a different, immediate anxiousness.

—It's beautiful, she said. Then she turned and looked up to him.

—Wyatt, you know you could do more, more than just the drafting, copying lines, wasting your time with . . .

—Look at it, he said, —do you see the way it seems to come out and meet itself, does it? He held his hands up in a nervous bridge, fingertips barely touching, the piece of string still hung from one of them. —Does it look that way to you? that sense of movement in stillness, that . . . tension at rest and still . . . do you know that Arab saying, "The arch never sleeps"? . . .

—Yes, it is dynamic. Wyatt, you, why can't you . . . Then her eyes, meeting his, seemed that abruptly to empty the enthusiasm from his face and his voice.

—It's derivative, the design, he said.

—Derivative?

—Of Maillart.

—I don't know him.

—A Swiss, there's a book of his work somewhere around here.

She looked at his hands, gone back to knotting the string, and watched a bowline form there. —Like a knot, she said, —pulling against itself.

—I'm going back to work, he said and turned away. She walked after him as far as the lighted doorway, and stood for a minute staring at the picture on the upright easel. —I've come to hate that thing, she said finally, and with no answer, left him removing corroded portions of the face with the sharp blade.

Most nights now Esther went to sleep alone, her consciousness carried in that direction by Handel and Palestina, William Boyce, Henry Purcell, Vivaldi, Couperin, music which connected them across the darkness in the stream where everything that had once brought them together returned to force them apart, back to the selves they could no longer afford to mistrust. Sometimes there was a long pause between the records; sometimes one was repeated, over and over again.

She woke to the same exquisitely measured contralto, —*When I am laid* . . . , that had lost her to sleep what seemed so many hours before. She lay in the dark and saw herself as she had been, a week before was it? sitting with an open book. —Wyatt . . . ? —What is it? When she said nothing he looked up at her. —What is it, Esther? She looked at him. —I just want you to talk to me. He looked at her; and looking at him she heard herself saying something she had said another time and wanted to repeat but there was no way to, for he simply sat, looking at her, and would not provoke it: —I wish you *would* lose your temper, she had said, —or *some*thing because this . . . this restraint, this pose, this control that you've cultivated, Wyatt, it becomes inhuman . . . He just looked at her.

The music, she realized now, was not the Purcell, not the contralto at all, but strident male voices in a Handel oratorio. Memories ran together, and she sat up in bed. Just her position, lying flat on her back, had advanced one memory, one evening and one conversation, into another, like streams commingling on an open plain. Bolt upright, everything stopped. She drew breath, and smelled lavender.

Esther got out of bed and went into the living room, where she sat down in the darkness. The door to the studio was open barely an inch. She sat, listening and remembering, as though he had been gone a long time. Would the music of Handel always recall sinful commission, the perpetration of some crime in illuminated darkness recognized as criminal only by him who committed it: Persephone, she sat now listening. And would the scent of lavender recall it? as it was doing now; for she felt that she was remembering, that this moment was long past, or that she was seated somewhere in the future, seated somewhere else and had suddenly caught the smell of lavender in the air, recalling this moment only in memory, that in another moment she would breathe deeply, destroying the delicate scent, that she would arise and go: queen of the shades, was her mother wandering in search of her? now where she waited, here on the other side of the door opening upon her husband's infernal kingdom.

She woke sitting straight up in the chair. The music was right where it had abandoned her: repeating? or had she been lost to it for no more than a transition of chords, as is the most alert consciousness. She stared at the shaft of light; and immediately she was up, and had pushed the door open.

Wyatt had modified his handwriting to a perverse version of Carolingian minuscule, in which the capital *S*'s, and *G*'s, and *Y*'s were indistinguishable, and among the common letters, *y*, *g*, and *f*. *The* looked like *M*, and *p* a declined bastard of *h*. (Esther wrote in one continuous line, interrupted by humps, depressions, lonely dots and misplaced streaks, remarkably legible.) There were specimens of his writing strewn about the room; still, his childhood hand was apparent as the child father to the man. On the length of the table made from a door, on top of large sheets of unfinished lines drafted in origins of design pinned to the table, among opened books, and books with slips of paper profusely stuck between their pages, *The Secret of the Golden Flower, Problems of Mysticism and Its Symbolism, Prometheus and*

Epimetheus, Cantilena Riplæi, beside an empty brandy bottle, lay open Foxe's *Book of Martyrs,* and there in the scrupulous hand of childhood, written on lined paper, a nursery rhyme which she suddenly had in her hand, standing alone in the room.

There was a man of double deed, it commenced.

> *Sowed his garden full of seed.*
> *When the seed began to grow,*
> *'Twas like a garden full of snow;*
> *When the snow began to melt,*
> *'Twas like a ship without a belt;*
> *When the ship began to sail,*
> *'Twas like a bird without a tail;*
> *When the bird began to fly,*

—Esther!

> *'Twas like an eagle in the sky;*
> *When the sky began to roar,*
> *'Twas like a lion at the door;*

—Esther . . .

> *When the door began to crack,*
> *'Twas like a stick across my back;*
> *When my back began to smart . . .*

—Esther, what is it? What are you doing here?

> *'Twas like a penknife in my heart;*
> *When my heart began to bleed,*
> *'Twas death and death and death indeed.*

—Esther . . .

—I just couldn't stop reading it, she said. He had her, supporting her with one arm.

—But what . . . why . . .

—Are you here now? she said, looking at him, into his eyes.

The music stopped, and the automatic arm lifted, paused, returned to the grooves it had just left. He reached over and turned it off.

—Wyatt . . . ?

—I thought you were asleep, I just went out to get this, he said, holding up a bottle of brandy. He looked down quickly at his table, at the undisturbed plans and the books there. —I thought you were asleep, he repeated, looking at her. Then he saw what she had in her hand. —That, he said taking it from her, —what are you reading it for, it . . . it's just something I found here, here in this old book of Aunt May's. It's nothing, it's just something . . . He set the brandy down on the table. —Something she made me copy out.

He had no coat, and was dressed in a black suit. The bones in his face were smaller than Esther's. His hair was cut short, and his skull looked almost square. —Esther? . . . She put her arms around him. —Come to bed.

The dream recurs.

—Darling . . . the same one?

—Yes. The same. Exactly the same.

She thinks then, Perhaps . . .

—It doesn't really hurt, there isn't any pain and there aren't any flames, but just that my hair is burning . . .

Perhaps the consecration has not taken place yet after all, and the substance is still there, caught up in accident, waiting. Bedded in darkness she drew him over, and sweating he performed, and lay back, silent, inert, distant. —There are some cigarettes on the dresser, she said. He walked there in the dark, found them and lit one, sitting on the edge of the bed he smoked.

—Wyatt?

—What.

—How are you?

—Fine.

—I mean how do you feel?

—Empty, he answered.

She said nothing, but pretended sleep. After minutes of sitting abandoned he turned open the disrupted covers, and was asleep before she was, dwelling close up against the exposure of her back.

EVAN S. CONNELL, JR.

"The Fisherman From Chihuahua," like *Young Men Waiting*, is another instance of multi-track understatement. What has been captured and presented here, and is indefinable in traditional terms, is that combination of sublime detachment and intense perception or involvement, of which the *mind itself* is capable, but which is rarely, if ever, experienced in Western cultures except as an effect of drugs.

Such a state of perception differs so markedly from the ordinary, and its occurrence is so infrequent, that the difference might almost be considered categorical, rather than of degree. Although we tend to think of "detachment" and "involvement" as contradictions, this is seen to be untrue when it is realized that "detachment" invariably applies to what is *general*, and "involvement" to what is *specific*. In physical terms, the movement of one's eyes, for example, takes in, under ordinary circumstances, a general view, and if, during the movement, there occurs a single point of focus, or involvement, it is subject to as many distractions as are actually present (or, are so defined) in the general view. As an effect of certain common drugs, however, the general view scarcely exists; the eyes move from one specific to another—that is to say, *each thing* within what was previously the general view becomes a specific—with, at any given moment, a relative immunity to distraction . . . an immunity, of course, which in its classic, or Eastern, attainment, may be absolute.

"The Fisherman From Chihuahua," however, does not represent this phenomenon in an Eastern, or in any way esoteric, form, but in a form extremely common within our own culture, one which has been observed by all—yet one almost never successfully treated in literature. If there is no mention of drugs in the story it is because, like the names of the streets of Paris in *Young Men Waiting*, it is irrelevant to larger issues.

250

THE FISHERMAN FROM CHIHUAHUA

Santa Cruz is at the top of Monterey Bay which is about 100 miles below San Francisco, and in the winter there are not many people in Santa Cruz. The boardwalk concessions are shuttered except for one counter-and-booth restaurant, the ferris wheel seats are hooded with olive green canvas and the powerhouse padlocked, and the rococo doors of the carousel are boarded over and if one peers through a knothole into its gloom the horses which buck and plunge through summer prosperity seem like animals touched by a magic wand that they may never move again. Dust dims the gilt of their saddles and sifts through cracks into their bold nostrils. About the only sounds to be heard around the waterfront in Santa Cruz during winter are the voices of Italian fishermen hidden by mist as they work against the long pier, and the slap of waves against the pilings of the ce-ment dance pavillon when tide runs high, or the squeak of a gull, or once in a long time bootsteps on the slippery boards as some person comes quite alone and usually slowly to the edge of the grey and fogbound ocean.

The restaurant is Pendleton's and white brush strokes on the glass announce *tacos, frijoles* and *enchiladas* as house specialities, these being mostly greens and beans and fried meat made arrogant with pepper. Smaller letters in pseudo-Gothic script say: *Se Habla Espanol* but this is not true; it was the man who owned the place before Pendleton who could speak Spanish. From him, though, Pendleton

did learn how to make the food and this is the reason a short fat
Mexican who worked as a mechanic at Ace Dillon's Texaco station
continued eating his suppers there. He came in every night just after
eight o'clock and sat at the counter, ate an astounding amount of
this food which he first splattered with tabasco sauce as casually as
though it were ketchup and then washed farther down with beer.
After that he would feel a little drunk and would spend as much as
two or even three dollars playing the pinball machine and the great
nickelodeon and dancing by himself, but inoffensively, contentedly,
just snapping his fingers and shuffling across the warped boards often
until Pendleton began pulling in the shutters. Then having had a
suitable evening he would half-dance his way home, or at least back
in the direction of town. He was a squat little man who waddled
like a duck full of eggs and he had a face like a blunt arrowhead
or a Toltec idol, and he was about the color of hot sand. His fingers
were much too thick for their length, seemingly without joints, only
creases where it was necessary for them to bend. He smelled princi-
pally of cold grease and of urine as though his pants needed some
air, but Pendleton who did not smell very good himself did not mind
and besides there were not many customers during these winter
months.

So every evening shortly after dark he entered for his food and
some amusement, and as he appeared to contain all God's world
within his own self Pendleton was not disinterested when another
Mexican came in directly behind him like a long shadow. This new
man was tall, very tall, possibly six feet or more, and much darker,
almost black in the manner of a sweat stained saddle. He was handsome, silent, and perhaps forty years of age. Also he was something
of a dandy: his trousers which were long and quite tight revealed
the fact that he was bowlegged, as befits certain types of men, and
made one think of him easily riding a large fast horse, not necessarily toward a woman but in the direction of something more remote and mysterious—bearing a significant message or something like
that. Exceedingly short black boots of finest leather took in his narrow trouser bottoms. For a shirt he wore long-sleeved white silk
unbuttoned to below the level of his nipples which, themselves, were
vaguely visible. The hair of his chest was so luxuriant that an enameled
crucifix there did not even rest on the skin.

These two men sat at the counter side by side. The tall one lifted
off his sombrero as if afraid of mussing his hair and he placed it on
the third stool. His hair was deeply oiled and comb tracks went all

the way from his temples to the back of his thin black neck, and he scented of a kind of green perfume. He had a mustache that consisted of nothing but two black strings hanging across the corners of his unforgiving mouth and ending in soft points about an inch below his chin. He seemed to think himself alone in the restaurant because, after slowly licking his lips and interlacing his fingers, he just sat looking somberly ahead. The small man ordered for them both.

After they had eaten supper the little one played the pinball machine while this strange man took from his shirt pocket a cigarillo only a little bigger than his mustache and smoked it with care, that is, he would take it from his mouth between his thumb and one finger as if he were afraid of crushing it, and after releasing the smoke he would replace it with the same care in the exact center of his mouth. It never dangled or rolled, he respected it. Nor was it a cheap piece of tobacco, its smoke ascended heavily, moist and sweet.

Suddenly the fat Mexican kicked the pinball game and with a surly expression walked over to drop a coin into the nickelodeon. The tall man had remained all this time at the counter with his long savage eyes half-shut, smoking and smoking the fragrant cigarillo. Now he did not turn around, in fact his single movement was to remove the stump from his lips, but clearly he was disturbed. When the music ended he sat totally motionless for several minutes. Then his head began to sink and was almost touching the counter before its direction reversed, and when his face was against the ceiling his throat began to swell like that of a mating pigeon.

Pendleton, sponging an ash tray, staggered as if a knife had plunged through his ribs.

The Mexican's eyes were squeezed altogether shut. His lips had peeled back from his teeth like those of a jaguar tearing meat and the veins of his neck looked ready to burst. In the shrill screams was a memory of Moors, the ching of Arab cymbals, of rags and of running feet through all the marketplaces of the East.

His song had no beginning; it had no end. All at once he was simply sitting on the stool looking miserably ahead.

After a while the small fat Mexican said to Pendleton "Be seeing you, man," and waddled through the door into darkness. A few seconds later the tall one's stool creaked. Without a sound he placed the high steepled sombrero like a crown on his hair and followed his friend through the door.

The next night there happened to be a pair of tourists eating in the back booth when the men entered. They were dressed as before except that the big one's shirt was lime green in color and Pendleton noticed his wrist watch, fastened not to his wrist actually but over the green cuff where it bulged like an oily bubble. They took the same stools and ate fried beans, tacos and enchiladas for almost an hour after which the short one who looked like his Toltec ancestors gently belched, smiled in a benign way and moved over to his machine. Failing to win anything he cursed it and kicked it before selecting his favorite records.

This time Pendleton was alert: as the music ended he got ready for the first shriek. The tourists, caught unaware, thought their time had come. When they recovered from the shock they looked fearfully over the top of the booth and then the woman stood up in order to see better. After the black Mexican's song was finished they all could hear the incoming tide, washing softly around the pillars of the pavilion.

Presently the two paid their bill and went out, the short one leading, into the dirty yellow fog and the diving, squeaking gulls.

"Why that's terrible," the woman laughed. "It wasn't musical." Anyone who looked at her would know she was still shuddering from the force of the ominous man.

Her husband too was frightened and laughed, "Somebody should play a little drum behind that fellow." Unaware of what a peculiar statement he had made he formed a circle of his thumb and forefinger to show how big the drum should be.

She was watching the door, trying to frown compassionately. "I wonder what's the matter with that poor man. Some woman must have hurt him dreadfully."

Pendleton began to wipe beer bracelets and splats of tabasco sauce from the lacquered plywood counter where the men had been. The restaurant seemed too quiet.

The woman remarked cheerily, "We're from Iowa City."

Pendleton tried to think of something but he had never been to Iowa City or anywhere near it even on a train, so he asked if they would like more coffee.

The husband wondered, "Those two fellows, do they come in here every night?"

Pendleton was seized with contempt and hatred for this domestic little man, though he did not know why, and walked stiffly away from their booth without answering. He stood with both hairy hands on the shining urn while he listened to the sea threshing and rolling under the night.

"Who?" he said gruffly. "Them two?"

A few minutes later while pouring coffee he said, "Sometimes I feel so miserable I could damn near roll up in a tube."

The couple, overpowered by his manner, looked up uneasily. The woman ventured: "It seems terribly lonely around."

On the third evening as they seated themselves before the counter Pendleton said to the one who spoke American, "Tell your friend he can't yowl in here any more."

"He's not my baby," this short fat man replied, not greatly interested. "Six tacos and four beers and a lot of beans."

"What do you think, I'm running a damn concert hall?"

For a moment the little Mexican became eloquent with his eyebrows, then both he and Pendleton turned their attention to the silent one who was staring somberly past the case of pies.

Pendleton leaned on his hands so that his shoulders budged. "Now looky, Pablo, give him the word and do it quick. Tell him to cut that noise out. You understand me?"

This enraged the small man whose voice rose to a snarl. "Pablo yourself. Don't give me that stuff."

Pendleton was not angry but set about cleaving greens for their tacos as though he were furious. While the blade chunked into the wood again and again beside his thumb he thought about the situation. He did not have anything particular in mind when all at once he banged down the cleaver and with teeth clenched began bending his eyes toward the two.

"*No debe cantar*," the little one said hurriedly, waggling a negative finger at his companion. No more singing. "*No mas.*"

"That's better, by God," muttered Pendleton as though he understood. He wished to say something in Spanish about the matter but he knew only *mañana, adios* and *señorita* and none of these seemed to fit. He resumed work, but doubtfully, not certain if the silent one had heard either of them. Over one shoulder he justified himself: "Folks come here to eat their suppers, not to hear any concert."

Abel W. Sharpe who had once been the sheriff of Coda City and who now ripped tickets for a movie house on Pacific came in the door alone but arguing harshly. The Toltec had started playing pinball so Sharpe took the vacant stool, looked up twice at the man beside him, and then dourly ordered waffles and hot milk. It was while he was pouring syrup into the milk that the nickelodeon music died and that the black Mexican did it again.

Pendleton was exasperated with himself for laughing and almost choked by trying to stop.

"Heh?" asked the old man, who at the first note had jumped off his stool and now crouched several feet away from the counter, a knife in one hand and his mug of sweet milk in the other. "I can't hear nothing. The bastard's deefened me."

The Toltec had not stopped playing pinball and paid none of them the least attention because he had lighted four pretty girls which meant he would probably win something. His friend now sat motionless on the stool and looked ahead as though he saw clear into some grief stricken time.

Not until the eighth or maybe the ninth night did Pendleton realize that the restaurant was drawing more people; there would be six or eight or even as many as a dozen in for dinner.

There came a night when the fat Toltec entered as always but no one followed. That night the restaurant was an uneasy place. Things spilled, and while cleaning up one of the tables Pendleton discovered a menu burned through and through with cigarette holes. By 10:30 the place was deserted.

Pendleton said, "Hey, Pablo."

The Toltec gave him a furious look.

"All right," Pendleton apologized, "what's your name?"

"What's yours?" he replied. He was deeply insulted.

"Whereabouts is your friend?"

"He's no friend of mine."

Pendleton walked down the counter behind a damp rag, wrung it over the sink, then very casually he did something he never did or never even thought of doing: he opened a bottle of beer for the Mexican and indicated without a word that it was free.

Toltec, though still grieved, accepted the gift, saying, "I just met the guy. He asked me where to get some decent cooking."

Pendleton wiped a table and for a time appeared to be idly picking his back teeth. When he judged the interval to be correct he asked, "Got tired of the grub here, I guess."

"No, tonight he's just drunk."

Pendleton allowed several more minutes, then, "He looks like a picture of a bullfighter I saw once in Tijuana called Victoriano Posada."

And this proved to be a shrewd inquiry because after drinking some more of the free beer the fat Mexican remarked, "He calls himself Damaso."

Pendleton, wondering if something else might follow, pretended to stretch and to yawn and smacked his chops mightily. He thought that tomorrow he would say, when the tall one entered, "Howdy, Damaso."

"Know what? He goes and stands by himself on the sea wall a lot of times. Maybe he's going to knock himself off. Wouldn't that be something?"

"Tell him not to do it in front of my place," Pendleton answered.

Through the screen door could be seen a roll of silvery yellow fog and above it the moon, but the water was hidden.

"These Santa Cruz winters," Pendleton said. Opening the icebox he selected a superior beer for himself and moved his high stool far enough away that his guest might not feel their friendship was being forced. Peeling off the wet label he rolled it into a soggy grey ball which he dropped into a bucket under the counter. "Singers make plenty money, I hear."

The Mexican looked at him slyly. "What are you talking about?"

Pendleton, scratching his head, sighed and yawned again. "Huh? Oh. I was just thinking about what's-his-name. That fellow you come in here with once or twice."

"I know it," the Mexican said, laughing.

For a while both of them drank away at their beers and listened to the combers, each of which sounded as if it would smash the door.

"Feels like there's something standing up in the ocean tonight," Pendleton said. "I could use a little summer."

"You want our beach full of tourists? Those sausages? Man, you're crazy. You're off the rocks."

Pendleton judged that the Mexican was about to insult the summer people still more so he manipulated the conversation once again: "Somebody told me your friend got himself a singing job at that nightspot near Capitola."

"Look," said the Toltec, patient but irritated, "I just met the guy a couple of weeks ago."

"He never said where he's from, I guess."

"Chihuahua, he says. That's one rough town. And full of sand, Jesus Christ."

Breakers continued sounding just beyond the door and the fog now stood against the screen like a person.

"What does he do?"

The Mexican lifted both fat little shoulders.

"Just traveling through?"

The Mexican lifted both hands.

"Where is he going?"

"All I know is he's got a pretty good voice."

"He howls like a god damn crazy wolf," Pendleton said, "howling for the moon."

"Yah, he's pretty good. Long time ago I saw a murder down south in the mountains and a woman screamed just like that."

Both of them thought about things and Pendleton, having reflected on the brevity of human affairs and the futility of riches, opened his icebox for two more drinks. The Mexican accepted one as though in payment for service. For some seconds they had been able to hear footsteps approaching, audible after every tunnel of water caved in. The footsteps went past the door but no one could be seen.

"Know what? There was an old man washed up on the beach the other day."

"That so?" said Pendleton. "Everything gets to the beach sooner or later."

The Mexican nodded. Somewhere far out on the bay a little boat sounded again and again. "What a night," he said.

Pendleton murmured and scratched.

"Know something, mister?"

Pendleton, now printing wet circles on his side of the counter, asked what that might be.

"Damaso is no Mexicano."

"I didn't think so," Pendleton lied.

"No, because he's got old blood. You know what I mean? I think he's a gypsy from Spain, or wherever those guys come from. He's dark in the wrong way. He just don't *feel* Mexicano to me. There's something about him, and besides he speaks a little Castellano."

Both of them considered all this.

"I suppose he's howling about some girl."

"No, it's bigger than that."

"What's the sound say?"

But here the little Mexican lost interest; he revolved on the stool, from which only his toes could reach to the floor, hopped off and hurried across to the nickelodeon. Having pushed a nickle through the slit he studied the wonderful colors and followed the bubbles which fluttered up the tubes to vanish, next he dialed *The Great Speckled Bird* and began shuffling around the floor snapping his fingers and undulating so that in certain positions he looked about five months pregnant.

"Who knows?" he asked of no one in particular while he danced.

The next night also he entered alone. When Pendleton mentioned this he replied the dark one was still drunk.

And the next night when asked if the drunk were going into its third day he replied that Damaso was no longer drunk, just sick from being so, that he was at present lying on the wet cement having vomited on his boots, that probably by sunrise he would be all right. This turned out to be correct because both of them came in for supper the following night. Toltec, smiling and tugging at his crotch, was rumpled as usual and smelled human while his tall companion was oiled and groomed and wearing the white silk again. A good many people were loitering about the restaurant—every booth was full—because this thing had come to be expected, and though all of them were eating or drinking or spending money in some way to justify themselves, and although no one looked up at the entrance of the two Mexicans there could be no doubt about the situation. Only these two men seemed not to notice anything; they ate voraciously and drank a lot of beer after which the one went across to his game, which had been deliberately vacated, and Damaso remained on the stool with his long arms crossed on the counter.

Later the nickelodeon lighted up. When at last its music died and the table stopped there was not a sound in all the restaurant. People watched the head of the dark man bow until it was hidden in his arms. The crucifix disentangled itself and dropped out the top of his gaucho shirt where it began to swing to and fro, glittering as it twisted on the end of its golden chain. He remained like that for almost an hour, finally raised his head to look at the ticket, counted away enough money, and with the sombrero loosely in one hand he stumbled out the door.

The other Mexican paid no attention; he called for more beer which he drank all at once in an attempt to interest a young girl with silver slippers and breasts like pears who was eating supper with her parents, but failing to win anything at this or again at the machine he suddenly grew bored of the evening and walked out.

The next night he entered alone. When asked if his companion had started another drunk he said that Damaso was gone.

Pendleton asked late in the evening, "How do you know?"

"I feel it," he said.

Big Pendleton then stood listening to the advancing tide which had begun to pat the pillars like someone gently slapping a dead drum. Taking off his apron he rolled it tight as he always did and put it beneath the counter. With slow fingers he untied the sweaty handkerchief from around his neck and folded it over the apron, but there his routine altered; before pulling in shutters he stood a while beside the screen and looked out and listened but of course received no more than he expected which was fog, the sound of the sea, and its odor.

Sharply the Toltec said, "I like to dance." And he began to do so. "Next summer I'm really going to cut it up. Nothing's going to catch me." He read Pendleton's face while dancing by himself to the odd and clumsy little step he was inventing, and counseled, "Jesus Christ, he's gone. Forget about it, man."

CHARLES FOSTER

THE TROUBLED MAKERS

Accusing. Two orange eyes set in dead white, staring up at him, accusing. And a rising curl of gray smoke past his eyes.

There was a tinkle of shells and a waft of air. Gray smoke eddied toward his face, rose up his nostrils. His nose twitched.

He sneezed. "Scope," he said.

His eyes blinked four times, rapidly.

He wiped his nose on the sleeve of his shirt and looked down at the counter that was tilting up toward him or away from him—which was it? And now he knew what the orange eyes were. Eggs. Sunny-side up. Hash-brown potatoes on the side. And coffee now, please, miss.

"Yes sir," she said, "right away, sir."

Had he said it out loud? And had he said it just now—or was he remembering having said it when he walked into this place, out of the awful rain? But she had already turned away, toward the terrace of six silexes in back of the counter.

She had short legs. Like goat legs? No. They were straight and rounded—not crooked or bony. But her trunk long in proportion. Erect she stood and walked. Rhythmic. Backstrap of her bra through the translucent nylon dimpled waitress dress going this way and that way as her shoulders went this way and that way.

Not slender, she wasn't. Young. Already too soft-rounded to be slender. And later on not slender at all. With love and children and food she'd spread. But with love. Black hair and skin in desert colors. Hints of ocher and sand and brown in the flesh. Desert Princess.

And brown eyes. Liquid brown. Not orange. Not accusing orange eyes idiot-set in frizzled mires of dead white with airholes.

He sneezed again.

He looked down. His right hand was resting on the edge of the counter, the counter that kept sloping this way and that way. Loving counter, nubile and waiting counter.

He saw the long thin cigar in his hand. That was the smoke. It had a soft gray ash three-quarters of an inch long and the smoke curled whitely toward his face. The firm brown wrapper of the slender cigar was faintly green in places.

"Seventy-five cents," he said.

"Did you say something to me, sir?" The girl turned back to him.

"Seventy-five cents, Desert Princess," he said. "Somewhere for this Havana Panatela . . . Havana Panatela . . . I paid seventy-five cents."

"Of course," Desert Princess said. "You got it here."

She was close to him, just above him across the yawing, shifting counter. Hips, waist, breasts, shoulders, liquid warm brown eyes and the clean smell of herself. How could anybody smell so much like herself?

"You bought it here, sir," she said with a smile hinting at the full flesh of her lips. "You said it might protect you from the rain. You bought it and then you lit it and you went out."

"I did? Nonchalant, into the red rain, smoking a seventy-five cent Havana Panatela. Devil a care . . . never a backward glance . . . leaving you flat? How could I do it, Desert Princess?"

"Oh, I didn't worry, sir. Your friend worried but I didn't worry. I knew you'd be back. At least, I was pretty sure you'd be back. And now you are back, aren't you?"

"Am I?" he said. "Yes, I suppose I am. And with a seventy-five cent Havana Panatela. But we'll soon fix that."

He grasped the panatela like a spear between the thumb and first two fingers of his right hand. So poised, he waited for the yaw and pitch of the counter to settle a little. And then he plunged it down, swiftly hard and true, down right into the center of the first of the two orange accusing eyes.

Liquid yolk spurted.

There was another musical tinkle of shells. He looked up and back along the deep, narrow lunchroom. The writhing counter ended four stools farther down—and there was an archway, ornate with plaster angels and lilies growing at its curving edges. Had he made it? He supposed so. And down from the arch hung a curtain made of shells. Shells that tinkled as, blown by air, they sounded one against another.

And now the shells had parted. And two brown hands were on the edges of the arch.

The Watusi Chief.

Six feet four inches tall he was. Maybe taller when he straightened up? But now he stooped under the arch.

"You shouldn't oughta done that, Boss," Watusi Chief said.

"Why not?" the man called Boss asked.

"Nobody oughta waste food, Boss. It ain't right, with people hungry."

"You call *this* food? And you call *them* out there people? I'll show you what's food and what's people!"

Boss lifted the dripping end of the Havana Panatela out of the egg yolk, leaving a mound of ash, gray slowly wetting to black. "I'll show you!"

And he plunged the end of the Havana Panatela deep into the center of the second orange eye. Again, liquid yolk spurted. It splashed on the heaving counter, the nylon of Desert Princess, the dirty, red-spattered khaki of the Boss's shirt.

"I'll show you what's food, you black bastard! I'll show you what's people! I'll show you what's what!"

Calmly, Watusi Chief took two big steps along the billowing counter. His long, evenly muscled right arm snaked down and under Boss's arms and around his belly. He lifted and hauled Boss up into the air, up over the counter. Desperately, Boss reached down to retrieve his Havana Panatela from the middle of the second orange eye. But his fingers only brushed it, knocking it off the edge of the plate onto the pulsing counter.

The counter surged and Havana Panatela flipped up on the crest of the surge and then off the counter and down, down between two stools.

Boss screamed in mid-air. "Something to suck. Gotta have something to suck. Something to mouth!" Boss screamed and screamed again.

"Maybe you better give him some mints," Desert Princess said.

"Could be," Watusi Chief said. "Gimme a box of 'em, please."

Desert Princess walked along the counter to the cash register, up at the front of the long narrow room.

Watusi Chief hoisted Boss up to his shoulder and let him hang there. "You try to calm down, Boss," he said. "You suck some mints and calm down, okay? Because we've got to find us a job before we run into the Town Marshal again—you remember, the bastard who stopped us out on the highway this morning?"

But Boss wasn't listening. Because down there in front of him was Desert Princess, one hand on the cash register, smiling up at him.

"Honey," he wailed to her, over the vast distances between them, the tremendous distances between everybody, "desert honey. Desert honey in the cool light and shadow of the oasis where the wild bees murmur. I must go now, I must leave thee, O desert princess of my honeycomb, dripping with desert ardor. I am borne on cruel wings of duty—but the memory of your sweet honey will stay ever on my tongue. Loved I not honor more, I'd curry and hurry the spice of your honey'd favor, and here I'd make my stand, to love or die for honey . . ."

"How much do we owe ya?" Watusi Chief asked.

"One eighty-seven," Desert Princess said. "Including the Havana Panatela and the sales tax."

Watusi Chief pulled two bills and a coin out of his pants pocket. "Here you are, miss. And you keep the change for your trouble."

"Oh, it wasn't hardly what you'd call trouble at all," Desert Princess said, smiling. "Why, gee, I kind of like him. The nice things he said, even if he did splash egg on my dress. I really do."

Boss began chanting, in a high falsetto. "Mints, mints, mints— mints pie in the mints sky when I mints mints mints die. Hot slices and slabs of mints sky girl princess of minks and princess of mints, succulent mints and singing minks. And when the mints sky was opened they all rained down—the shining furs of mints, the running laughter of the minks. And all the kings began to sing, O what a princess dish to set before the minsky pie of my mint-deminted eye . . ."

"Here's your mints, Boss. You can simmer down, now."

Boss saw the pink palm of Watusi Chief's brown left hand coming up toward his mouth. Two round white mints in the palm. Boss craned down, mouth open, tongue out. He lapped up and sucked up the two mints. And then he twisted his neck up and around till he could see the ceiling.

"Well, miss, I guess we'll be running along now," Watusi Chief said. "Could you tell me how we get to the state employment office from here?"

"Why, surely," Desert Princess said. "You just cross Main at the next crossing—the one with the light. That's Second. Walk two blocks down and turn left on Elm. Employment office's in the middle of the block. You can't miss it."

Desert Princess looked up at Boss, on Watusi Chief's shoulder. And then, beyond him, she saw what was happening on the ceiling. Or in the ceiling. She gasped.

There was a dwarf apple tree. Not exactly painted on—or in— the ceiling. It was in bas-relief, half in and half out, as if the ceiling were wet cement and a real apple tree had been picked up by a giant hand and pushed on its side halfway into the cement. Except instead of cement, or ceiling, there was a yellow sky behind—or above—the tree.

Desert Princess felt sure—if she could only reach up that high— she could pick one of the apples and bite into it and it would be a real apple. A tremendously real apple. Suddenly, she wanted one of the apples very much.

And she wanted the blossoms, the gigantic white-and-gold apple blossoms that nestled in sets of three around each of the big round red ripe apples. Whoever heard of apple blossoms and ripe apples growing together? And never on any tree, either apples or blossoms like these.

But instead of reaching up she just stared, mouth open. Because on the gnarled and crooked lowest limb of the dwarf apple tree a girl was suddenly sitting.

Bare feet and bare legs dangled down from the low limb, almost touching the ground. But the girl's body was wrapped in a short cape. Desert Princess had never in her life seen a cape anything like that cape but she was immediately sure that she had to have one just like it. For when she stared at it, all she could think of was a fan coral with delicate tracery veins of blood, taken from the turquoise deeps of a warm and liquid tropic sea, carried up and up to the surface of the world of air, and there transformed to texture sheer and smooth as incredible silk, silk passed by gentle hands through an adhering cloud of dust of butterfly wings.

"At it again," Watusi Chief groaned. "Jesus Christ, Boss, don't you *ever* relax?"

But Desert Princess hardly heard Watusi Chief. Because now she saw the face of the girl. And it was her face. Duplicated exactly in every detail, right down to the almost imperceptible forceps mark on her left cheek bone. But somehow, through the perfection of the likeness, there glowed a beauty, both ethereal and sexy, that Desert Princess had never herself discerned when she looked into her mirror.

"Gee," Desert Princess said, "am I *really* like that?"

"Boss says so, why then it's *so*," Watusi Chief said. "But he's sure takin' a long time saying it."

"Was I really like that—before? Or—did he, just now—did he just now *make* me that way?"

Watusi Chief sighed, resigned. "The Boss only brings out what's really there all the time, miss. He knows it's there because he can see it. And then he makes you see it too—with words, or colors, or sounds—or little scenes like this . . ."

"Goddamnit," Boss said, "I wanna nother mint. Gotta have something to *suck!*"

As Watusi Chief handed another mint up to Boss, Desert Princess saw a new figure appearing on the ceiling. Was it what they called a 'centaur'? It had four legs—but they sure weren't horse legs. They looked more like the legs of a goat. And instead of hide—horsehide or goathide—the body was covered with the finest of white feathers. Pure white, except around the brisket. There they were tipped with scarlet. And above the brisket a man's body—covered with a swirling cape of feathers. A cape cut along the same lines as the cape of Desert-Princess-in-the-apple-tree.

The head above the cape was the head of Boss—except that the single twisted spear of a unicorn horn grew out of the middle of the forehead, just below the wind-tangled hair.

Two massively muscled arms held a shiny clarinet to the lips. And goat-legged, horned, feathered and caped, Boss galloped across the ceiling toward Desert Princess on the apple tree, his head thrown far back, blowing joy into the clarinet. The sound he made filled the lunchroom.

That sound—it seemed to well up from the floor, to travel up from the toes along the quivers of nets of nerves of legs and body, to be heard by all the body, bone and flesh and glands and nerves, before it even reached the drums of the ears. Because who could ever *hear* such sounds without feeling them first?

"Hey, that's something new you got on that clarinet, ain't it, Boss," Watusi Chief said. "What is it, chrome?"

"Purest silver," Boss said. "Silver pillaged by marauding barbarian hordes of the sun as they struck down in rapine the long-forgotten mountain fastness of an ancient race, an ancient people."

"Christmas sakes!" Desert Princess breathed, "a pure silver clarinet!"

"Nah," Boss said. "I was exaggerating. Kind of a pure silver alloy. I sort of threw in a little tungsten and platinum and antimony to, well, to give it body and feel and weight and touch and resonance and timbre. Stuff like that. Gimme another mint." Boss seemed calmer now, absorbed in his work.

Desert Princess herself handed up two more mints to Boss and his lips brushed across her fingers as he took them. She looked up and saw that now her cape was opening, opening wider as Boss the centaur approached closer and closer.

But it was not really a cape at all. It was a pair of wings! They fluttered up and down, opened wide and up and out over her shoulders and back, then down, closing in and around her bare shoulders. Up and down, with a movement like the flutter of a cape and the beat of wings at the same time—keeping the beat and the time of the sound from the silver and platinum and tungsten and antimony clarinet, swooping up and down.

Under her wings, Desert Princess' arms were folded over her naked breasts. In her hands she held a short bow and an arrow, both blood red. The feathers of the arrow with their scarlet tips might have been plucked from the centaur's chest.

With the centaur galloping closer across the ceiling, Desert Princess unfolded her arms. She fitted a blood red arrow to the gold string of the blood red bow. She pulled back till the bow bent and strained in a tense arc. Bowstring taut as a song, nipples of her bare breasts taut as the bowstring, taut as the red skin of the apples, taut apples bursting with ripeness.

She released the string and the arrow sang higher than the clarinet.

But in the midflight instant, they sang together—the arrow and the clarinet. Their songs blended into one new sound. And then both stopped. Stopped in shattering silence.

"Judas Priest! What have I done now!" Desert Princess screamed. She covered her eyes and leaned forward, bending over the cash register. "Oh, I can't bear it. I can't bear to look."

"Go ahead and look," Watusi Chief said. "You didn't do no harm. Boss is having too good a time right now to let anything tragic happen."

Desert Princess peered up, between her fingers. Watusi Chief was right. Now the silver and tungsten and antimony and platinum clarinet was clenched in Boss's right hand. And the blood red arrow he had caught, caught in midflight and at the midpoint of its shaft, between his teeth.

Boss trotted forward, lifting his goat legs high, prancing triumphantly. The golden point of the blood red arrow glinted at the sun while his eyes, under the single unicorn horn, glinted at Desert Princess. . . .

"Sque-e-e-e-ak—BANG!" said the screen door.

"What the hell is going on here?" said the fat man who came in through the door.

"Why nothin' at all, Uncle," Desert Princess said. "Fellers, this is my uncle, the Town Marshal."

"We've met," Watusi Chief said.

"What d'ya mean—nothin' at all? If it's nothin' at all, then what's that tree doin' growin' outa my ceiling?"

"Your ceiling?" Watusi Chief said. "Looks to me like it's mostly Boss's ceiling now."

"Fifty-one percent of the stock in this here lunchroom's mine," the Town Marshal said. "I guess that makes it my ceiling, don't it? Well, don't it?"

"But forty-nine percent is *mine*," Desert Princess said, "so I guess I got *some* say in what . . ." Desert Princess broke off, her voice choked with disappointment. She was staring at the ceiling.

The Town Marshal looked up. The ceiling, one hundred percent of it, was just as it had always been. The plaster wore the dead gray, powdery gray coat of dirt and calcimine it had always worn. The three big brown stains and the five small brown stains were back, where they had always been. Over the stove and grill, behind the counter, the same layer of smoke and slimy grease spread out in its half-circle, just as it had for years and years and years.

"Now look what you've gone and done!" Desert Princess screamed. "Just *look* what you've done!"

"Now *you* look, girl," the Town Marshal said. "You look and you listen to me. I'm a lot more to you than just the fifty-one percent controlling co-owner of this here lunchroom. I'm your uncle, girl, and don't you forget it. And I raised you up from the time you was a three-years-old orphan. And even besides all that—me bein' the law here—it's up to me to keep a little order. . . ."

"Order!" she said scornfully, "what do you know about order?" She gazed wistfully for a moment at Boss, still hanging over the shoulder of Watusi Chief. When she spoke again her voice was softer. "Nobody ever made me like that before. Why, for a minute there, I knew the way I really was. The way I really am . . ."

"Trouble!" the Town Marshal broke in. "Trouble. From the moment I laid eyes on you two out on the highway this morning, I could smell trouble." The anger was rising in the Town Marshal's voice, the red flush working itself up into his face. "Didn't I tell you two to keep moving? Didn't I? Didn't I tell you two to keep agoin' right through my town, and not to stop for nothin'?"

Boss said, "Scope." Then he said, "You got seventy-five cents left, Watusi Chief?"

"Scope? What's he mean by scope?" the Town Marshal demanded.

"With the exception of seven cents, Boss," Watusi Chief said, "we're broke."

"I'll bet I know what he wants," Desert Princess said, "Another Havana Panatela."

"I guess so," Watusi Chief said. "When things get bad, mints just ain't enough."

"I asked you what you meant by *scope*," the Town Marshal shouted, "and by God I want an answer!"

"Before you start talkin' that way, uncle, maybe you ought to kind of remember that I'm a Sunday school teacher," Desert Princess said. "What would my class think, do you think, if they heard my own uncle a talkin' like that?"

"Maybe so," the Town Marshal said, breathing hard, "and maybe *you* ought to remember it too—that you're a Sunday school teacher— when you're having all these dirty pictures made on your ceiling. My ceiling." He paused and looked up at Boss. "But I still ain't found out what you mean by . . ."

"There's no call at all to look at him with them mean, accusing eyes of yours . . ."

"I wasn't doing anything of the sort," the Town Marshal said, "I was just trying to find out . . ."

"And what's more," Desert Princess said, "I'm going to *give* him a Havana Panatela, even if it is fifty-one percent yours. After what he showed me about myself, why it's little enough to do."

The Town Marshal stared at her in silence for a moment. When he spoke his voice was lower, placating. "Honey," he said, "you don't know what you're saying. I raised you up and I loved you and took care of you all these years. I slaved and sacrificed for you so you'd have all the advantages. I even took this here thankless Town Marshal's job, to make the money so's you could have a nice little business of your own and a place where you could meet nice young fellers. And now, after all that, you stand up there, defying me, mocking me like a jaybird. And for what? For a good for nothing, no good at all *stranger*. A *maker*. That you never even laid eyes on before . . ."

He paused for breath. Desert Princess was staring down at her feet and there was a blush of guilt on her face.

"I guess," she said, "I guess what you say—well—I guess you're right." Her voice was small, subdued.

"You *guess* I'm right?" the Town Marshal said, louder now and with more of his old confidence. "You *know* I'm right. What I said to you, why, it's just plain common-sense facts. And there's no disputin' facts, is there, honey?"

"No," she said, her voice even smaller and quieter, "I guess not."

"Boss is gonna get kinda disturbed if he don't get a Havana Panatela pretty soon," Watusi Chief said.

"Oh, he *is*, is he?" the Town Marshal said. "Well, goddam. That just about does it. First thing, you two come into my town, without even a by-your-leave. Then, you try to turn the head of my own niece, the little girl I raised up from a baby—as good a girl as you could ask for—teaches in the Sunday school every Sunday. Next, you grow trees in the ceiling of my lunchroom. And now—to top it all off—you go 'round demandin' Havana Panatelas. Okay. Now I'll tell you what I'm goin' to do. I'm gonna run you both in. Let's go!"

"You mind telling me what the charge is?" Watusi Chief asked.

"Charge? I'll give you plenty of charges. Vagrancy . . ."

"They still got seven cents!" Desert Princess said. "It ain't as if they was broke!"

". . . And vagrancy's only the beginning," the Town Marshal went on. "Apple trees in the ceiling without a permit. Pornography. Disturbance of the peace—why, what do you think the other folks in this town would think? Supposing they was to come into this respectable lunchroom and see a apple tree growing out of the ceiling?"

"But, Uncle!" Desert Princess said, "these boys ain't bums. They're willing to work. Why, just before you came in here and made such a ruckus, they was on their way to the state employment office. And I'll bet they was goin' there to get jobs!"

"Boss ain't gonna be in a good mood *at* all if he don't get a Havana Panatela pretty quick," Watusi Chief said.

"He sure *ain't* gonna be in a good mood, where I'm taking him," the Town Marshal said, "and neither are you. Lessen you like bars, chilled steel bars. And you're gonna stay right there behind 'em, too—till the judge gets back from deer hunting."

"Bars ain't so bad," Watusi Chief said, "not when Boss gets through with 'em."

"Oh—maybe you think my bars won't hold you, huh? Chilled steel . . ."

"Oh yeah, they'll *hold* all right. Boss he got a lot of respect for reality, including bars. I don't think he's about to bust out through 'em. But he'll kind of decorate 'em—so you'll be able to see what they *really* look like—what they *feel* like. And then maybe you won't be able to stand the sight of 'em yourself. . . ."

"Oh, bars, bars, *bars!*" Desert Princess said. "Why can't you men ever talk sense? Chilled steel! I never heard so much nonsense in all my life. Bars or no bars, Uncle, you just can't lock these men up when they're honestly looking for work. You just can't! It ain't fair!"

"I can't, huh? What makes you think I can't?" The Town Marshal's face was livid now and he was shouting. "I'll show you what I can do and what I can't do."

"You can't lock 'em up," Desert Princess said, calmly, quietly, positively, "not if you expect to get any peace at home for the next month or two of Sundays."

The Town Marshal stared at her. "After all I've done, after all I've said, you're still taking up for these strangers . . ."

"Fair's fair!" Desert Princess said, "and it was you taught me to be fair!"

"Okay. *Okay.* I'll tell you what I'll do. I'll escort these two around to the state employment office myself. Right now. If they get themselves jobs, I'm all done with them. But if they don't, I'm locking 'em both up!"

"Unless he gets a Havana Panatella, Boss is gonna feel . . ."

"Boss can damn well *earn* his Havana Panatela," the Town Marshal broke in, "provided he gets a job. And if you ask me, that's a pretty big provided."

The skinny man with the straw-colored hair toyed nervously with the painted wedge on his desk that said INTERVIEWER. His worried eyes shifted from the two men seated beside his desk to the fat Town Marshal standing behind both of them.

It was pretty obvious the Town Marshal didn't want these two to get jobs—but the Interviewer was determined not to let that sway him. It was up to him to match men to jobs, come hell or high water.

That was *his* job and he took pride in doing it well. Of course, it was a small town and a man had to live with his neighbors. And he did owe the Marshal a few favors. And the Marshal did have one of the prettiest girls in town for a niece. . . .

But naturally, he wasn't going to be influenced by any of these considerations. If there had been a job for these two—the maker and his assistant—he wouldn't hesitate a minute. But of course, in a town like this, there just weren't any jobs for makers.

"I sure wish I *did* have something in your line," he said, his voice trembling a little with sincerity, "but the honest truth of the matter is that we haven't had a call for a maker in all the three years I've been holding down this desk."

"Scope," Boss said. His moist eyes blinked as he stared at the plain, blank, ivory-colored wall at the back of the state employment office. His voice was indistinct because of the five mints he was sucking.

"What in hell do you mean by *scope?*" roared the Town Marshal.

"Don't let it excite you, Marshal," the Interviewer said hastily. "Makers often say things that seem—uh—a little obscure to folks." He turned to the two seated men. "Isn't there—uh—something else you could do? Short order cooking? Certified Public Accounting?"

"He's tried 'em," Watusi Chief said, "but his mind sort of wanders. And then he'll put bacon fat into the coffee or coffee into the frying pan. Or he'll use the wrong set of books to make out the income tax forms. Things like that. And I've got to work with him and kind of watch out for him."

"Scope," Boss said. He was still staring at the back wall and it was beginning to shimmer a little now and didn't look quite so ivory as it had a moment before.

"I'll *scope* you when I get you locked up, the Town Marshal said. "And it's time we were going right now. You heard what the man said, didn't you? He ain't got a thing for you!"

And then the Interviewer's phone rang.

He smiled and talked into the phone and listened and when he put it down he looked like a man who's just squared a circle or filled an inside straight.

"That was your niece," he said to the Town Marshal. "Says she needs a maker and maker's assistant. Right away."

"What the hell do you mean!" the Town Marshal said. "Without my say-so she can't hire any . . ."

"O Desert Princess," said the Boss, "O wild heart of desert honey. Golden goddess of Havana Panatelas . . ."

"Shut up, you! I'm the controlling co-owner of that lunchroom . . ."

"It isn't for the lunchroom," the Interviewer said. "It's for the Sunday school. Remember, way back last fall, when the Sunday School Board voted fifty dollars for an Audio Visual Training Aid? Well, she's scouted around and never found anything decent for that price. But she thought, maybe, now with a maker right here in town and all . . ."

"Fifty bucks," Watusi Chief said, "will buy one hell of a mess of Havana Panatelas. We'll take it."

"What do you mean—*we'll* take it?" the Town Marshal demanded. "Who the hell asked you?"

"I got his power of attorney," said Watusi Chief. "Want I should show it to you?"

"Nah. Nah. Never mind. But I'll tell you one thing. You'd better deliver the goods, because every one of those charges is still hanging over both your heads. I'm giving you till Sunday to get this Audio Visual thing done and done right!"

"But that's only a third the usual time for a job like this," Watusi Chief said. "Think you can handle it, Boss?"

"Scope," Boss said.

"Where's the man responsible for this?" the Mayor asked as he strode up to Watusi Chief and the Town Marshal. It was Sunday morning. The mayor had just finished his dedication speech for the new Audio Visual Aid.

"That's him, out there." Watusi Chief pointed out through the Sunday school window.

For a moment, the Mayor continued to stare in wonder at the enormous Audio Visual Aid which filled the air of the Sunday school, hanging over the class that Desert Princess was now teaching. Then the Mayor looked out the window. The Boss was stretched out on the grass, flat on his back, eyes closed, a box of Havana Panatelas for a pillow. One of the cigars was lit and between his teeth. He was blowing pink smoke rings. Sometimes he would blow a green figure eight. Once in awhile a dancing girl, all colors.

"Looks kinda beat, don't he?" the Town Marshal said.

"It takes it out of a man, making as big an Audio Visual Aid as that with such a close deadline," Watusi Chief said. "And when a maker gets through working, he's put so much of himself into what he's done that there just ain't very much left over."

"Well, he's certainly made something that'll boost this town," the Mayor said. "Tourist business alone that it'll bring in—just that alone oughta pay off the bonded debt in two-three years. This sure was a damn fine idea of yours, Marshal."

"Hell, Mr. Mayor, it was mainly just using a little persuasion at the right moment," the Town Marshal said.

The man on the grass stirred. In a lazy circle, one hand swung up and took the cigar from his mouth. Gently, with the other hand, he thumbed his nose at the Marshal and the Mayor. He winked at Watusi Chief. Then he turned his face back up to the sky. He smiled wearily, happily. "Scope," he said.

Sunday school was over but the Smallest Girl was still there, staring in wonder—the stars in her eyes as bright as the millions and tens of millions of stars that shone out of the Audio Visual Aid, above and all around her.

At random, she picked out one, a medium-sized yellow star with nine tiny dots revolving around it. Pointing to it, she turned toward Desert Princess.

"Do you really think there are people like us on this one?"

"Sure," Desert Princess said with a smile. "Audio Visual Aids can't exist without people, any more than you can rightly say that people can exist without Audio Visual Aids. Leastways, that's what the Boss said. And seein' how he's the maker, I guess he knows."

"Do you think they're as good as us? Or better? Or worse?"

"From what Boss says, I'm afraid they're just about as bad. He told me he figured they'd have just as much trouble with money and cheating and bombs and plain ignorance and fancy cussedness as us."

"But why couldn't he make 'em *better*, while he was at it?"

"Well—they're supposed to be a kind of model for us and of us. And if they're too much better, then they ain't no model at all, is they? And besides, Boss says he can only make 'em as good as his own vision is good. And I guess it sounds kind of funny, but he says his vision was none too good when he made this one, on account of he didn't have no Havana Panatelas to keep him calm."

"But why didn't he, if that was all he needed?" the Smallest Girl asked.

"Folks was a little stiff-necked, I guess, child. And you know what? Boss says he figures something like that was what happened when *we* was made. Any time, he says, that a maker gets a real big job, why, it just doesn't seem as if things are set up so he'll be in a peaceful mood. Or he'll have a close deadline to meet. All kinds of things."

"Gee, you talked to him a whole *lot*," the Smallest Girl said. "Are you going to get yourself married up to him?"

"No, course not. It's been wonderful knowing him—and someday when you're big you'll know *how* wonderful. But makers just ain't very good husband material. I'll always remember him, though, I always will. Because it was him showed me who I really am. And that's the most important thing can happen to anybody ever. Even after I'm married to the Interviewer—and it isn't going to be long now before he asks me, but don't you dare tell him—I won't ever forget how the Boss showed me who I really was."

But the Smallest Girl was no longer really listening. She had turned back to the Audio Visual Aid. Across the whole ceiling of the Sunday school it stretched. In the center a great, slowly revolving pinwheel of stars, throwing off little sparks of stars. And stretching out in every direction were the smaller pinwheels and clusters.

It was funny, the Smallest Girl thought. If you looked straight at the walls of the Sunday school, there they were, looking solid and real.

But if you focused your eyes on the Audio Visual Aid, it wasn't like that at all. Your eyes started at the great star cloud in the center, your eyes caught by its foams and whirlpools and running rivulets of stars, all in motion, millions of stars. And as you looked there was a sound, a sound that your *eyes* seemed to hear, a new sound, a music that you knew had always been there but was always new.

Accusing. Two green eyes set in unhealthy magenta, staring up at him. And a slosh of gin, a bare finger of gin in the bottle before his eyes.

He drank the gin in one gulp. Then he turned the empty bottle upside down, letting the last drop drip on the counter.

"Scope," he said.

"Did you speak to me, sir?" the waitress behind the wavering counter asked.

"Scope!" he said again, savagely. He looked up at her. "If I had scope enough, if I could only do once, just once, what I'm trying to do, I could build whole universes. Endless islands of universes!"

In sudden anger he jabbed the neck of the bottle he held into one of the accusing green eyes on the plate before him and then into the other. Green ichor spurted across his shirt, over the counter, onto the skirt of the waitress.

"Scope!" he cried, and the shells at his back tinkled with a faint music. The tall sunburnt white man was coming toward him. Trader Horn.

He turned back to the waitress and regarded her. A gazelle of the far veldt she was, and in her eyes the moon of the eastern sea. "Enough scope," he said, "O Moon of the Eastern Sea, and I'd make a dozen island universes for you, just for you, for you—and string them in a bracelet for your wrist . . ."

"Come on, Chief, let's go," Trader Horn said, his big sunblistered hand on Chief's shoulder, "we gotta make the employment office before it closes, if we're gonna get a gig for tomorrow."

The Smallest Girl felt the sad tears coming and she let them come and she cried for a long time after the two men had left—but the stars in her eyes, the stars of wonder, the stars of her passage, they stayed bright through the tears.

EDWARD DAHLBERG

from *THE SORROWS OF PRIAPUS*

Man must be classed among the brutes, for he is still a very awkward and salacious biped. What shape he will assume in the future is vague. There are many traits of early man he has lost, and it is plain that he is much more given to falsehood, robbery and law-suits than the primitive. The first two-legged man scratched himself because he had an itch. Men now lie and steal for this pleasure. Primeval natures wallowed without thought, but soon as men began thinking how pleasant it was to rub themselves and to have deliriums from mud, they employed their minds to achieve what paleolithic mankind did without being lascivious.

Men lie, not alone for profit, but to root in Circe's mire. No pygmy or cave-dweller wears more bizarre or dirty raiment than present-day man. He is often as offensive as the gland on the back of the Brazil peccary. He would rather tell a lie than the truth because his sole purpose is to be a grub.

He is the most ridiculous beast on the earth, and the reason for this is his mind and his pudendum. He sacks nations, or throws away his reason to see the petticoat of Aspasia or Helen empurpled by murex or the lichen at Madeira. The procreative organ in the camel is behind, but in man it is in front, and unless he is too fat to look over his belly, he pays more attention to this gibbous organ than to his arms, his talus, or anything else. He frequently forgets how his arms look, and is surprised to find a wen on his jaw, and he rarely knows whether his pupils are brown or ocherous, but he is always mindful of his testes hanging between his legs like folly.

In the *Book of Enoch* the scribe says that the first two-legged creatures had the private parts of great studs, and it may well be that Methuselah and Jared and Mahalalel were mountains and that from their middles hung hills which were their organs of generation. Otherwise, it is impossible for one to imagine how they could live for nine hundred years without wearing out their genitals. It is known that Og, King of Bashan, had an iron bedstead seven cubits long, and that the giants of Anak had six fingers.

Adam bare stones long before he begat Seth. Human life began as procreative mud, and later man was a shark with a human face. There was a human species with a lion's mouth and the legs of a giraffe, for anterior to the neolithic period diverse animals mingled. Many of our traits are found in the countenance of the bear and in the lip of the pard. The story that the pygmies were chased from the River Strymon by cranes is also a fable of our bird origin.

The old gods were ocean, rivers, animals, fish, birds; Noah was a fish, and Plato supposed that Oceanus was the father of Saturn, and there is as much natural history in this as mythology. Men and rivers are demigods and beasts; the Scamander is the river's mortal name; Zeus called the fierce water Xanthus; in the *Iliad* it is reported that the bird, said to be named *chalcis* by the gods, was Cymindis among men. This is the heroic conception of human fate.

Pleasure brings about the most violent transport in men, and of all the animals in the earth none is so brutish as man when he seeks the delirium of coition. Democritus of Abdera, unable to bear being stung by any female foot in sandals, or round skirt, was said to have plucked out his eyes. He was as mad as a boar for the shape of Venus; when the testicles of the boar are swollen he is at times so beside himself that he rubs them against a tree until he is castrated. The female deer hates copulation because the penis of the stag is as tough and spinous as a palm leaf; the pain the stag gives her is considerable but she cannot overcome her passion for him.

One marvels what man will do to have his skin scraped. Antony lay with Cleopatra at Daphne for this foolishness, and though he gave all his force to her, his delights were not as long as those of the ordinary fly. One cannot submit a little to sexual excitement without hankering after more such raptures. When birds are continent their testes are internal, but after sexual intercourse the penis is very conspicuous.

Whether man is more lecherous than the partridge is doubtful, but he is not as chaste as the raven, who bleeds from the eyes during coition. The man of sensibility is not satisfied with ordinary coupling;

all the arts of Lais of Corinth cannot furnish his skin and veins with the infinite sensations he demands. Pain affords him infatuate happiness unknown to four-legged creatures. He is almost the only animal that cohabits at all times. With the exception of the pigeon, a bird which abstains only a few days in the year, man has the most lickerish tail of all beasts. This has made him very unruly, and double in his words and deeds. Unlike the elephant he has no seasons for his venery. This pachyderm, after impregnating the female, avoids this excitement for two years.

The elephant is an exemplary teacher. It is in many respects a rational animal, and repents of its anger, which is rare among men; when it kills its master, it grieves and sometimes starves to death. The dam suckles her young six years, and many elephants live as long as people. When an elephant is sick he is given wine to drink, and when he has an eye disease, these warm, friendly orbs are bathed in cow's milk. His wounds are healed by butter. These are the simples that the Homeric heroes gave to each other at Troy, and the poet of the *Iliad*, as well as Plato, would have paid the tenderest regard to this superior beast whose diet, medicines and habits are far better than those of the vast multitudes in the earth. The elephant, doubtless, was no less a monitor than the heifer which is so often seen beside the seated Buddha.

Countless adulteries are committed without lust, and with no thought to the peril which attends this folly. Animals do not give each other the pox; when men attempt to lie with a beast it rejects the malady that is said to be the companion of human genius. The adulterer is more senseless than the earthworm who keeps part of his tail in the hole he inhabits when copulating so he can disappear at once should he see an adversary. The tibulae hide in the hedges all day, and seek the delights of the female at dusk.

Most people are furtive, but very few are ashamed; the elephant prefers to copulate near an obscure river bank, and the camel retires to the desert to rut. Modesty has been undermined because it is not generally known that the camel, more continent in his thoughts than a modern vestal, requires a whole day to complete such exercises.

Few labor for anything else but to exchange their sexual properties with blowzy dowds, or to rival the fox which has a bony penis: even the impotent are like the aged boar who waits for the tired female to lie down before he will risk his feeble appendage.

When the camel opens its mouth it looks like the greatest ass, though the ancients made the strongest bowstrings out of its pudendum. The egg of the *sepia* pretends to be blake myrtle seeds; the vine the polypus deposits is its ovum.

The rhyades remain quiet until the equinox, and the grasshopper is said to sit upon the olive and reeds when it casts its skin, but man now stays in one place only long enough to void or feed. His irregular habits and haste make him the inferior of the polypi which unite only in winter, and these creatures conceal themselves for this reason for two months.

The tortoise gives a month to coition. The moose cannot have commerce with a red deer that is too short, but men and women of sundry sizes are suitable to each other. Andromache had too long a body, but not for Hector. Nubian dwarfs were ravishing morsels in Egypt. The pygmies who rode on the backs of partridges, which was a way of saying they were concupiscent, satisfied the giantesses of the Thermodon.

The puma never utters a cry when he mingles with the female. Bucks and does herd separately after the rutting season; man is incontinent whenever he has the occasion.

Men are more obscure to themselves than the elm or marine shells. The *solens* perish after they have been taken away from their borning place; the fir is comely in the sun, and the cedar is a Saul in the mountains. Man does not know when he should plant, or from whom he can glean, or what town is his stony Medusa. The *sepia* deposit their ova near the river Thermodon, for its waters are warm and potable; the eels seek reedy ponds, and the pregnant red mullet lies among the rockweed. Paul the Fourth was an ascetic until his eightieth year, but when he became pope, he sported for hours at table as any mare in heat.

Men are too unstable to be just; they are crabbed because they have not passed water at the usual time, or testy because they have not been stroked or praised. The habits of animals can be ascertained better than the mien of a philosopher. When stags are bitten by the *phalangius* they eat crabs and are healed, but if a man has had a poor or dour sleep, he is waspish the whole day, and is likely to curse his parents.

There are certain fish that only breed in the Pontus, and many of the tunnies run to the Pillars to spawn. The halcyon appears only at the setting of the Pleiades and during the solstice. The crocodile is a modest brute whose penis and testicles are internal, and he could be regarded the peer of saints did he keep these members there. The polypus hides its ova in holes, which is a lesson for modern

women who, when they are with child, go through the streets showing the results of their shame. When the mare wants to sport with
the stallion she makes water. But this lubricous mammal is continent
compared with man, and he eats herbs, barley and oats which is a
diet similar to the sacred table of Pythagoras. One has to travel to
India to find a savant as herbivorous and savory as this extraordinary
brute.

We scoff at Alexander for burying his horse Bucephalus, but the
stone of that stallion shows that he had the separate toes of a human
being, and this monument stands in front of the temple of Venus
Genetrix. Bucephalus was so named because of the breadth of its
head. Plato means wide forehead, and it is interesting to add that
the philosopher came of the family of Hippias who were horsemen.
The horse is so marvelous to behold that Semiramis was seized with
the wildest passions when looking upon this carnal beast.

The horse goes mad pasturing by himself; separated from the
human flock man loses his reason. Nietzsche, the wildest intellect of
his century, lived in solitude, a Dionysiac disease which in crazy
horses was known as the hippomania. In his last Bacchic throes he
flung his insane arms about a horse standing in the gutters of Turin.

No one but a perverse person takes exception to horse manure.
Droppings of many animals are more healthful than those of people.
Human dung, except that of primitive races, is unclean. When the
stag's horns are most perfect he has a very offensive odor; unlike
man, who wears the same skin all his life, the stag casts his horns,
the bird molts, and the despised python sloughs off his vile coat;
man's despair is that he smells, he is garbed in the same skin until
he rots in the tomb.

The Aztecs sold pots of human excrement for working their
leather. Civilized nations regarded primitive man as a savory beast.
The ancients, having the highest esteem for the offal of kine, said
the oxen of the Sun were stalled near the Ocean where the seascum
resembled dung.

Man imagines that because he stands on his legs he is intellectual,
but the penguin is a biped who feeds until he can scarcely move;
the bear too can stand up. Man's passion for disorder, upheaval and
bedlam explains his greed. He attempts to prove that whatever man
does is for his advantage. This is not true of him, and sometimes
quadrupeds, generally reasonable, are demented or perverse. It is
fabled that the mongoose breaks the eggs which the crocodile hatches
in the mud though it does not eat them nor derive profit from this

act. Man's neck is as long as Plutus: Solomon said, his eyes cannot
be filled with seeing nor his ears with hearing. He is so bored that
he seeks the naïve existence of the sow. Having devoured all the
experiences possible to the biped, he now wants to be primitive,
which he thinks is the same as being chaotic, torpid, or supine the
whole day. Baudelaire asserted that he had the wildest desire to be
aboriginal, because standing on two legs was too trivial and average
for him. Man imagines that could he crawl again as an infant or as
any brute in the field, he could recapture a primeval existence. Others
are only content with the testicles of animals. Could man molt his
skin as the bird its feathers, and have new flesh, he would be innocent. The stag casts his horns every year, and the horse may lose
his hoof, but each acquires what he has shed. When the teeth or
the hair of men decay, they do not grow the tusks they show whenever they desire sexual frenzies, or the hair that makes them prance
and sport and neigh. Were it possible for man to shed his feet or
his hands he could have a naïve heart.

Man pines to live but cannot endure the days of his life. The
learned, crouched over their inkpots, covet the customs of the savage
who cohabits with a Lais or Aspasia of the Amazons whenever he
pleases, or envy the panther. The poet wants to be an animal. "Submit,
my heart, sleep the sleep of the brute," said Charles Baudelaire.

Men have more sorrow from their entrails than animals; except
backward people or ancient races they have fewer rites pertaining
to their ordure. They excrete when they are bored or want a savage
pleasure. The father of Beatrice Cenci drew the close-stool over to
the fireplace and voided in the presence of his wife and daughter.

The Mohammedan of the old order wipes his buttocks with his
left hand since he uses the right one to handle food, plant vines, or
to greet people. A Moslem woman can divorce a man with a reeking
breath, a fault unknown among the natives of Otaheite. Modern man
rushes to the water closet, and after the most summary ablutions,
extends his hand to the first person he meets. The ancient Essenes
had strict tenets regarding defecation and its burial in secret places.
Man at present dungs in his own house and considers himself
a delicate creature.

The anthropoid is arrogant, and when he finds a remedy for a
malady that is the consequence of a cormorant throat he is elated.
Tantalus can never eat or drink enough countries, rivers, or carcasses,
and this gluttony is the cause of nearly all human woes.

When the sow has a certain disease, it goes to the mulberry for relief, and when the horse falls into a declining melancholy, the sound of the flute will assuage this fever for which men have found no nostrum. The river horse, after overeating, comes ashore and presses its hide against the sharp rushes until blood flows from a vein in the leg. When ill the stork sups upon marjoram; and stags also, in failing health, graze upon wild artichoke. The pigeon has exquisite revulsions, and at times disrelishes his table as much as men, and then turns to bay leaves for food.

Despite all the spital houses in the world, if a man suffers from strangury, can he do much more than the Sudanese who entreat their idols to let them urinate without difficulty. If it please Zeus may we pass water; to prevent chafing, if Cato be true, put a small branch of Pontic wormwood under the anus.

Socrates described love as the sting of a tarantula. We see that desire dominates the old as well as youth; the senile forget to button their clothes, and leave the door of their trousers ajar, showing what is no more than a relic of a quondam tower. Men lose their goatish powers long before their minds; Montaigne complained that when he was somewhere in his fifties he could not raise that sleepy animal more than three times a week.

The anthropoid is more luckless and unintelligent than animals, and the remedy for his ills is not progress, going forward, which is always to his grave, but turning backward. He has extirpated most of the beasts which he no longer has as tutors. As a result he does not know whether to cohabit with woman, with man, or with sheep, and there are some who are enormously aroused by the sight of a mare. There is a breed of dog that will copulate with a wolf, and it is believed that a species of dog is derived from a tiger, and there is the Babylonian cameleopard; but, for the most part, the stallion seeks the female of its kind, and the elephant hankers after the same sort of animal that bore him.

Man is more incoherent than any beast in the earth. Schopenhauer has said that pleasure is the absence of pain, but it is not true. Man is not content with negative delights or even with positive transports. Some of his immoral deeds lacerate him, and he finds much satisfaction in being wounded. Man hates what he does, and that is what is moral in him, but he continues to do it, which is why he is Euripides, a spider, or the *Dryophis fulgida*. Man lies in ambush for all creatures, for he is the hunter; the Psalmist cries out that he is the turtledove about to be devoured by the multitude.

The whelp is most greedy for the soul that has fallen down to the ground. In the *Psalms* the soul flees to a hiding place in the mountains. The prophet rides upon a Cherub who is one of the fowls of the air. Man who is the master of the sheep and the oxen has the tender feet of the hind. He crouches before the bulls of Bashan and dreads man continually. But a little while he is a tree planted by the rivers of water, for all lurk in lairs to harm his branches.

Man is either too stupid or vain to know himself, and too self-loving to understand anyone. He cannot endure his own vices in others, and he is least just when he is railing at the faults of people.

Man is the tragic brute because he can never be as sure of others as the ass or the bull who knows that he is the booty of the wolf. A strong foe is better than a weak friend; the heron is always on guard against the eagle; the *anthus* is a reliable opponent of the horse since both covet the pasture. The deer when it has produced the fawn hides, for she knows what beast will hurt it. The wolf is the enemy of the ass, bull and fox; a mountain cat will embowel a porcupine; in a narrow defile the panther will leap upon a small dog instead of a human being. Men have no such certainties, and the more erudite they are the fewer companions they have. Aristotle in his old age said, "O my friends, there is no friend."

Everything in man is double because he has testes. The old Nile God had the form of a man with a woman's breast wearing a cluster of water plants. The Egyptians extracted from the meanest worm the paint to design jars and the sacred, funeral amphorae. In the time of the Pharaohs dense thickets were said to be the resort of male-factors. This was a proverb, and yet among the Quiche Mayans the gods were seated in the ravines, the forests and among the mosses. Not everyone that goes into the wilderness is Elijah or John.

If one considers the acts of his youth he wonders why he was ever young; or if he ponders his later vices he asks himself why he is still alive. In what manner is Messalina superior to the puma, or is anyone any better than a beetle which takes such pleasure in the fungus, called the English phallus, which has a most odious smell. The testicles of the American lizard give off a musky odor, and the monkeys in Brazil when stroked have as pleasant a scent as Alexander of Macedon. Priam had fifty bedchambers, and despite such opulent amorous experiences had no more sense than to select as his consort the termagant Hecuba. Solomon's bed linen was fragrant with Sheba and the perspiration of a hundred concubines, but were they any dearer to the nostrils than the musky testes of the lizard? There is a paradox: the Egyptians claimed that their land was infested with scorpions until it was settled by Apis. The serpent in Eden gave Eve knowledge of the phallus, and this is the source of art, science, poetry, wisdom, and perfidy.

We weep because the human race is no better than it is. The aquatic frog has the tail of a fish until he makes a twig or a blade of grass his house, then he loses his tail and grows legs. Nature advises the frog far better than man; a noddle endeavors to employ faculties he does not possess, and the eunuch burns for Jezebel.

Where is Apollo who rested his foot on the skull of an ox; where are the wild horses, the fawn, the roe, the cubs of bears that were brought to the altars of Artemis? Shall we wed, or woo, or tremble?

H. L. MENCKEN

THREE PERTINENT ESSAYS

from THE NATIONAL LETTERS

So far, the disease. As to the cause, I have delivered a few hints. I now describe it particularly. It is, in brief, a defect in the general culture of the country—one reflected, not only in the national literature, but also in the national political theory, the national attitude toward religion and morals, the national habit in all departments of thinking. It is the lack of a civilized aristocracy, secure in its position, animated by an intelligent curiosity, skeptical of all facile generalizations, superior to the sentimentality of the mob, and delighting in the battle of ideas for its own sake.

The word I use, despite the qualifying adjective, has got itself meanings, of course, that I by no means intend to convey. Any mention of an aristocracy, to a public fed upon democratic fustian, is bound to bring up images of stockbrokers' wives lolling obscenely in opera boxes, or of haughty Englishmen slaughtering whole generations of grouse in an inordinate and incomprehensible manner, or of Junkers with tight waists elbowing American schoolmarms off the sidewalks of German beer towns, or of perfumed Italians coming over to work their abominable magic upon the daughters of breakfast-food and bathtub kings. Part of this misconception, I suppose, has its roots in the gaudy imbecilities of the yellow press, but there is also a part that belongs to the general American tradition, along with the oppression of minorities and the belief in political panaceas. Its depth and extent are constantly revealed by the naïve assumption that the so-called fashionable folk of the large cities—chiefly wealthy industrials in the interior-decorator and country-club stage of culture—constitute an aristocracy, and by the scarcely less remarkable assumption that the peerage of England is identical with the gentry—that is, that

286

such men as Lord Northcliffe, Lord Iveagh and even Lord Reading are English gentlemen, and of the ancient line of the Percys.

Here, as always, the worshiper is the father of the gods, and no less when they are evil than when they are benign. The inferior man must find himself superiors, that he may marvel at his political equality with them, and in the absence of recognizable superiors *de facto* he creates superiors *de jure*. The sublime principle of one man, one vote must be translated into terms of dollars, diamonds, fashionable intelligence; the equality of all men before the law must have clear and dramatic proofs. Sometimes, perhaps, the thing goes further and is more subtle. The inferior man needs an aristocracy to demonstrate not only his mere equality, but also his actual superiority. The society columns in the newspapers may have some such origin: they may visualize once more the accomplished journalist's understanding of the mob mind that he plays upon so skillfully, as upon some immense and cacophonous organ, always going *fortissimo*. What the inferior man and his wife see in the sinister revels of those amazing first families, I suspect, is often a massive witness to their own higher rectitude—to their relative innocence of cigarette-smoking, poodle-coddling, child-farming and the more abstruse branches of adultery—in brief, to their firmer grasp upon the immutable axioms of Christian virtue, the one sound boast of the nether nine-tenths of humanity in every land under the cross.

But this bugaboo aristocracy, as I hint, is actually bogus, and the evidence of its bogusness lies in the fact that it is insecure. One gets into it only onerously, but out of it very easily. Entrance is effected by dint of a long and bitter struggle, and the chief incidents of that struggle are almost intolerable humiliations. The aspirant must school and steel himself to sniffs and sneers; he must see the door slammed upon him a hundred times before ever it is thrown open to him. To get in at all he must show a talent for abasement—and abasement makes him timorous. Worse, that timorousness is not cured when he succeeds at last. On the contrary, it is made even more tremulous, for what he faces within the gates is a scheme of things made up almost wholly of harsh and often unintelligible taboos, and the penalty for violating even the least of them is swift and disastrous. He must exhibit exactly the right social habits, appetites and prejudices, public and private. He must harbor exactly the right political enthusiasms and indignations. He must have a hearty taste for exactly the right sports. His attitude toward the fine arts must be properly tolerant and yet not a shade too eager. He must read and like exactly the right books, pamphlets and public journals. He must put up at the right hotels when he travels. His wife must patronize the right milliners. He himself must stick to the right haberdashery. He must live in the right neighborhood. He must even embrace the right doctrines of religion. It would ruin him, for all opera box and society column purposes, to set up a plea for justice to the Bolsheviki, or even for ordinary decency. It would ruin him equally to wear celluloid collars, or to move to Union Hill, N.J., or to serve ham and cabbage at his table. And it would ruin him, too, to drink coffee from his saucer, or to marry a chambermaid with a gold tooth, or to join the Seventh Day Adventists. Within the boundaries of his curious order he is worse fettered than a monk in a cell. Its obscure conception of propriety, its nebulous notion that this or that is honorable, hampers him in every direction, and very narrowly. What he resigns when he enters, even when he makes his first deprecating knock at the door, is every right to attack the ideas that happen to prevail within. Such as they are, he must accept them without question. And as they shift and change in response to great instinctive movements (or perhaps, now and then, to the punished but not to be forgotten revolts of extraordinary rebels) he must shift and change with them, silently and quickly. To hang back, to challenge and dispute, to preach reforms and revolutions—these are crimes against the brummagem Holy Ghost of the order.

Obviously, that order cannot constitute a genuine aristocracy, in any rational sense. A genuine aristocracy is grounded upon very much different principles. Its first and most salient character is its interior security, and the chief visible evidence of that security is the freedom that goes with it—not only freedom in act, the divine right of the aristocrat to do what he jolly well pleases, so long as he does not violate the primary guarantees and obligations of his class, but also and more importantly freedom in thought, the liberty to try and err, the right to be his own man. It is the instinct of a true aristocracy, not to punish eccentricity by explusion, but to throw a mantle of protection about it—to safeguard it from the suspicions and resentments of the lower orders. Those lower orders are inert, timid, inhospitable to ideas, hostile to changes, faithful to a few maudlin superstitions. All progress goes on on the higher levels. It is there that salient personalities, made secure by artificial immunities, may oscillate most widely from the normal track. It is within that entrenched fold, out of reach of the immemorial certainties of the mob, that extraordinary men of the lower orders may find their city of refuge, and breathe a clear air. This, indeed, is at once the hall-mark and the justification of an aristocracy—that it is beyond responsibility to the general masses of men, and hence superior to both their degraded longings and their no less degraded aversions. It is nothing if it is not autonomous, curious, venturesome, courageous, and everything if it is. It is the custodian of the qualities that make for change and experiment; it is the class that organizes danger to the service of the race; it pays for its high prerogatives by standing in the forefront of the fray.

No such aristocracy, it must be plain, is now on view in the United States. The makings of one were visible in the Virginia of the later eighteenth century, but with Jefferson and Washington the promise died. In New England, it seems to me, there was never any aristocracy, either in being or in nascency: there was only a theocracy that degenerated very quickly into a plutocracy on the one hand and a caste of sterile *Gelehrten* on the other—the passion for God splitting into a lust for dollars and a weakness for mere words. Despite the common notion to the contrary—a notion generated by confusing literacy with intelligence—New England has never shown the slightest sign of a genuine enthusiasm for ideas. It began its history as a slaughter-house of ideas, and it is to-day not easily distinguishable from a cold-storage plant. Its celebrated adventures in mysticism, once apparently so bold and significant, are now seen to have been little more than an elaborate hocus-pocus—respectable Unitarians shocking the peasantry and scaring the horned cattle in the fields by masquerading in the robes of Rosicrucians. The ideas that it embraced in those austere and far-off days were stale, and when it had finished with them they were dead: to-day one hears of Jakob Bohme almost as rarely as one hears of Allen G. Thurman. So in politics. Its glory is Abolition—an English invention, long under the interdict of the native plutocracy. Since the Civil War its six states have produced fewer political ideas, as political ideas run in the Republic, than any average county in Kansas or Nebraska. Appomattox seemed to be a victory for New England idealism. It was actually a victory for the New England plutocracy, and that plutocracy has dominated thought above the Housatonic ever since. The sect of professional idealists has so far dwindled that it has ceased to be of any importance, even as an opposition. When the plutocracy is challenged now, it is challenged by the proletariat.

Well, what is on view in New England is on view in all other parts of the nation, sometimes with ameliorations, but usually with the colors merely exaggerated. What one beholds, sweeping the eye over the land, is a culture that, like the national literature, is in three layers—the plutocracy on top, a vast mass of undifferentiated human blanks at the bottom, and a forlorn *intelligentsia* gasping out a precarious life between. I need not set out at any length, I hope, the intellectual deficiencies of the plutocracy—its utter failure to show anything even remotely resembling the makings of an aristocracy. It is badly educated, it is stupid, it is full of low-caste superstitions and indignations, it is without decent traditions or informing vision; above all, it is extraordinarily lacking in the most elemental independence and courage. Out of this class comes the grotesque fashionable society of our big towns, already described. Imagine a horde of peasants incredibly enriched and with almost infinite power thrust into their hands, and you will have a fair picture of its habitual state of mind. It shows all the stigmata of inferiority—moral certainty, cruelty, suspicion of ideas, fear. Never did it function more revealingly than in the late *pogrom* against the so-called Reds, *i.e.*, against humorless idealists who, like Andrew Jackson, took the platitudes of democracy quite seriously. The machinery brought to bear upon these feeble and scattered fanatics would have almost sufficed to repel an invasion by the united powers of Europe. They were hunted out of their sweat-shops and coffee-houses as if they were so many Carranzas or Ludendorffs, dragged to jail to the tooting of horns, arraigned before quaking judges on unintelligible charges, condemned to deportation without the slightest chance to defend themselves, torn from their dependent families, herded into prison-ships, and then finally dumped in a snow waste, to be rescued and fed by the Bolsheviki. And what was the theory at the bottom of all these astounding proceedings? So far as it can be reduced to comprehensible terms it was much less a theory than a fear—a shivering, idiotic, discreditable fear of a mere banshee—an overpowering, paralyzing dread that some extra-eloquent Red, permitted to emit his balderdash unwhipped, might eventually convert a couple of courageous men, and that the courageous men, filled with indignation against the plutocracy, might take to the highroad, burn down a nail-factory or two, and slit the throat of some virtuous profiteer. In order to lay this fear, in order to ease the jangled nerves of the American successors to the Hapsburgs and Hohenzollerns, all the constitutional guarantees of the citizen were suspended, the statute-books were burdened with laws that surpass anything heard of in the Austria of Maria Theresa, the country was handed over to a frenzied mob of detectives, informers and *agents provoca-*

teurs—and the Reds departed laughing loudly, and were hailed by the Bolsheviki as innocents escaped from an asylum for the criminally insane.

Obviously, it is out of reason to look for any hospitality to ideas in a class so extravagantly fearful of even the most palpably absurd of them. Its philosophy is firmly grounded upon the thesis that the existing order must stand forever free from attack, and not only from attack, but also from mere academic criticism, and its ethics are as firmly grounded upon the thesis that every attempt at any such criticism is a proof of moral turpitude. Within its own ranks, protected by what may be regarded as the privilege of the order, there is nothing to take the place of this criticism. A few feeble platitudes by Andrew Carnegie and a book of moderate merit by John D. Rockefeller's press-agent constitute almost the whole of the interior literature of ideas. In other countries the plutocracy has often produced men of reflective and analytical habit, eager to rationalize its instincts and to bring it into some sort of relationship to the main streams of human thought. The case of David Ricardo at once comes to mind. There have been many others: John Bright, Richard Cobden, George Grote, and, in our own time, Walther von Rathenau. But in the United States no such phenomenon has been visible. There was a day, not long ago, when certain young men of wealth gave signs of an unaccustomed interest in ideas on the political side, but the most they managed to achieve was a banal sort of Socialism, and even this was abandoned in sudden terror when the war came, and Socialism fell under suspicion of being genuinely international—in brief, of being honest under the skin. Nor has the plutocracy of the country ever fostered an inquiring spirit among its intellectual valets and footmen, which is to say, among the gentlemen who compose headlines and leading articles for its newspapers. What chiefly distinguishes the daily press of the United States from the press of all other countries pretending to culture is not its lack of truthfulness or even its lack of dignity and honor, for these deficiencies are common to the newspaper everywhere, but its incurable fear of ideas, its constant effort to evade the discussion of fundamentals by translating all issues into a few elemental fears, its incessant reduction of all reflection to mere emotion. It is, in the true sense, never well-informed. It is seldom intelligent, save in the arts of the mob-master. It is never courageously honest. Held harshly to a rigid correctness of opinion by the plutocracy that controls it with less and less attempt at disguise, and menaced on all sides by censorships that it dare not flout, it sinks rapidly into formalism and feebleness. Its yellow section is perhaps its most respectable section for there the only vestige of the old free journalist survives. In the more conservative papers one finds only a timid and petulant animosity to all questioning of the existing order, however urbane and sincere—a pervasive and ill-concealed dread that the mob now heated up against the orthodox hobgoblins may suddenly begin to unearth hobgoblins of its own, and so run amok. For it is upon the emotions of the mob, of course, that the whole comedy is played. Theoretically the mob is the repository of all political wisdom and virtue; actually it is the ultimate source of all political power. Even the plutocracy cannot make war upon it openly, or forget the least of its weaknesses. The business of keeping it in order must be done discreetly, warily, with delicate technique. In the main that business consists of keeping alive its deep-seated fears—of strange faces, of unfamiliar ideas, of unhackneyed gestures, of untested liberties and responsibilities. The one permanent emotion of the inferior man, as of all the simpler mammals, is fear—fear of the unknown, the complex, the inexplicable. What he wants beyond everything else is safety. His instincts incline him toward a society so organized that it will protect him at all hazards, and not only against perils to his hide but also against assaults upon his mind—against the need to grapple with the unaccustomed problems, to weigh ideas, to think things out for himself, to scrutinize the platitudes upon which his everyday thinking is based. Content under kaiserism so long as it functions efficiently, he turns, when kaiserism falls, to some other and perhaps worse form of paternalism, bringing to its benign tyranny only the docile tribute of his pathetic allegiance. In America it is the newspaper that is his boss. From it he gets support for his elemental illusions. In it he sees a visible embodiment of his own wisdom and consequence. Out of it he draws fuel for his simple moral passion, his congenital suspicion of heresy, his dread of the unknown. And behind the newspaper stands the plutocracy, ignorant, unimaginative and timorous.

Thus at the top and at the bottom. Obviously, there is no aristocracy here. One finds only one of the necessary elements, and that only in the plutocracy, to wit, a truculent egoism. But where is intelligence? Where are ease and surety of manner? Where are enterprise and curiosity? Where, above all, is courage, and in particular, moral courage—the capacity for independent thinking, for difficult problems, for what Nietzsche called the joys of the labyrinth? As well look for these things in a society of half-wits. Democracy, obliterating the old aristocracy, has left only a vacuum in its place; in a century and a half it has failed either to lift up the mob to intellectual autonomy and dignity or to purge the plutocracy of its inherent stupidity and swinishness. It is precisely here, the first and favorite scene of the Great Experiment, that the culture of the individual has been reduced to the most rigid and absurd regimentation. It is precisely here, of all civilized countries, that eccentricity in demeanor and opinion has come to bear the heaviest penalties. The whole drift of our law is toward the absolute prohibition of all ideas that diverge in the slightest from the accepted platitudes, and behind that drift of law there is a far more potent force of growing custom, and under that custom there is a national philosophy which erects conformity into the noblest of virtues and the free functioning of personality into a capital crime against society.

THE ANGLO-SAXON

When I speak of Anglo-Saxons, of course, I speak inexactly and in the common phrase. Even within the bounds of that phrase the American of the dominant stock is Anglo-Saxon only partially, for there is probably just as much Celtic blood in his veins as Germanic, and his norm is to be found, not south of the Tyne and west of the Severn, but on the two sides of the northern border. Among the first English colonists there were many men of almost pure Teutonic stock from the east and south of England, and their influence is yet visible in many characteristic American folkways, in certain traditional American ideas—some of them now surviving only in national hypocrisies —and, above all, in the fundamental peculiarities of the American dialect of English. But their Teutonic blood was early diluted by Celtic strains from Scotland, from the north of Ireland, from Wales, and from the west of England, and today those Americans who are regarded as being most thoroughly Anglo-Saxons—for example, the mountaineers of the Appalachian slopes from Pennsylvania to Georgia —are obviously far more Celtic than Teutonic, not only physically but also mentally. They are leaner and taller than the true English, and far more given to moral obsessions and religious fanaticism. A Methodist revival is not an English phenomenon; it is Welsh. So is the American tendency, marked by every foreign student of our history, to turn all political combats into moral crusades. The English themselves, of course, have been greatly polluted by Scotch, Irish and Welsh blood during the past three centuries, and for years past their government has been largely in the hands of Celts, but though this fact, by making them more like Americans, has tended to conceal the difference that I am discussing, it has certainly not sufficed to obliterate it altogether. The English notion of humor remains different from the American notion, and so does the English view of personal liberty, and on the same level of primary ideas there are many other obvious differences.

But though I am thus convinced that the American Anglo-Saxon wears a false label, and grossly libels both of the great races from which he claims descent, I can imagine no good in trying to change it. Let him call himself whatever he pleases. Whatever he calls himself, it must be plain that the term he uses designates a genuinely distinct and differentiated race—that he is separated definitely, in character and habits of thought, from the men of all other recognizable strains—that he represents, among the peoples of the earth, almost a special species, and that he runs true to type. The traits that he developed when the first mixture of races took place in colonial days are the traits that he still shows; despite the vast changes in his material environment, he is almost precisely the same, in the way he thinks and acts, as his forefathers were. Some of the other great races of men, during the past two centuries, have changed very noticeably, but the American Anglo-Saxon has stuck to his hereditary guns. Moreover, he tends to show much less variation than other races between man and man. No other race, save it be the Chinese, is so thoroughly regimented.

The good qualities of this so-called Anglo-Saxon are many, and I am certainly not disposed to question them, but I here pass them over without apology, for he devotes practically the whole of his literature and fully a half of his oral discourse to celebrating them himself, and so there is no danger that they will ever be disregarded. No other known man, indeed, is so violently the blowhard, save it be his English kinsman. In this fact lies the first cause of the ridiculous figure he commonly cuts in the eyes of other people: he brags and blusters so incessantly that, if he actually had the combined virtues of Socrates, the Cid and the Twelve Apostles, he would still go beyond the facts, and so appear a mere Bombastes Furioso. This habit, I believe, is fundamentally English, but it has been exaggerated in the Americano by his larger admixture of Celtic blood. In late years in America it has taken on an almost pathological character, and is to be explained, perhaps, only in terms of the Freudian necromancy. Braggadocio, in the 100% American—"we won the war," "it is our duty to lead the world," and so on—is probably no more than a protective mechanism erected to conceal an inescapable sense of inferiority.

That this inferiority is real must be obvious to any impartial observer. Whenever the Anglo-Saxon, whether of the English or of the American variety, comes into sharp conflict with men of other stocks, he tends to be worsted, or, at best, to be forced back upon extraneous and irrelevant aids to assist him in the struggle. Here in the United States his defeat is so palpable that it has filled him with vast alarms, and reduced him to seeking succor in grotesque and extravagent devices. In the fine arts, in the sciences and even in the more complex sorts of business the children of the later immigrants are running away from the descendants of the early settlers. To call the roll of Americans eminent in almost any field of human endeavor above the most elemental is to call a list of strange and often outlandish names; even the panel of Congress presents a startling example. Of the Americans who have come into notice during the past fifty years as poets, as novelists, as critics, as painters, as sculptors and in the minor arts, less than half bear Anglo-Saxon names, and in this minority there are few of pure Anglo-Saxon blood. So in the sciences. So in the higher reaches of engineering and technology. So in philosophy and its branches. So even in industry and agriculture. In those areas where the competition between the new and the old bloodstreams is most sharp and clearcut, say in New York, in seaboard New England and in the farming States of the upper Middle West, the defeat of the so-called Anglo-Saxon is overwhelming and unmistakable. Once his predominance everywhere was actual and undisputed; today, even where he remains superior numerically, it is largely sentimental and illusory.

The descendants of the later immigrants tend generally to move upward; the descendants of the first settlers, I believe, tend plainly to move downward, mentally, spiritually and even physically. Civilization is at its lowest mark in the United States precisely in those areas where the Anglo-Saxon still presumes to rule. He runs the whole South—and in the whole South there are not as many first-rate men as in many a single city of the mongrel North. Wherever he is still firmly in the saddle, there we look for such pathological phenomena as Fundamentalism, Prohibition and Ku Kluxery, and there they flourish. It is not in the northern cities, with their mixed population, that the death-rate is highest, and politics most corrupt, and religion nearest to voodooism, and every decent human aspiration suspect; it is in the areas that the recent immigrations have not penetrated, where "the purest Anglo-Saxon blood in the world" still flows. I could pile up evidences, but they are not necessary. The fact is too plain to be challenged. One testimony will be sufficient: it comes from two inquirers who made an exhaustive survey of a region in southeastern Ohio, where "the people are more purely Americans than in the rest of the state":

> Here gross superstition exercises strong control over the thought and action of a large proportion of the people. Syphilitic and other venereal diseases are common and increasing over the whole counties, while in some communities nearly every family is afflicted with inherited or infectious disease. Many cases of incest are known; imbreeding is rife. Imbeciles, feeble-minded, and delinquents are numerous, politics is corrupt, and selling of votes is common, petty crimes abound, the schools have been badly managed and poorly attended. Cases of rape, assault, and robbery are of almost weekly occurrence within five minutes' walk of the corporation limits of one of the county seats, while in another county political control is held by a self-confessed criminal. Alcoholic intemperance is excessive. Gross immorality and its evil results are by no means confined to the hill districts, but are extreme also in the towns.[1]

As I say, the American of the old stock is not unaware of this steady, and, of late, somewhat rapid deterioration—this gradual loss of his old mastery in the land his ancestors helped to wring from

[1] Since the above was written there has been unqualified confirmation of it by a distinguished English authority, to wit, Arnold J. Toynbee. See his Study of History, Vol. I, pp. 466–67, and Vol. II, pp. 311–12.

the Indian and the wildcat. He senses it, indeed, very painfully, and, as if in despair of arresting it in fact, makes desperate efforts to dispose of it by denial and concealment. These efforts often take grotesque and extravagant forms. Laws are passed to hobble and cage the citizen of newer stocks in a hundred fantastic ways. It is made difficult and socially dangerous for him to teach his children the speech of his fathers, or to maintain the cultural attitudes that he has inherited from them. Every divergence from the norm of the low-cast Anglo-Saxon is treated as an *attentat* against the commonwealth, and punished with eager ferocity.

It so happens that I am myself an Anglo-Saxon—one of far purer blood, indeed, than most of the half-bleached Celts who pass under the name in the United States and England. I am in part Angle and in part Saxon, and what else I am is safely white, Nordic, Protestant and blond. Thus I feel free, without risk of venturing into bad taste, to regard frankly the *soi-disant* Anglo-Saxon of this incomparable Republic and his rather less dubious cousin of the Motherland. How do the two appear to me, after years spent largely in accumulating their disfavor? What are the characters that I discern most clearly in the so-called Anglo-Saxon type of man? I may answer at once that two stick out above all others. One is his curious and apparently incurable incompetence—his congenital inability to do any difficult thing easily and well, whether it be isolating a bacillus or writing a sonata. The other is his astounding susceptibility to fears and alarms—in short, his hereditary cowardice.

To accuse so enterprising and successful a race of cowardice, of course, is to risk immediate derision; nevertheless, I believe that a fair-minded examination of its history will bear me out. Nine-tenths of the great feats of derring-do that its sucklings are taught to venerate in school—that is, its feats as a race, not the isolated exploits of its extraordinary individuals, most of them at least partly of other stocks—have been wholly lacking in even the most elementary gallantry. Consider, for example, the events attending the extension of the two great empires, English and American. Did either movement evoke any genuine courage and resolution? The answer is plainly no. Both empires were built up primarily by swindling and butchering unarmed savages, and after that by robbing weak and friendless nations. Neither produced a hero above the average run of those in the movies; neither exposed the folks at home to any serious danger of reprisal. Almost always, indeed, mercenaries have done the Anglo-Saxon's fighting for him—a high testimony to his common sense, but scarcely flattering, I fear, to the truculence he boasts of. The British empire was won mainly by Irishmen, Scotchmen and native allies, and the American empire, at least in large part, by Frenchmen and Spaniards. Moreover, neither great enterprise cost any appreciable amount of blood; neither presented grave and dreadful risks; neither exposed the conqueror to the slightest danger of being made the conquered. The British won most of their vast dominions without having to stand up in a single battle against a civilized and formidable foe, and the Americanos won their continent at the expense of a few dozen puerile skirmishes with savages. The total cost of conquering the whole area from Plymouth Rock to the Golden Gate and from Lake George to the Everglades, including even the cost of driving out the French, Dutch, English and Spaniards, was less than the cost of defending Verdun.

So far as I can make out there is no record in history of any Anglo-Saxon nation entering upon any great war without allies. The French have done it, the Dutch have done it, the Germans have done it, the Japs have done it, and even such inferior nations as the Danes, the Spaniards, the Boers and the Greeks have done it, but never the English or Americans. Can you imagine the United States resolutely facing a war in which the odds against it were as huge as they were against Spain in 1898? The facts of history are wholly against any such fancy. The Anglo-Saxon always tries to take a gang with him when he goes into battle, and even when he has it behind him he is very uneasy, and prone to fall into panic at the first threat of genuine danger. Here I put an unimpeachably Anglo-Saxon witness on the stand, to wit, the late Charles W. Eliot. I find him saying, in an article quoted with approbation by the *Congressional Record*, that during the Revolutionary War the colonists now hymned so eloquently in the school-books "fell into a condition of despondency from which nothing but the steadfastness of Washington and the Continental army *and the aid from France* saved them," and that "when the War of 1812 brought grave losses a considerable portion of the population experienced a moral collapse, from which they were rescued only by the exertions of a few thoroughly patriotic statesmen and the exploits of three or four American frigates on the seas"—to say nothing of an enterprising Corsican gentleman, Bonaparte by name.

In both these wars the Americans had enormous and obvious advantages, in terrain, in allies and in men; nevertheless, they fought, in the main, very badly, and from the first shot to the last a majority of them stood in favor of making peace on almost any terms. The

Mexican and Spanish Wars I pass over as perhaps too obscenely ungallant to be discussed at all; of the former, U. S. Grant, who fought in it, said that it was "the most unjust war ever waged by a stronger against a weaker nation." Who remembers that, during the Spanish War, the whole Atlantic Coast trembled in fear of the Spaniards' feeble fleet—that all New England had hysterics every time a strange coal-barge was sighted on the sky-line, that the safe-deposit boxes of Boston were emptied and their contents transferred to Worcester, and that the Navy had to organize a patrol to save the coast towns from depopulation? Perhaps those Reds, atheists and pro-Germans remember it who also remember that during World War I the entire country went wild with fear of an enemy who, without the aid of divine intervention, obviously could not strike it a blow at all—and that the great moral victory was gained at last with the assistance of twenty-one allies and at odds of eight to one.[2]

But the American Civil War remains? Does it, indeed? The almost unanimous opinion of the North, in 1861, was that it would be over after a few small battles; the first soldiers were actually enlisted for but three months. When, later on, it turned unexpectedly into a severe struggle, recruits had to be driven to the front by force, and the only Northerners remaining in favor of going on were Abraham Lincoln, a few ambitious generals and the profiteers. I turn to Dr. Eliot again. "In the closing year of the war," he says, "large portions of the Democatic party in the North *and of the Republican party,* advocated surrender to the Confederacy, *so downhearted were they.*" Downhearted at odds of three to one! The South was plainly more gallant, but even the gallantry of the South was largely illusory. The Confederate leaders, when the war began, adopted at once the traditional Anglo-Saxon device of seeking allies. They tried and expected to get the aid of England, and they actually came very near succeeding. When hopes in that direction began to fade (*i.e.,* when England concluded that tackling the North would be dangerous), the common people of the Confederacy threw up the sponge, and so the catastrophe, when it came at last, was mainly internal. The South failed to bring the quaking North to a standstill because, to borrow

---

[2] The case of World War II was even more striking. The two enemies that the United States tackled had been softened by years of a hard struggle with desperate foes, and those foes continued to fight on. Neither enemy could muster even a tenth of the materials that the American forces had the use of. And at the end both were outnumbered in men by odds truly enormous.

a phrase that Dr. Eliot uses in another connection, it "experienced a moral collapse of unprecedented depth and duration." The folks at home failed to support the troops in the field, and the troops in the field began to desert. Even so early as Shiloh, indeed, many Confederate regiments were already refusing to fight.

This reluctance for desperate chances and hard odds, so obvious in the military record of the English-speaking nations, is also conspicuous in times of peace. What a man of another and superior stock almost always notices, living among so-called Anglo-Saxons, is (a) their incapacity for prevailing in fair rivalry, either in trade, in the fine arts or in what is called learning—in brief, their general incompetence, and (b) their invariable effort to make up for this incapacity by putting some inequitable burden upon their rivals, usually by force. The Frenchman, I believe, is the worst of chauvinists, but once he admits a foreigner to his country he at least treats that foreigner fairly, and does not try to penalize him absurdly for his mere foreignness. The Anglo-Saxon American is always trying to do it; his history is a history of recurrent outbreaks of blind rage against peoples who have begun to worst him. Such movements would be inconceivable in an efficient and genuinely self-confident people, wholly assured of their superiority, and they would be equally inconceivable in a truly gallant and courageous people, disdaining unfair advantages and overwhelming odds. Theoretically launched against some imaginary inferiority in the non-Anglo-Saxon man, either as patriot, as democrat or as Christian, they are actually launched at his general superiority, his greater fitness to survive in the national environment. The effort is always to penalize him for winning in fair fight, to handicap him in such a manner that he will sink to the general level of the Anglo-Saxon population, and, if possible, even below it. Such devices, of course, never have the countenance of the Anglo-Saxon minority that is authentically superior, and hence self-confident and tolerant. But that minority is pathetically small, and it tends steadily to grow smaller and feebler. The communal laws and the communal *mores* are made by the folk, and they offer all the proof that is necessary, not only of its general inferiority, but also of its alarmed awareness of that inferiority. The normal American of the "pure-blooded" majority goes to rest every night with an uneasy feeling that there is a burglar under the bed, and he gets up every morning with a sickening fear that his underwear has been stolen.

This Anglo-Saxon of the great herd is, in many important respects, the least civilized of white men and the least capable of true civilization. His political ideas are crude and shallow. He is almost wholly devoid of esthetic feeling. The most elementary facts about the visible universe alarm him, and incite him to put them down. Educate him, make a professor of him, teach him how to express his soul, and he still remains palpably third-rate. He fears ideas almost more cravenly than he fears men. His blood, I believe, is running thin; perhaps it was not much to boast of at the start; in order that he may exercise any functions above those of a trader, a pedagogue or a mob orator, it needs the stimulus of other and less exhausted strains. The fact that they increase is the best hope of civilization in America. They shake the old race out of its spiritual lethargy, and introduce it to disquiet and experiment. They make for a free play of ideas. In opposing the process, whether in politics, in letters or in the ages-long struggle toward the truth, the prophets of Anglo-Saxon purity and tradition only make themselves ridiculous.

THE LIBIDO FOR THE UGLY

On a Winter day some years ago, coming out of Pittsburgh on one of the expresses of the Pennsylvania Railroad, I rolled eastward for an hour through the coal and steel towns of Westmoreland county. It was familiar ground; boy and man, I had been through it often before. But somehow I had never quite sensed its appalling desolation. Here was the very heart of industrial America, the center of its most lucrative and characteristic activity, the boast and pride of the richest and grandest nation ever seen on earth—and here was a scene so dreadfully hideous, so intolerably bleak and forlorn that it reduced the whole aspiration of man to a macabre and depressing joke. Here was wealth beyond computation, almost beyond imagination—and here were human habitations so abominable that they would have disgraced a race of alley cats.

I am not speaking of mere filth. One expects steel towns to be dirty. What I allude to is the unbroken and agonizing ugliness, the sheer revolting monstrousness, of every house in sight. From East Liberty to Greensburg, a distance of twenty-five miles, there was not one in sight from the train that did not insult and lacerate the eye. Some were so bad, and they were among the most pretentious—churches, stores, warehouses, and the like—that they were downright startling; one blinked before them as one blinks before a man with his face shot away. A few linger in memory, horrible even there: a crazy little church just west of Jeannette, set like a dormer-window on the side of a bare, leprous hill; the headquarters of the Veterans of Foreign Wars at another forlorn town, a steel stadium like a huge rat-trap somewhere further down the line. But most of all I recall the general effect—of hideousness without a break. There was not a single decent house within eye-range from the Pittsburgh suburbs to the Greensburg yards. There was not one that was not misshapen, and there was not one that was not shabby.

The country itself is not uncomely, despite the grime of the endless mills. It is, in form, a narrow river valley, with deep gullies running up into the hills. It is thickly settled, but not noticeably overcrowded. There is still plenty of room for building, even in the larger towns, and there are very few solid blocks. Nearly every house, big and little, has space on all four sides. Obviously, if there were architects of any professional sense or dignity in the region, they would have perfected a chalet to hug the hillsides—a chalet with a high-pitched roof, to throw off the heavy winter snows, but still essentially a low and clinging building, wider than it was tall. But what have they done? They have taken as their model a brick set on end. This they have converted into a thing of dingy clapboards, with a narrow, low-pitched roof. And the whole they have set upon thin, preposterous brick piers. By the hundreds and thousands these abominable houses cover the bare hillsides, like gravestones in some gigantic and decaying cemetery. On their deep sides they are three, four and even five stories high; on their low sides they bury themselves swinishly in the mud. Not a fifth of them are perpendicular. They lean this way and that, hanging on to their bases precariously. And one and all they are streaked in grime, with dead and eczematous patches of paint peeping through the streaks.

Now and then there is a house of brick. But what brick! When it is new it is the color of a fried egg. When it has taken on the patina of the mills it is the color of an egg long past all hope or caring. Was it necessary to adopt that shocking color? No more than it was necessary to set all of the houses on end. Red brick, even in a steel town, ages with some dignity. Let it become downright black, and it is still sightly, especially if its trimmings are of white stone, with soot in the depths and the high spots washed by the rain. But in Westmoreland they prefer that uremic yellow, and so they have the most loathsome towns and villages ever seen by mortal eye.

I award this championship only after laborious research and incessant prayer. I have seen, I believe, all of the most unlovely towns of the world; they are all to be found in the United States. I have seen the mill towns of decomposing New England and the desert towns of Utah, Arizona and Texas. I am familiar with the back streets of Newark, Brooklyn and Chicago, and have made scientific explorations to Camden, N.J. and Newport News, Va. Safe in a Pullman, I have whirled through the gloomy, God-forsaken villages of Iowa and Kansas, and the malarious tide-water hamlets of Georgia. I have been to Bridgeport, Conn., and to Los Angeles. But nowhere on this earth, at home or abroad, have I seen anything to compare to the villages that huddle along the line of the Pennsylvania from the Pittsburgh yards to Greensburg. They are incomparable in color, and they are incomparable in design. It is as if some titanic and aberrant genius, uncompromisingly inimical to man, had devoted all the ingenuity of Hell to the making of them. They show grotesqueries of ugliness that, in retrospect, become almost diabolical. One cannot imagine mere human beings concocting such dreadful things, and one can scarcely imagine human beings bearing life in them.

Are they so frightful because the valley is full of foreigners— dull, insensate brutes, with no love of beauty in them? Then why didn't these foreigners set up similar abominations in the countries that they came from? You will, in fact, find nothing of the sort in Europe—save perhaps in the more putrid parts of England. There is scarcely an ugly village on the whole Continent. The peasants, however poor, somehow manage to make themselves graceful and charming habitations, even in Spain. But in the American village and small town the pull is always toward ugliness, and in that Westmoreland valley it has been yielded to with an eagerness bordering upon passion. It is incredible that mere ignorance should have achieved such masterpieces of horror.

On certain levels of the American race, indeed, there seems to be a positive libido for the ugly, as on other and less Christian levels there is a libido for the beautiful. It is impossible to put down the wallpaper that defaces the average American home of the lower middle class to mere inadvertence, or to the obscene humor of the manufacturers. Such ghastly designs, it must be obvious, give a genuine delight to a certain type of mind. They meet, in some unfathomable way, its obscure and unintelligible demands. They caress it as "The Palms" caresses it, or the art of the movie, or jazz. The taste for them is as enigmatical and yet as common as the taste for dogmatic theology and the poetry of Edgar A. Guest.

Thus I suspect (though confessedly without knowing) that the vast majority of honest folk of Westmoreland county, and especially the 100% Americans among them, actually admire the houses they live in, and are proud of them. For the same money they could get vastly better ones, but they prefer what they have got. Certainly there was no pressure upon the Veterans of Foreign Wars to choose the dreadful edifice that bears their banner, for there are plenty of vacant buildings along the track-side, and some of them are appreciably better. They might, indeed, have built a better one of their own. But they chose that clapboarded horror with their eyes open, and having chosen it, they let it mellow into its present shocking depravity. They like it as it is: beside it, the Parthenon would no doubt offend them. In precisely the same way the authors of the rat-trap stadium that I have mentioned made a deliberate choice. After painfully designing and erecting it, they made it perfect in their own sight by putting a completely impossible pent-house, painted a staring yellow, on top of it. The effect is that of a fat woman with a black eye. It is that of a Presbyterian grinning. But they like it.

Here is something that the psychologists have so far neglected: the love of ugliness for its own sake, the lust to make the world intolerable. Its habitat is the United States. Out of the melting pot emerges a race which hates beauty as it hates truth. The etiology of this madness deserves a great deal more study than it has got. There must be causes behind it; it arises and flourishes in obedience to biological laws, and not as a mere act of God. What, precisely, are the terms of those laws? And why do they run stronger in America than elsewhere? Let some honest *Privat Dozent* in pathological sociology apply himself to the problem.

HUBERT SELBY, JR.

On August 17, 1961, a young trollop walked out of the obscurity of the back alleys of New York City into the equally obscure court-room of Provincetown, Massachusetts. Tralala was not a flesh and blood creature, but her brief career, lived out in the pages of the *Provincetown Review,* was so horrendous to the local interpreters of public morality that they brought her to trial.

Because it was impossible for her to appear in person, I was tried in her place. Poor Tralala, after a loveless life of mechanical lust which brought her to an early death, was not destined to rest in peace. Her shame was resurrected by a town in which the reality of her life was twisted into an obscenity.

WILLIAM V. WARD
Editor
Provincetown Review

"The prosecution of the editors of the *Provincetown Review,*" testified Allen Tate at the trial, "raises once more an issue which it seems that societies throughout history have not been able to settle. The issue may be stated as follows: Is a literary work of high merit to be condemned and suppressed because it presents odious scenes from human life, in odious language? . . .

"Everybody agrees that society has both the right and the duty to protect itself from the menace of disorder, whether the menace expresses itself in action or in print. But the agency, by means of which a democratic society may protect the immature mind from the corrupting influence of salacious literature, must be established with an authority which can be accepted as reasonable, objective, and superior to individual prejudice. In a civilized society, the police are not equipped to exercise this authority, but only to execute it. It is an authority which entails a complex responsibility with which they should not be burdened.

"The criterion by which such a work as 'Tralala' must be judged is not a criterion of what happens, to the subject as such, but rather a criterion of the total meaning of the work, a criterion of how the action progresses toward what end, not specific passages which in isolation may be offensive. I submit that the action, so understood, of 'Tralala' is deeply within the Christian scheme of morality. The destruction of the principal character is one of the most powerful scenes that I have anywhere read. I do not know of a more deeply realized exemplum of the Christian aphorism that the wages of sin is death. . . .

"If any young person could be attracted to sexual sin by this story, he would be a psychopathic case before he read it. I assume that the law exists for the protection of the public, not of psychopaths or the criminally insane."

TRALALA

Tralala was 15 the first time she was laid. There was no real passion. Just diversion. She hungout in the Greek's, an all nite diner near the Bklyn. Army base, with the other neighborhood kids. Nothing to do. Sit and talk. Listen to the Jukebox. Drink coffee. Bum cigarettes. Everything a drag. She said yes. In the park. 3 or 4 couples finding their own tree and grass. Yes. Actually she didn't say yes. She said nothing. Tony or Vinnie or whoever it was just continued. They all met later at the exit. They grinned at each other. The guys felt real sharp. The girls walked in front and talked about it. They giggled and alluded. Tralala shrugged her shoulders. Getting laid was getting laid. Why all the bullshit? She liked it but why the bullshit? She went to the park often. She always had her pick. The other girls were as willing, but played games. They liked to tease. And giggle. Tralala didn't fuckaround. Nobody likes a cockteaser. Either you put out or you don't. That's all. And she had big tits. She was built like a woman. Not like some kid. They preferred her. And even before the first summer was over she played games. Different ones though. She didn't tease the guys. No sense in that. Or money. Some of the girls bugged her and she broke their balls. If a girl liked one of the guys or tried to get him for any reason Tralala cut in. For kicks. The girls hated her. So what. Who needs them. The guys had what she wanted. Especially when they lushed a drunk. Or pulled a small burglary. She always got something out of it. They'd take her to the movies. Buy cigarettes. Go

to a PIZZERIA for pie. There was no end of drunks. Everybody had
money during the war. The waterfront was filled with drunken seamen. And of course the base was filled with doggies. And they were
always good for a few bucks at least. Sometimes more. And Tralala
always got her share. No tricks. All very simple. The guys had a ball
and she got a few bucks. If there was no room to go to there was
always the Wolffe Bldg. cellar. Miles and miles of cellar. One screwed
and the others played chick. Sometimes for hours. But she got what
she wanted. All she had to do was put out. It was kicks too. Sometimes.
If not, so what? It made no difference. Lay on your back. Or bend over
a garbage can. Better than working. And it's kicks. For a while anyway. But time always passes. They grew older. Weren't satisfied with
the few bucks they got from drunks. Why wait for a drunk to passout
after they've spent most of their loot. Drop them on their way back
to the Army base. Everynite dozens left Willies, a bar across the street
from the Greek's. They'd get them on their way back to the base or
the docks. They usually let the doggies go. They didn't have too much.
But the seamen were usually loaded. If they were too big or too sober
they'd hit them over the head with a brick. If they looked easy one
would hold him and the other(s) would lump him. A few times they got
one in the lot on 57th street. That was a ball. It was real dark back by
the fence. They'd hit him until their arms were tired. Good kicks. Then
a pie and beer. And Tralala. She was always there. As more time
passed they acquired valuable experience. They were more selective.
And stronger. They didn't need bricks anymore. They'd make the
rounds of the bars and spot some guy with a roll. When he left they'd
lush him. Sometimes Tralala would set him up. Walk him to a doorway. Sometimes through the lot. It worked beautifully. They all had
new clothes. Tralala dressed well. She wore a clean sweater every
few days. They had no trouble. Just stick to the seamen. They come
and go and who knows the difference. Who gives a shit. They have
more than they need anyway. And what's a few lumps. They might
get killed so what's the difference. They stayed away from the doggies.
Usually. They played it smart and nobody bothered them. But Tralala
wanted more than the small share she was getting. It was about time
she got something on her own. If she was going to get laid by a couple
of guys for a few bucks she figured it would be smarter to get laid
by one guy and get it all. All the drunks gave her the eye. It would
be a slopeout. Just be sure to pick a live one. Not some bum with a few
lousy bucks. None of that shit. She waited, alone, in the Greek's. A
doggie came in and ordered coffee and a hamburger. He asked her

if she wanted something. Why not. He smiled. He pulled a bill from
a thick roll and dropped it on the counter. She pushed her chest out.
He told her about his ribbons. And medals. Bronze star. And a purple-
heart with 2 oakleaf clusters. Been overseas 2 years. Going home. He
talked and slobbered and she smiled. She hoped he didn't have all
ones. She wanted to get him out before anybody else came. They got in
a cab and drove to a downtown hotel. He bought a bottle of whiskey and
they sat and drank and he talked. She kept filling his glass. He kept
talking. About the war. How he was shot up. About home. What he
was going to do. About the months in the hospital and all the operations. She kept pouring but he wouldn't pass out. The bastard. He said
he just wanted to be near her for a while. Talk to her and have a few
drinks. She waited. Cursed him and his goddam mother. And who
gives a shit about your leg getting all shotup. She had been there over
an hour. If he'd fucker maybe she could get the money out of his
pocket. But he just talked. The hell with it. She hit him over the head
with the bottle. She emptied his pockets and left. She took the money
out of his wallet and threw the wallet away. She counted it on the
subway. 50 bucks. Not bad. Never had this much at once before.
Should've gotten more though. Listenin to all that bullshit. Yeah. That
sonofabitch. I shoulda hitim again. A lousy 50 bucks and he's talkin
like a wheel or somethin. She kept 10 and stached the rest and hurried
back to the Greek's. Vinnie and Al were there and asked her where
she was. Alex here says ya cutout with a drunken doggie a couple
a hours ago. Yeah. Some creep. I thought he was loaded. Didju score?
Yeah. How much? 10 bucks. He kept bullshitin how much he had and
all he had was a lousy 10. Yeah? Let's see. She showed them the
money. Yasure that's all yagot? Ya wanna search me. Yathink I got
somethin stached up my ass or somethin? We'll take a look later.
Yeah. How about you? Score? We got a few. But you don't have to
worry about it. You got enough. She said nothing and shrugged her
shoulders. She smiled and offered to buy them coffee. And? Krist.
What a bunch of bloodsuckers. O.K. Hey Alex . . . They were still
sitting at the counter when the doggie came in. He was holding a
bloodied handkerchief to his head and blood had caked on his wrist
and cheek. He grabbed Tralala by the arm and pulled her from the
stool. Give me my wallet you goddamn whore. She spit in his face and
told him ta go fuck himself. Al and Vinnie pushed him against the
wall and asked him who he thought he was. Look, I don't know you
and you don't know me. I got no call to fight with you boys. All I
want is my wallet. I need my I D card or I can't get back in the base.

You can keep the goddamn money. I don't care. Tralala screamed in his face that he was a no good mother-fuckin sonofabitch and then started kicking him, afraid he might say how much she had taken. Ya lousy fuckin hero. Go peddle a couple a medals if yaneed money so fuckin bad. She spit in his face again, no longer afraid he might say something, but mad. Goddam mad. A lousy 50 bucks and he was cryin. And anyway, he should've had more. Ya lousy fuckin creep. She kicked him in the balls. He grabbed her again. He was crying and bent over struggling to breathe from the pain of the kick. If I don't have the pass I can't get in the base. I have to get back. They're going to fly me home tomorrow. I haven't been home for almost 3 years. I've been all shot up. Please PLEASE. Just the wallet. That's all I want. Just the I D card. PLEASE PLEASE!!! The tears streaked the caked blood and he hung on Vinnie's and Al's grip and Tralala swung at his face spitting, cursing, and kicking. Alex yelled to stop and get out. I don't want any trouble in here. Vinnie grabbed the doggie around the neck and Al shoved the bloodied handkerchief in his mouth and they dragged him outside and into a darkened doorway. He was still crying and begging for his I D card and trying to tell them he wanted to go home when Vinnie pulled his head up by his hair and Al punched him a few times in the stomach and then in the face, then held him up while Vinnie hit him a few times; but they tired of it soon, not afraid that the cops might come, but they knew he didn't have any money and they were tired from hitting the seaman they had lushed earlier, so they dropped him and he fell to the ground on his back. Before they left Tralala stomped on his face until both eyes were bleeding and his nose was split and broken then kicked him a few times in the balls. Ya rotten scumbag, then left and walked slowly to 4th avenue and took a subway to Manhattan. Just in case somebody might put up a stink. In a day or two he'll be shipped out and nobody'll know the difference. Just another fuckin doggie. And anyway he deserved it. They ate in a cafeteria and went to an all nite movie. The next day they got a couple of rooms in a hotel on the east side and stayed in Manhattan until the following nite. When they went back to the Greek's Alex told them some M.P.'s and a detective were in asking about the guys who beat up a soldier the other nite. They said he was in bad shape. Had to operate on him and he may go blind in one eye. Ain't that just too bad. The M.P.'s said if they get ahold of the guys who did it they'd killem. Those fuckin punks. Whad the law say. Nothing. You know. Yeah. Killus! The creeps. We outta dumpem on general principles. Tralala laughed. I shoulda pressed charges fa rape.

I won't be 18 for a week. He raped me the dirty freaky sonofabitch. They laughed and ordered coffee and when they finished Al and Vinnie figured they'd better make the rounds of a few of the bars and see what was doin. In one of the bars they noticed the bartender slip an envelope in a tin box behind the bar. It looked like a pile of bills on the bottom of the box. They checked the window in the MENS ROOM and the alley behind it then left and went back to the Greek's. They told Tralala what they were going to do and went to a furnished room they had rented over one of the bars on 1st Avenue. When the bars had closed they took a heavy duty screwdriver and walked to the bar. Tralala stood outside and watched the streets while they broke in. It only took a few minutes to force open the window, drop inside, crawl to the bar, pick up the box and climb out the window and drop to the alley. They pried open the box in the alley and started to count. They almost panicked when they finished counting. They had almost 2 thousand dollars. They stared at it for a moment then jammed it into their pockets. Then Vinnie took a few hundred and put it into another pocket and told Al they'd tell Tralala that that was all they got. They smiled and almost laughed then calmed themselves before leaving the alley and meeting Tralala. They took the box with them, and dropped it into a sewer then walked back to the room. When they stepped from the alley Tralala ran over to them asking them how they made out and how much they got. Vinnie told her to keep quiet that they got a couple a hundred and to play it cool until they got back to the room. When they got back to the room Al started telling her what a snap it was and how they just climbed in and took the box but Tralala ignored him and kept asking how much they got. Vinnie took the lump of money from the pocket and they counted it. Not bad eh Tral. 250 clams. Yeah. How about giving me 50 now? What for. You ain't going no where now. She shrugged and they went to bed. The next afternoon they went to the Greek's for coffee and two detectives came in and told them to come outside. They searched them took the money from their pockets and pushed them in their car. The detectives waved the money in front of their faces and shook their heads. Don't you know better than to knock over a bookie joint? Huh? Huh, Huh! Real clever aren't you. The detectives laughed and actually felt a professional amazement as they looked at their dumb expressions and realized that they really didn't know who they had robbed. Vinnie slowly started to come out of the coma and started to protest that they didn't do nothin. One of the detectives slapped his face and told him to shut up. For Christ's

sake don't give us any of that horseshit. I suppose you found a couple
of grand lying in an empty lot? Tralala screeched a what. The detectives looked at her briefly then turned back to Vinnie and Al. You
can lush a few drunken seamen now and then and get away with it,
but when you start taking money from my pocket you're going too far
Sonny. What a pair of stupid punks . . . OK sister, beat it. Unless you
want to come along for the ride? She automatically backed away from
the car, still staring at Vinnie and Al. The doors slammed shut and
they drove away. Tralala went back to the Greek's and sat at the
counter cursing Vinnie and Al and then the bulls for pickinem up before she could get hers. Didn't even spend a penny of it. The goddam
bastards. The rotten stinkin sonofabitches. Those thievin flatfooted
bastards. She sat drinking coffee all afternoon then left and went across
the street to Willie's. She walked to the end of the bar and started
talking with Rosie, the barmaid, telling her what happened, stopping
every few minutes to curse Vinnie, Al, the bulls and her lousy luck.
The bar was slowly filling and Rosie left her every few minutes to pour a
drink and when she came back Tralala would repeat the story from the
beginning, yelling about the 2 grand and they never even got a chance
ta spend a penny. With the repeating of the story she forgot about
Vinnie and Al and just cursed the bulls and her luck and an occasional
seaman or doggie who passed by and asked her if she wanted a drink or
just looked at her. Rosie kept filling Tralala's glass as soon as she
emptied it and told her to forget about it. That's the breaks. But there's
no sense in beatin yahead against the wall about it. There's plenty
more. Maybe not that much, but enough. Tralala snarled, finished her
drink and told Rosie to fill it up. Eventually she absorbed her anger
and quieted down and when a young seaman staggered over to her
she glanced at him and said yes. Rosie brought them two drinks and
smiled. Tralala watched him take the money out of his pocket and
figured it might be worthwhile. She told him there were better places
to drink than this crummy dump. Well lez go baby. He gulped his
drink and Tralala left hers on the bar and they left. They got into a cab
and the seaman asked her whereto and she said she didn't care, anywhere. O.K. Take us to Times Square. He offered her a cigarette and
started telling her about everything. His name was Harry. He came
from Idaho. He just got back from Italy. He was going to— She didn't
bother smiling but watched him trying to figure out how soon he
would pass out. Sometimes they last all nite. Can't really tell. She
relaxed and gave it thought. Can't konckim here. Just have to wait
until he passes out or maybe just askim for some money. The way

they throw it around. Just gotta getim in a room alone. If he don't pass out I'll just rapim with somethin—and you should've seen what we did to that little ol . . . He talked on and Tralala smoked and the lampposts flicked by and the meter ticked. He stopped talking when the cab stopped in front of the Crossroads. They got out and tried to get in the Crossroads but the bartender looked at the seaman and shook his head no. So they crossed the street to Diamond Jims. The bar was jammed, but they found a small table in the rear and sat down. They ordered drinks and Tralala sipped her then pushed her unfinished drink across the table to him when he finished his. He started talking again but the lights and the music slowly changed the subject matter and he started tellin Tralala what a lovely girl she was and what a good time he was going to show her; and she told him that she would show him the time of his life and didn't bother to hide a yawn. He beamed and drank faster and Tralala asked him if he would give her some money. She was broke and had to have some money or she'd be locked out of her room. He told her not to worry that he'd find a place for her to stay tonite and he winked and Tralala wanted to shove her cigarette into his face, the cheap sonofabitch, but figured she'd better wait and get his money before she did anything. He toyed with her hand and she looked around the bar and noticed an Army Officer staring at her. He had a lot of ribbons just like the one she had rolled and she figured he'd have more money than Harry. Officers are usually loaded. She got up from the table telling Harry she was going to the Ladies Room. The Officer swayed slightly as she walked up to him and smiled. He took her arm and asked her where she was going. Nowhere. O we can't have a pretty girl like you going nowhere. I have a place that's all empty and a sack of whiskey. Well . . . She told him to wait and went back to the table. Harry was almost asleep and she tried to get the money from his pocket and he started to stir. When his eyes opened she started shaking him, taking her hand out of his pocket, and telling him to wakeup. I thought yawere goin to show me a good time. You bet. He nodded his head and it slowly descended toward the table. Hey Harry, wakeup. The waiter wants to know if yahave any money. Show'em ya money so I won't have to pay. You bet. He slowly took the crumpled mess of bills from his pocket and Tralala grabbed it from his hand and said I toldya he had money. She picked up the cigarettes from the table, put the money in a pocket and walked back to the bar. My friend is sleeping so I don't think he'll mind, but I think we'd better leave. They left the bar and walked to his hotel. Tralala hoped she didn't make a mistake.

Harry mightta had more money stached somewhere. The Officer should have more though and anyway she probably got everything Harry had and she can get more from this jerk if he has any. She looked at him trying to determine how much he could have, but all Officers look the same. That's the trouble with a goddamn uniform. And then she wondered how much she had gotten from Harry and how long she would have to wait to count it. When they got to his room she went right into the bathroom, smoothed out the bills a little and counted it. 45. Shit. Fuckit. She folded the money, left the bathroom and stuffed the money in a coat pocket. He poured two small drinks and then sat and talked for a few minutes then put the lite out. Tralala figured there was no sense in trying anything now so she relaxed and enjoyed herself. They were having a smoke and another drink when he turned and kissed her and told her she had the most beautiful pair of tits he had ever seen. He continued talking for a few minutes, but she didn't pay any attention. She thought about her tits and what he had said and how she could get anybody with her tits and the hell with Willies and those slobs, she'd hang around here for a while and do alright. They put out their cigarettes and for the rest of the nite she didn't wonder how much money he had. At breakfast the next morning he tried to remember everything that had happened in Diamond Jims, but Harry was only vaguely remembered and he didn't want to ask her. A few times he tried speaking, but when he looked at her he started feeling vaguely guilty. When they had finished eating he lit her cigarette, smiled, and asked her if he could buy her something. A dress or something like that. I mean, well you know—I'd like to buy you a little present. He tried not to sound maudlin or look sheepish, but he found it hard to say what he felt now, in the morning, with a slight hangover, and she looked to him pretty and even a little innocent. Primarily he didn't want her to think he was offering to pay her or think he was insulting her by insinuating that she was just another prostitute; but much of his loneliness was gone and he wanted to thank her. You see, I only have a few days leave left before I go back and I thought perhaps we could—that is I thought we could spend some more together . . . He stammered on apologetically hoping she understood what he was trying to say but the words bounced off her and when she noticed that he had finished talking she said sure. What the fuck. This is much better than wrestlin with a drunk and she felt good this morning, much better than yesterday (briefly remembering the bulls and the money they took from her) and he might even give her his money before he went overseas (what could he do with it) and with her tits she could always makeout and what the hell, it was the best screwin she ever had. . . . They went shopping and she bought a dress, a couple of sweaters (2 sizes too small) shoes, stockings, a pocketbook and an overnight bag to put her clothes in. She protested slightly when he told her to buy a cosmetic case (not knowing what it was when he handed it to her and she saw no sense in spending money on that when he could just as well give her cash), and he enjoyed her modesty in not wanting to spend too much of his money; and he chuckled at her childlike excitement at being in the stores, looking and buying. They took all the packages back to the hotel and Tralala put on her new dress and shoes and they went out to eat and then to a movie. For the next few days they went to movies, restaurants (Tralala trying to make a mental note of the ones where the Officers hungout), a few more stores and back to the hotel. When they woke on the 4th day he told her he had to leave and asked her if she would come with him to the station. She went thinking he might give her his money and she stood awkwardly on the station with him, their bags around them, waiting for him to go on the train and leave. Finally the time came for him to leave and he handed her an envelope and kissed her before boarding the train. She felt the envelope as she lifted her face slightly so he could kiss her. It was thin and she figured it might be a check. She put it in her pocketbook, picked up her bag and went to the waiting room, sat on a bench and opened the envelope. She opened the paper and started reading: Dear Tral: There are many things I would like to say and should have said but— A letter. A goddamn LETTER. She ripped the envelope apart and turned the letter over a few times. Not a cent. I hope you understand what I mean and am unable to say—she looked at the words—if you do feel as I hope you do I'm writing my address at the bottom. I wanted to ask for yours but— Shit. Not vehemently but factually. She dropped the letter and rode the subway to Brooklyn. She went to Willies to display her finery. Ruthy was behind the bar and Waterman Annie was sitting in a booth with a seaman. She stood at the bar talking with Ruthy for a few minutes answering her questions about the clothes and telling her about the rich john she was living with and how much money he gave her and where they went. Ruthy left occasionally to pour a drink and when she came back Tralala continued her story, but soon Ruthy tired of listening to her bullshit as Tralala's short imagination bogged down. Tralala turned and looked at Annie and asked her when they leter out. Annie told her to go screw herself. Your the only one who would. Annie laughed and Tralala told her ta keep her shiteatin mouth shut. The seaman got up from the booth and staggered toward Tralala. You shouldn't talk to my girl friend like that. That Douchebag? You should be able ta do betteran that. She smiled and pushed her chest out. The seaman laughed and leaned on the bar and asked her if she would like a drink. Sure. But not in this crummy place. Lets go ta some place that's not crawlin with stinkin whores. The seaman roared, walked back to the table, finished his drink and left with Tralala. Annie screamed at them and tried to throw a glass at Tralala but someone grabbed her arm. Tralala and Jack (he was an oiler and he . . .) got into a cab and drove downtown. Tralala thought of ditching him rightaway (she only wanted to break Annie's balls), but figured she ought to wait and see. She stayed with him and they went to a hotel and when he passed out she took what he had and went back uptown. She went to the Crossroads and sat at the bar. It was filled with servicemen and a few drunken sailors smiled at her as she looked around, but she ignored them and the others in the bar ignored her. She wanted to be sure she picked up a live one. No drunken two bit sailor or doggie for her. O no. You bet ya-sweetass no. With her clothes and tits? Who inthehell do those punks think they are. I outta go spit in their stinkin faces. Shit! They couldn't kiss my ass. She jammed her cigarette out and took a short sip of her drink. She waited. She smiled coyly at a few Officers she thought might have loot, but they were with women. She cursed the dames under her breath, pulled her dress down, looked around and sipped her drink. Even with sipping the drink was soon gone and she had to order another. The bartender refilled her glass and marked her for an amateur. He smiled and was almost tempted to tell her that she was trying the wrong place, but didn't. He just refilled her glass thinking somebody should tell her that she would be better off in one of the 8th Avenue bars. She sipped the new drink and lit another cigarette. Why was she still alone? What was with this joint? Everybody with a few bucks had a dame. Goddamn pigs. Not one of em had a pair half as big as hers. She could have any sonofabitch in Willies or any bum stumbling into the Greek's. What's with the creeps in here. They should be all around her. She shouldn't be sitting alone. She'd been there 2 hours already. She felt like standing up and yelling fuck you to everybody in the joint. You're all a bunch of goddamn creeps. She snarled at the women who passed. She pulled her dress tight and forced her shoulders back. Time still passed. She still ignored the drunks figuring somebody with gelt would popup. She didn't touch her third drink, but sat looking around, cursing every sonofabitch in the joint and growing more defiant and desperate. Soon she was screaming in her mind and wishing takrist she had a blade, she'd cut their goddamn balls off. A CPO came up to her and asked her if she wanted a drink and she damn near spit in his face, but just mumbled as she looked at the clock and said shit. Yeah, yeah, lets go. She gulped down her drink and they left. Her mind was still such a fury of screechings (and that sonofabitch gives me nothin but a fuckin letter) that she just lay in bed staring at the ceiling and ignored the sailor as he screwed her and when he finally rolled off for the last time and fell asleep she continued staring and cursing for hours before falling asleep. The next afternoon she demanded that he giver some money and he laughed. She tried to hit him but he grabbed her arm, slapped her across the face and told her she was out of her mind. He laughed and told her to take it easy. He had a few days leave and he had enough money for both of them. They could have a good time. She cursed him and spit and he told her to grab her gear and shove off. She stopped in a cafeteria and went to the ladies room and threw some water on her face and bought a cup of coffee and a bun. She left and went back to the Crossroads. It was very crowded, being filled mostly with servicemen trying to drink away hangovers, and she sat and sipped a few drinks until the bar started filling. She tried looking for a live one, but after an hour or so, and a few drinks, she ignored everyone, and just waited. A couple of sailors asked her if she wanted a drink and she said whatthefuck and left with them. They roamed around for hours drinking and then she went to a room with the two of them and they gave her a few bucks in the morning so she stayed with them for a few days, 2 or 3, staying drunk most of the time and going back to the room now and then with them and their friends. And then they left or went somewhere and she went back to the Crossroads to look for another one or a whole damn ship. What's the difference. She pulled her dress tight, but didn't think of washing. She hadn't reached the bar when someone grabbed her arm, walked her to the side door and told her to leave. She stood on the corner of 42nd & Broadway cursing them and wanting to know why they let those scabby whores in but kick a nice young girl out, ya lousy bunch apricks. She turned and crossed the street, still mumbling to herself, and went in Diamond Jim's. It was jammed and she worked her way to the back near the juke box and looked. When someone came back to play a number she smiled, threw her shoulders back and pushed the hair from her face. She stood there drinking and smiling and eventually left with a drunken soldier. They screwed most of the night, slept for a short time then awoke and started drinking and screwing again. She stayed with him for a day or two or perhaps longer, she wasn't sure and it didn't make any difference anyway, then he was gone and she was back in a bar looking. She bounced from one bar to another still pulling her dress tight and occasionally throwing some water on her face before leaving a hotel room, slobbering drinks and soon not looking but just saying yeah, yeah, whathefuck and pushing an empty glass toward the bartender and sometimes never seeing the face of the drunk buying her drinks and rolling on and off her belly and slobbering over her tits; just drinking then pulling off her clothes and spreading her legs with the habit of a machine and drifting off to sleep or a drunken stupor with the first lunge. Time passed— months, maybe years, who knows, and even seasons changed and the dress was gone and just a beatup skirt and sweater and the Broadway bars were 8th Avenue bars; but soon even these joints with their hustlers, pushers, pimps, queens and would be thugs kicked her out and the inlaid linoleum turned to wood and then was covered with sawdust and she hung over a beer in a dump on the waterfront, snarling and cursing every sonofabitch who fucked her up and left with anyone who looked at her or had a place to flop. The honeymoon was over and still she pulled the sweater tight but there was no one there to look. When she crawled out of a flophouse she fell in the nearest bar and stayed until another offer of a flop was made. But each night she would shove her tits out and look around for a live one, not wanting any goddamn wino but the bums only looked at their beers and she waited for the live one who had an extra 50¢ he didn't mind spending on beer for a piece of ass and she flopped from one joint to another growing dirtier and scabbier. She was in a South Street bar and a seaman bought her a beer and his friends who depended on him for their drinks got panicky fearing he would leave them and spend their beer money on her so when he went to the head they took the beer from her and threw her out into the street. She sat on the curb yelling until a cop came along and kicked her and told her to move. She sprawled to her feet cursing every sonofabitch and his brother and told them they could stick their fuckin beer up their ass. She didn't need any goddamn skell to buy her a drink. She could get anything she wanted in Willies. She had her kicks. She'd go back to Willies where what she said goes. That was the joint. There was always somebody in there with money. No bums like these cruds. Did they think she'd let any goddamn bum in her pants and play with her tits just for a few bucks. Shit! She could get a seaman's whole payoff just sittin in Willies. People knew who she was in Willies. You bet yasweet ass they did. She stumbled down the subway and rode to Brooklyn, muttering and cursing, sweat streaking the dirt on her face. She walked up the 3 short steps to the door and was briefly disappointed that the door wasn't closed so she could throw it open. She stood for just a second in the doorway looking around then walked to the rear where Annie, Ruthy and a seaman were sitting. She stood beside the seaman, leaned in front of him and smiled at Annie and Ruthy then ordered a drink. The bartender looked at her and asked her if she had any money. She told him it was none of his goddamn business. My friend here is going to pay for it. Wontya honey. The seaman laughed and pushed a bill forward and she got her drink and sneered at the ignorant sonofabitching bartender. The rotten scumbag. Annie pulled her aside and told her if she tried cuttin her throat she'd dump her guts on the floor. Me and Ruth's gonna leave as soon as Jack's friend comes and if ya screw it up you'll be a sorry sonofabitch. Tralala yanked her arm away and went back to the bar and leaned against the seaman and rubbed her tits against his arm. He laughed and told her to drink up. Ruthy told Annie not ta bother witha, Fred'll be here soon and we'll go, and they talked with Jack and Tralala leaned over and interrupted their conversation and snarled at Annie hoping she burns like hell when Jack left with her and Jack laughed at everything and pounded the bar and bought drinks and Tralala smiled and drank and the jukebox blared hillbilly songs and an occasional blues number, and the red and blue neon lights around the mirror behind the bar sputtered and winked and the soldiers, seamen and whores in the booths and hanging on the bar yelled and laughed and Tralala lifted her drink and said chuckalug and banged her glass on the bar and she rubbed her tits against Jack's arm and he looked at her wondering how many blackheads she had on her face and if that large pimple on her cheek would burst and ooze and he said something to Annie then roared and slapped her leg and Annie smiled and wrote Tralala off and the cash register kachanged and the smoke just hung and Fred came and joined the party and Tralala yelled for another drink and asked Fred how he liked her tits and he poked them with a finger and said I guess they're real and Jack pounded the bar and laughed and Annie cursed Tralala and tried to get them to leave and they said let's stay for a while, we're having fun and Fred winked and someone rapped a table and roared and a glass fell to the floor and the smoke fell when it reached the door and Tralala opened Jack's fly and smiled and he closed it 5, 6, 7 times

laughing and stared at the pimple and the lights blinked and the cash
register crooned kachang kachang and Tralala told Jack she had big
tits and he pounded the bar and laughed and Fred winked and
laughed and Ruthy and Annie wanted to leave before something
screwed up their deal and wondered how much money they had and
hating to see them spend it on Tralala and Tralala gulped her drinks
and yelled for more and Fred and Jack laughed and winked and
pounded the bar and another glass fell to the floor and someone be-
moaned the loss of a beer and two hands fought their way up a skirt
under a table and she blew smoke in their faces and someone passed
out and his head fell on the table and a beer was grabbed before it
fell and Tralala glowed she had it made and she'd shove it up Annie's
ass or anybody elses and she gulped another drink and it spilled down
her chin and she hung on Jack's neck and rubbed her chest against
his cheek and he reached up and turned them like knobs and roared
and Tralala smiled and O she had it made now and piss on all those
motherfuckers and someone walked a mile for a smile and pulled the
drunk out of the booth and dropped him out the back door and
Tralala pulled her sweater up and bounced her tits on the palms of
her hands and grinned and grinned and grinned and Jack and Fred
whooped and roared and the bartender told her to put those goddamn
things away and get the hell outahere and Ruthy and Annie winked
and Tralala slowly turned around bouncing them hard on her hands
exhibiting her pride to the bar and she smiled and bounced the biggest
most beautiful pair of tits in the world on her hands and someone
yelled is that for real and Tralala shoved them in a face and everyone
laughed and another glass fell from a table and guys stood and
looked and the hands came out from under the skirt and beer was
poured on Tralala's tits and someone yelled that she had been christened and the beer ran down her stomach and dripped from her
nipples and she slapped his face with her tits and someone yelled you'll
smotherim to death—what a way to die—hey, what's for dessert—I
said taput those goddamn things away ya fuckin hippapotmus and
Tralala told him she had the prettiest tits in the world and she fell
against the juke box and the needle scraped along the record sounding like a long belch and someone yelled all tits and no cunt and
Tralala told him ta comeon and find out and a drunken soldier banged
out of a booth and said comeon and grabbed her by the arm and he
yelled to his buddies to comeon and glasses fell and Jack knocked
over his stool and fell on Fred and they hung over the bar nearing
hysteria and Ruthy hoped she wouldn't get fired because this was a

good deal and Annie closed her eyes and laughed relieved that they wouldn't have to worry about Tralala and they didn't spend too much money and Tralala still bounced her tits on the palms of her hands turning to everyone as she was dragged out the door by the arm by 2 or 3 and she yelled to Jack to comeon and she'd fuckim blind not like that fuckin douchebag he was with and someone yelled we're coming and she was dragged down the steps tripping over someone's feet and scraping her ankles on the stone steps and yelling but the mob not slowing their pace and still dragging her by an arm and Jack and Fred still hanging on the bar roaring and Ruthie taking off her apron and getting ready to leave before something happened to louse up their deal and the 10 or 15 drunks dragged Tralala to a wrecked car in the lot on the corner and yanked her clothes off and pushed her inside and a few guys fought to see who would be first and finally a sort of a line was formed everyone yelling and laughing and someone yelled to the guys on the end to go get some beer and they left and came back with cans of beer which were passed around the daisy chain and the guys from the Greek's came over and some other kids from the neighborhood stood around watching and waiting and Tralala yelled and shoved her tits into the faces as they occurred before her and beers were passed around and the empties dropped or thrown and guys left the car and went back on line and had a few beers and waited their turn again and more guys came from Willies and a phone call to the Army base brought more seamen and doggies and more beer was brought from Willies and Tralala drank beer while being laid and someone asked if anyone was keeping score and someone yelled who can count that far and Tralala's back was streaked with dirt and sweat and her ankles stung from the sweat and dirt in the scrapes from the steps and sweat and beer dripped from the faces onto hers but she kept yelling she had the biggest goddamn pair of tits in the world and someone answered ya bet ya sweet ass ya do and more came 40 maybe 50 and they screwed her and went back on line and had a beer and yelled and laughed and someone yelled that the car stunk of cunt so Tralala and the seat were taken out of the car and laid in the lot and she lay there naked on the seat and their shadows hid her pimples and scabs and she drank flipping her tits with the other hand and somebody shoved the beer can against her mouth and they all laughed and Tralala cursed and spit out a piece of tooth and someone shoved it again and they laughed and yelled and the next one mounted her and her lips were split this time and the blood trickled to her chin and someone mopped her brow with a beer

soaked handkerchief and another can of beer was handed to her and
she drank and yelled about her tits and another tooth was chipped
and the split in her lips was widened and everyone laughed and she
laughed and she drank more and more and soon she passed out and
they slapped her a few times and she mumbled and turned her head
but they couldn't revive her so they continued to fuck her as she lay
unconscious on the seat in the lot and soon they tired of the dead
piece and the daisy chain brokeup and they went back to Willie's the
Greek's and the base and the kids who were watching and waiting to
take a turn took out their disappointment on Tralala and tore her
clothes to small scraps put out a few cigarettes on her nipples pissed
on her jerked off on her jambed a broomstick up her snatch then bored
they left her lying amongst the broken bottles rusty cans and rubble
of the lot and Jack and Fred and Ruthy and Annie stumbled into a
cab still laughing and they leaned toward the window as they passed
the lot and got a good look at Tralala lying naked covered with
blood urine and semen and a small blot forming on the seat between
her legs as blood seeped from her crotch and Ruthie and Annie were
happy and completely relaxed now that they were on their way downtown and their ideal wasn't loused up and they would have plenty of
money and Fred looking through the rear window and Jack pounding
his leg and roaring with laughter. . . .

WILLIAM BURROUGHS

on *NAKED LUNCH*   by E. S. Seldon

Naked Lunch is not the most impressive American literary debut
in Paris since 1934, date of *Tropic of Cancer;* it's one of the most
impressive literary debuts of the past century. At a moment when, I
think, we have no lack of talents, Mr. Burroughs comes along and
reminds us of what was lacking, all the same: not names to remember,
but works. *Naked Lunch* is a finished work of literature, original,
mature, challenging. The writer has something unusual and important
to say, and he has found the only right way of saying it. This is one
contemporary writer who can drop dead tomorrow, confident not in
promise, but in fulfillment.

And I should think he might very well drop dead, William Burroughs. Not just from the strain of sustained originality (all traces
of labor, of course, have been scrupulously removed), but from
nervous exhaustion. This is a strenuous book, in a sense Teddy Roose-
velt and Jack London might not have appreciated, a spiritual sense,
and its exploration of frontiers beyond statistical mediocrity and institutional culture is hair-raising, both in perils run and alarming
discoveries made. This is a case of overcivilization so extreme as to
have blown off the top of the thermostat. Not to be mealy-mouthed,
this is a book calculated to scare the shit out of anyone old enough to
read it, and to set the behavioral scientists to counting over their
methodological beads with new urgency. In other words, this is a book
to the scale of world literature in an age of flight to outer space.

There are "influences," of course, but they have been fully assimilated. Henry Miller, what we used to call the "surrealist" Miller, he of the
Cosmodemonic Telegraph Company and the other genial satires of life
in what Rimbaud called the *raw, new metropolises* of the late-modern

world. Burroughs has concentrated the old man's gift, boiled it down, writes with a better ear, and fires off salvos of such episodes at a time. Orwell must have provided clues for such divertissements as "techno-logical surgery," and for the unforgettable day "the electronic brain went berserk playing six-dimensional chess with the Technician and released every subject in the R.C." thus precipitating a scene of mass carnage that Burroughs handles with easy mastery in a set piece worthy of Zola. This is the last paragraph:

> Rock and Roll adolescent hoodlums storm the streets of all nations. They rush into the Louvre and throw acid in the Mona Lisa's face. They open zoos, insane asylums, prisons, burst water mains with air hammers, chop the floor out of passenger plane lavatories, shoot out lighthouses, file elevator cables to one thin wire, turn sewers into the water supply, throw sharks and sting rays, electric eels and candiru into swimming pools . . . in nautical costumes ram the *Queen Mary* full speed into New York harbor, play chicken with passenger planes and busses, rush into hospitals in white coats carrying saws and axes and scalpels three feet long, throw paralytics out of iron lungs (mimic their suffocations flopping about on the floor and rolling their eyes up), ad-minister injections with bicycle pumps, disconnect artificial kidneys, saw a woman in half with a two-man surgical saw, they drive herds of squealing pigs into the Curb, they shit on the floor of the United Nations and wipe their ass with treaties, pacts, alliances.

There is no lack of characters or events in *Naked Lunch,* and Mr. Burroughs never lets his knife-edge plain style dull into rhetoric. The nothing-if-not extreme situations and states of consciousness he treats are neither glamorized nor watered down. Intensely readable at whatever point you open it, his book is nonetheless put together in a completely original way which, to describe abstractly, sounds hopelessly confusing. All that really baffles, however, is his awe-inspiring artistry. He takes us on a very lively, scary, broadening journey, not in space and time, but from one particular kind of withdrawal from familiar existence out into what the analysts call the "real" world—way, way out into the social, collective world—and then right back again to where we started, staring fixedly at one shoe, or a crack in the wall.
Somewhere in the background, we are dimly aware of changing

locales, just as, in the foreground, we are aware of shifting, splitting, and all but merging characters who might be either facets of a single character never portrayed as such (but presumably the author) or sole remaining fragments of different, individual characters in literal dissolution. What is so extraordinary is that this lack of a central character as such, as well as of a conventional narrative as such, produces nothing like blurriness or lack of coherence. To the contrary, it serves to sharpen the points of what Mr. Burroughs has to say; it leaves no possible *out* for the reader who might wish to pretend that Mr. Burroughs is saying something else than what, by this means, he so unequivocally gets said.

The purpose of all this, I am pretty sure, is not to make a hero, or an anti-hero, of the drug addict. Extreme addiction, which only in its terminal stages resembles the terminal stages of schizophrenia, is in its intermediate stages a cure for schizophrenia. Is this junky logic? I have no idea, but it is quite enough logic—and quite compellingly enough demonstrated in *Naked Lunch*—to create a unique angle of vision. We who are not addicts think of dope as an escape into nothing, an evasion of responsibility, a kind of ultimate selfishness. Well, this may not be the case, or rather, it may leave out an important aspect of the total case, which is betrayed by our ferocious persecution of the addict. After all, why should we care? Is individual self-destruction of such moment in a world of organized collective destruction—worse, of culturally defended *absolute* preconditions for collective destruction? From this point of view—where addiction, not idealized but literalized, is one pole of a conduct of life, the other pole of which is an adequately comprehended "reality" of much more savage scale and much more unmistakably *dangerous* cast—from this point of view, life appears as a choice between methods of arriving at the same disastrous conclusion. And there may be a little more dignity (certainly a more nearly traditional *kind* of dignity) in the cool refusal to participate in going to hell your own way, patiently running through the pharmacopoeia and using up your own veins, than there is in projecting your inadequacies and dissatisfactions into socio-political and scientific schemes of what Burroughs calls a variously "Liquefactionist" or "Divisionist" character.

If I am not mistaken, this is a completely secular, truly scientific, historical *and* psychological restatement of the human predicament mankind once thought of religiously, as a choice between desiccation in the Thebaid or the anchorite's cell, for example, and wallowing in the world-historical brutalities of empire. Only such "extreme" statements, of course, can illuminate the human condition, caught up as we are at any given moment in the illusion that the five or ten degrees of the scale we occupy constitutes the full range of human possibility, from zero to infinity.

Much more unmistakable is the fact that Burroughs is a superb writer, and *Naked Lunch* a novel of revolt in the best late-modern sense. He is a much less genial writer than Henry Miller, and a much more intelligent one than Céline. And I had better insist: for all his spiritual strength, he invokes no fuzzy, subliminal powers, whether of a transcendental or an unconscious variety. He is quite as aware of what he is revolting against as of the individual human predicament he sympathizes with sufficiently not to understate its gravity. On the one hand, he gives a stunning going over to the objective, "scientifically" reinforced madness of institutional culture, while on the other, he shows the doomed individual desperately trying to preserve his own identity, at whatever cost—if necessary, all else failing, within the private world of his own skin:

> The body knows what veins you can hit and conveys this knowledge in the spontaneous movements you make preparing to take a shot. . . . Sometimes the needle points like a dowzer's wand. Sometimes I must wait for the message. But when it comes I always hit blood.

These lines are written with love; and to all, in the months and years to come, who try to tell you *Naked Lunch* is "a nasty book," just reply as I do, "Don't you mean lucid?"

Not too far beneath the hard, glittering bitter surface of this original work, it is possible to hear a desperate cry not unlike that of the poet Artaud from the madhouse at Rodez. It is the cry of every as yet "uninstitutionalized" man everywhere to the impersonal collective forces which have him in their grip: just let us possess what at least exists, "the actual body of our immediate being in sempiternal time and space." American, more privileged than Artaud, and a generation younger (i.e., older), Burroughs understands also what desperation there is in studied deafness to this cry, as Artaud did not. Even more than Sade, he "mixes up" the executioners and the victims. *Naked Lunch* is a very worldly-wise, late-modern, nothing-if-not civilized version of the cannibal feast.

If, nonetheless, there should be a twenty-first century, this is one of the few works of our day historians could turn to for a grasp, both imaginative and intelligent, of the strange historical phase of the human condition we are living through: when reason is in official, institutional alliance with brute force, and the individual psyche systematically reduced to a garbage pail for the "negative" contents of life—i.e., whatever science cannot "use." There is no complacency here about "the present state of our knowledge."

from *NAKED LUNCH*

The Meet Café occupies one side of the Plaza, a maze of kitchens, restaurants, sleeping cubicles, perilous iron balconies and basements opening into the underground baths.

On stools covered in white satin sit naked Mugwumps sucking translucent, colored syrups through alabaster straws. Mugwumps have no liver and nourish themselves exclusively on sweets. Thin, purple-blue lips cover a razor-sharp beak of black bone with which they frequently tear each other to shreds in fights over clients. These creatures secrete an addicting fluid from their erect penises which prolongs life by slowing metabolism. (In fact all longevity agents have proved addicting in exact ratio to their effectiveness in prolonging life.) Addicts of Mugwump fluid are known as Reptiles. A number of these flow over chairs with their flexible bones and black-pink flesh. A fan of green cartilage covered with hollow, erectile hairs through which the Reptiles absorb the fluid sprouts from behind each ear. The fans, which move from time to time touched by invisible currents, serve also some form of communication known only to Reptiles.

During the biennial Panics when the raw, pealed Dream Police storm the City, the Mugwumps take refuge in the deepest crevices of the wall sealing themselves in clay cubicles and remain for weeks in biostasis. In those days of grey terror the Reptiles dart about faster and faster, scream past each other at supersonic speed, their flexible skulls flapping in black winds of insect agony.

The Dream Police disintegrate in globs of rotten ectoplasm swept away by an old junky, coughing and spitting in the sick morning. The Mugwump Man comes with alabaster jars of fluid and the Reptiles get smoothed out.

The air is once again still and clear as glycerine.

The Sailor spotted his Reptile. He drifted over and ordered a green syrup. The Reptile had a little, round disk mouth of brown gristle, expressionless green eyes almost covered by a thin membrane of eyelid. The Sailor waited an hour before the creature picked up his presence.

"Any eggs for Fats?" he asked, his words stirring through the Reptile's fan hairs.

It took two hours for the Reptile to raise three pink transparent fingers covered with black fuzz.

Several Meat Eaters lay in vomit, too weak to move. (The Black Meat is like a tainted cheese, overpoweringly delicious and nauseating so that the eaters eat and vomit and eat again until they fall exhausted.)

A painted youth slithered in and seized one of the great black claws sending the sweet, sick smell curling through the café.

HOSPITAL

Disintoxication Notes. Paranoia of early withdrawal. . . . Everything looks blue. . . . Flesh dead, doughy, toneless.

Withdrawal Nightmares. A mirror-lined café. Empty. . . . Waiting for something. . . . A man appears in a side door. . . . A slight, short Arab dressed in a brown jellaba with grey beard and grey face. . . . There is a pitcher of boiling acid in my hand. . . . Seized by a convulsion of urgency, I throw it in his face. . . .

Everyone looks like a drug addict. . . .

Take a little walk in the hospital patio. . . . In my absence someone has used my scissors, they are stained with some sticky, red
brown gick. . . . No doubt that little bitch of a criada trimming her
rag.

Horrible-looking Europeans clutter up the stairs, intercept the
nurse when I need my medicine, empty piss into the basin when I am
washing, occupy the toilet for hours on end—probably fishing for
a finger stall of diamonds they have stached up their asshole. . . .

In fact the whole clan of Europeans has moved in next to me.
. . . The old mother is having an operation, and her daughter move
right in to see the old gash receive proper service. Strange visitors,
presumably relatives . . . One of them wears as glasses those gadgets
jewellers screw into their eyes to examine stones. . . . Probably a
diamond-cutter on the skids . . . The man who loused up the Throck-
morton Diamond and was drummed out of the industry . . . All these
jewelers standing around the Diamond in their frock coats, waiting
on The Man. An error of one thousandth of an inch ruins the rock
complete and they have to import this character special from Amster-
dam to do the job. . . . So he reels in dead drunk with a huge air
hammer and pounds the diamond to dust. . . .

I don't check these citizens. . . . Dope peddlers from Aleppo?
. . . Slunk traffickers from Buenos Aires? Illegal diamond buyers from
Johannesburg? . . . Slave traders from Somaliland? Collaborators at
the very least . . .

Continual dreams of junk: I am looking for a poppy field. . . .
Moonshiners in black Stetsons direct me to a Near East café. . . .
One of the waiters is a connection for Yugoslav opium. . . .

Buy a packet of heroin from a Malay Lesbian in white belted
trenchcoat. . . . I cop the paper in Tibetan section of a museum. She
keeps trying to steal it back. . . . I am looking for a place to fix. . . .

The critical point of withdrawal is not the early phase of acute
sickness, but the final step free from the medium of junk. . . . There
is a nightmare interlude of cellular panic, life suspended between two
ways of being. . . . At this point the longing for junk concentrates
in a last, all-out yen, and seems to gain a dream power: circumstances
put junk in your way. . . . You meet an old-time Schmecker, a
larcenous hospital attendant, a writing croaker. . . .

A guard in a uniform of human skin, black buck jacket with
carious yellow teeth buttons, an elastic pullover shirt in burnished
Indian copper, adolescent-nordic-sun-tan slacks, sandals from calloused

foot soles of young Malayan farmer, an ash-brown scarf knotted and tucked in the shirt. (Ash-brown is a color like grey *under* brown skin. You sometimes find it in mixed Negro and white stock, the mixture did not come off and the colors separated out like oil on water....)

The Guard is a sharp dresser, since he has nothing to do and saves all his pay to buy fine clothes and changes three times a day in front of an enormous magnifying mirror. He has a Latin handsome-smooth face with a pencil line mustache, small black eyes, blank and greedy, undreaming insect eyes.

When I get to the frontier the Guard rushes out of his casita, a mirror in a wooden frame slung round his neck. He is trying to get the mirror off his neck. . . . This has never happened before, that anyone reached the frontier. The Guard has injured his larynx taking off the mirror frame. . . . He has lost his voice. . . . He opens his mouth, you can see the tongue jumping around inside. The smooth blank young face and the open mouth with the tongue moving inside are incredibly hideous. The Guard holds up his hand. His whole body jerks in convulsive negation. I go over and unhook the chain across the road. It falls with a clank of metal on stone. I walk through. The Guard stands there in the mist looking after me. Then he hooks the chain up again, goes back into the casita and starts plucking at his mustache.

They just bring so-called lunch. . . . A hard-boiled egg with the shell off revealing an object like I never seen it before. . . . A very small egg of a yellow-brown color . . . Perhaps laid by the duck-billed platypus. The orange contained a huge worm and very little else. . . . He really got there firstest with the mostest. . . In Egypt is a worm gets into your kidneys and grows to an enormous size. Ultimately the kidney is just a thin shell around the worm. Intrepid gourmets esteem the flesh of The Worm above all other delicacies. It is said to be unspeakably toothsome. . . . An Interzone coroner known as Autopsy Ahmed made a fortune trafficking The Worm.

The French school is opposite my window and I dig the boys with my eight-power field glasses. . . . So close I could reach out and touch them. . . . They wear shorts. . . . I can see the goose-pimples on their legs in the cold Spring morning. . . . I project myself out through the glasses and across the street, a ghost in the morning sunlight, torn with disembodied lust.

Did I ever tell you about the time Marv and me pay two Arab

kids sixty cents to watch them screw each other? So I ask Marv, "Do you think they will do it?"

And he says, "I think so. They are hungry."

And I say, "That's the way I like to see them."

Makes me feel sorta like a dirty old man but, "*Son cosas de la vida,*" as Soberba de la Flor said when the fuzz upbraids him for blasting this cunt and taking the dead body to the Bar O Motel and fucking it. . . .

"She play hard to get already," he say . . . "I don't hafta take that sound." (Soberba de la Flor was a Mexican criminal convict of several rather pointless murders.)

The lavatory has been locked for three hours solid. . . . I think they are using it for an operating room. . . .

Nurse: "I can't find her pulse, doctor."

Dr. Benway: "Maybe she got it up her snatch in a finger stall."

Nurse: "Adrenalin, doctor?"

Dr. Benway: "The night porter shot it all up for kicks." He looks around and picks up one of those rubber vacuum cups at the end of a stick they use to unstop toilets. . . . He advances on the patient. . . . "Make an incision, Doctor Limpf," he says to his appalled assistant. . . . "I'm going to massage the heart."

Dr. Limpf shrugs and begins the incision. Dr. Benway washes the suction cup by swishing it around in the toilet-bowl. . . .

Nurse: "Shouldn't it be sterilized, doctor?"

Dr. Benway: "Very likely but there's no time." He sits on the suction cup like a cane seat watching his assistant make the incision. . . . "You young squirts couldn't lance a pimple without an electric vibrating scalpel with automatic drain and suture. . . . Soon we'll be operating by remote control on patients we never see. . . . We'll be nothing but button pushers. All the skill is going out of surgery. . . . All the know-how and make-do . . . Did I ever tell you about the time I performed an appendectomy with a rusty sardine can? And once I was caught short without instrument one and removed a uterine tumor with my teeth. That was in the Upper Effendi, and besides . . ."

Dr. Limpf: "The incision is ready, doctor."

Dr Benway forces the cup into the incision and works it up and down. Blood spurts all over the doctors, the nurse and the wall. . . . The cup makes a horrible sucking sound.

Nurse: "I think she's gone, doctor."

Dr. Benway: "Well, it's all in the day's work." He walks across the room to a medicine cabinet. . . . "Some fucking drug addict has cut my cocaine with Saniflush! Nurse! Send the boy out to fill this RX on the double!"

Dr. Benway is operating in an auditorium filled with students: "Now, boys, you won't see this operation performed very often and there's a reason for that. . . . You see it has absolutely no medical value. No one knows what the purpose of it originally was or if it had a purpose at all. Personally I think it was a pure artistic creation from the beginning.

"Just as a bull fighter with his skill and knowledge extricates himself from danger he has himself invoked, so in this operation the surgeon deliberately endangers his patient, and then, with incredible speed and celerity, rescues him from death at the last possible split second. . . . Did any of you ever see Dr. Tetrazzini perform? I say perform advisedly because his operations were performances. He would start by throwing a scalpel across the room into the patient and then make his entrance like a ballet dancer. His speed was incredible: 'I don't give them time to die,' he would say. Tumors put him in a frenzy of rage. 'Fucking undisciplined cells!' he would snarl, advancing on the tumor like a knife-fighter."

A young man leaps down into the operating theatre and, whipping out a scalpel, advances on the patient.

DR. BENWAY: "An espontaneo! Stop him before he guts my patient!"

(Espontaneo is a bull-fighting term for a member of the audience who leaps down into the ring, pulls out a concealed cape and attempts a few passes with the bull before he is dragged out of the ring.)

The orderlies scuffle with the espontaneo, who is finally ejected from the hall. The anesthetist takes advantage of the confusion to pry a large gold filling from the patient's mouth. . . .

I am passing room 10 they moved me out of yesterday. . . . Maternity case I assume . . . Bedpans full of blood and Kotex and nameless female substances, enough to pollute a continent . . . If someone comes to visit me in my old room he will think I gave birth to a monster and the State Department is trying to hush it up. . . .

Music from *I Am an American* . . . An elderly man in the striped pants and cutaway of a diplomat stands on a platform draped with the American flag. A decayed, corseted tenor—bursting out of a Daniel Boone costume—is singing the *Star Spangled Banner*, accompanied by a full orchestra. He sings with a slight lisp. . . .

THE DIPLOMAT (reading from a great scroll of ticker tape that keeps growing and tangling around his feet): "And we categorically deny that *any* male citizen of the United States of America . . ."

TENOR: "Oh thay can you thee . . ." His voice breaks and shoots up to a high falsetto.

In the control room the Technician mixes a bicarbonate of soda and belches into his hand: "God damned tenor's a brown artist!" he mutters sourly. "Mike! rumph," the shout ends in a belch. "Cut that swish fart off the air and give him his purple slip. He's through as of right now. . . . Put in that sex-changed Liz athlete. . . . She's a fulltime tenor at least. . . . *Costume?* How in the fuck should I know? I'm no dress designer swish from the costume department! *What's that?* The entire costume department occluded as a security risk? What am I, an octopus? Let's see . . . How about an Indian routine? Pocahontas or Hiawatha? . . . No, that's not right. Some citizen cracks wise about giving it back to the Indians. . . . A Civil War uniform the coat North and the pants South like it show they got together again? She can come on like Buffalo Bill or Paul Revere or that citizen wouldn't give up the shit, I mean the ship, or a G.I. or a Doughboy or the Unknown Soldier. . . . That's the best deal. . . . Cover her with a monument, that way nobody has to look at her. . . ."

The Lesbian, concealed in a *papier mâché* Arc de Triomphe fills her great lungs and looses a tremendous bellow.

"Oh say do that Star Spangled Banner yet wave . . ."

A great rent rips the Arc de Triomphe from top to bottom. The Diplomat puts a hand to his forehead. . . .

THE DIPLOMAT: "That any male citizen of the United States has given birth in Interzone or at any other place. . . ."

"O'er the land of the FREEEEEEEEEEEE . . ."

The Diplomat's mouth is moving but no one can hear him. The Technician clasps his hands over his ears: "Mother of God!" he screams. His plate begins to vibrate like a Jew's harp, suddenly flies out of his mouth. . . . He snaps at it irritably, misses and covers his mouth with one hand.

The Arc de Triomphe falls with a ripping, splintering crash, reveals the Lesbian standing on a pedestal clad only in a leopard-skin jockstrap with enormous falsie basket. . . . She stands there smiling stupidly and flexing her huge muscles. . . . The Technician is crawling around on the control room floor looking for his plate and shouting unintelligible orders: "Thess thupper thonic!! Thut ur oth thu thair!"

THE DIPLOMAT (wiping sweat from his brow): "To any creature of any type or description . . ."

"And the home of the brave."

The diplomat's face is grey. He staggers, trips in the scroll, sags against the rail, blood pouring from eyes, nose and mouth, dying of cerebral hemorrhage.

THE DIPLOMAT (barely audible): "The Department denies . . . un-American . . . It's been destroyed . . . I mean it never was . . . Categor . . ." *Dies.*

In the Control Room instrument panels are blowing out . . . great streamers of electricity crackle through the room. . . . The Technician, naked, his body burned black, staggers about like a figure in *Götterdämmerung*, screaming: "Thubber thonic!! Oth thu thair!!!" A final blast reduces the Technician to a cinder.

> *Gave proof through the night*
> *That our flag was still there. . . .*

Habit Notes. Shooting Eukodol every two hours. I have a place where I can slip my needle right into a vein, it stays open like a red, festering mouth, swollen and obscene, gathers a slow drop of blood and pus after the shot. . . .

Eukodol is a chemical variation of codeine—dihydrooxy-codeine.

This stuff comes on more like C than M. . . . When you shoot Coke in the mainline there is a rush of pure pleasure to the head. . . . Ten minutes later you want another shot. . . . The pleasure of morphine is in the viscera. . . . You listen down into yourself after a shot. . . . But intravenous C is electrically through the brain, activating cocaine pleasure connections. . . . There is no withdrawal syndrome with C. It is a need of the brain alone—a need without body and without feeling. Earthbound ghost need. The craving for C lasts only a few hours as long as the C channels are stimulated. Then you forget it. Eukodol is like a combination of junk and C. Trust the Germans to concoct some really evil shit. Eukodol like morphine is six times stronger than codeine. Heroin six times stronger than morphine. Di-hydro-oxy-heroin should be six times stronger than heroin. Quite possible to develop a drug so habit-forming that one shot would cause lifelong addiction.

Habit Note continued: Picking up needle I reach spontaneously for the tie-up cord with my left hand. This I take as a sign I can

hit the one usable vein in my left arm. (The movements of tying up
are such that you normally tie up the arm with which you reach for the
cord.) The needle slides in easily on the edge of a callous. I feel
around. Suddenly a thin column of blood shoots up into the syringe,
for a moment sharp and solid as a red cord.

The body knows what veins you can hit and conveys this
knowledge in the spontaneous movements you make preparing to take
a shot. . . . Sometimes the needle points like a dowzer's wand. Sometime I must wait for the message. But when it comes I always hit
blood.

A red orchid bloomed at the bottom of the dropper. He hesitated
for a full second, then pressed the bulb, watching the liquid rush into
the vein as if sucked by the silent thirst of his blood. There was an
iridescent, thin coat of blood left in the dropper, and the white paper
collar was soaked through with blood like a bandage. He reached
over and filled the dropper with water. As he squirted the water out,
the shot hit him in the stomach, a soft sweet blow.

Look down at my filthy trousers, haven't been changed in months.
. . . The days glide by strung on a syringe with a long thread of
blood. . . . I am forgetting sex and all sharp pleasures of the body—a
grey, junk-bound ghost. The Spanish boys call me El Hombre Invisible—the Invisible Man. . . .

Twenty push ups every morning. Use of junk removes fat, leaves
muscle more or less intact. The addict seems to need less tissue. . . .
Would it be possible to isolate the fat-removing molecule of junk?

More and more static at the Drug Store, mutterings of control like
a telephone off the hook . . . Spent all day until 8 P.M. to score for
two boxes of Eukodol. . . .

Running out of veins and out of money.

Keep going on the nod. Last night I woke up with someone
squeezing my hand. It was my other hand. . . . Fall asleep reading
and the words take on code significance. . . . Obsessed with codes.
. . . Man contracts a series of diseases which spell out a code message. . . .

Take a shot in front of D.L. Probing for a vein in my dirty bare
foot. . . . Junkies have no shame. . . . They are impervious to the
repugnance of others. It is doubtful if shame can exist in the absence
of sexual libido. . . . The junky's shame disappears with his nonsexual
sociability which is also dependent on libido. . . . The addict regards

his body impersonally as an instrument to absorb the medium in which he lives, evaluates his tissue with the cold hands of a horse trader. "No use trying to hit there." Dead fish eyes flick over a ravaged vein.

Using a new type sleeping pill called Soneryl. . . . You don't feel sleepy. . . . You shift to sleep without transition, fall abruptly into the middle of a dream. . . . I have been years in a prison camp suffering from malnutrition. . . .

The President is a junky but can't take it direct because of his position. So he gets fixed through me. . . . From time to time we make contact, and I recharge him. These contacts look, to the casual observer, like homosexual practices, but the actual excitement is not primarily sexual, and the climax is the separation when the recharge is completed. The erect penises are brought into contact—at least we used that method in the beginning, but contact points wear out like veins. Now I sometimes have to slip my penis under his left eyelid. Of course I can always fix him with an Osmosis Recharge, which corresponds to a skin shot, but that is admitting defeat. An O.R. will put the President in a bad mood for weeks, and might well precipitate an atomic shambles. And the President pays a high price for the Oblique Habit. He has sacrificed all control, and is dependent as an unborn child. The Oblique Addict suffers a whole spectrum of subjective horror, silent protoplasmic frenzy, hideous agony of the bones. Tensions build up, pure energy without emotional content finally tears through the body throwing him about like a man in contact with high tension wires. If his charge connection is cut off cold, the Oblique Addict falls into such violent electric convulsions that his bones shake loose, and he dies with the skeleton straining to climb out of his unendurable flesh and run in a straight line to the nearest cemetery.

The relation between an A.O. (Oblique Addict) and his R.C. (Recharge Connection) is so intense that they can only endure each other's company for brief and infrequent intervals—I mean aside from recharge meets, when all personal contact is eclipsed by the recharge process.

Reading the paper. . . . Something about a triple murder in the rue de la Merde, Paris: "An adjusting of scores." . . . I keep slipping away. . . . "The police have identified the author . . . Pepe El Culito . . . The Little Ass Hole, an affectionate diminutive." Does it really say that? . . . I try to focus the words . . . they separate in meaningless mosaic. . . .

IONESCO

THE AVANT-GARDE THEATRE

I am, it seems, an avant-garde dramatist. It would even seem obvious since I am present here at discussions on the avant-garde theatre as a representative of this avant-garde. It is all entirely official.

But what does the term avant-garde mean? I am not a Doctor of Theatrology, nor Philosophy, nor Art: nor am I what is commonly called a "man-of-the-theatre." Perhaps I am a kind of mason, knowing certain laws of dramatic construction, but in an empirical or instinctive manner.

If I have formed certain ideas about the theatre, they refer above all to my theatre for they have sprung from my own creative experience: they are hardly normative, but rather descriptive. I hope, of course, that rules which apply to me will also apply to others, for the others are all contained in each one of us.

In any case, any laws of theatre which I may discover are provisional and mobile; they come after, not before, artistic creation. If I write a new play, my point of view may be profoundly modified. I may be obliged to contradict myself and I may no longer know whether I still think what I think.

I hope, nevertheless, that some fundamental principles may remain upon which I can lean consciously and instinctively. And here again I can only share with you a purely personal experience.

However, so that I would not make any serious blunders, I looked up the word "avant-garde" in my Larousse dictionary before I came. I found that the avant-garde, or the van-guard, "are the troops which precede an armed land, sea or air force and prepare the way for its entry into action."

Thus, by analogy, in the theatre, the avant-garde would consist of a small shock force of dramatists and sometimes directors, followed at a certain distance by the main body of actors, playwrights and producers. This analogy is perhaps valid when we see what Albérès has stated in his book, *L'Aventure intellectulle du XXe Siècle:* "by a phenomenon which no one has troubled to explain (and which indeed would seem difficult) literary sensibility (and artistic of course) has always, in our century, preceded the historic events which were later to corroborate them." Indeed Baudelaire, Kafka, Pirandello ("who took apart the machinery of lofty family sentiments, etc. . . ."), and Dostoyevsky were regarded with good reason as writer-prophets.

Thus the avant-garde would seem to be an artistic and cultural phenomenon of a precursory nature, which tallies with its literal meaning. It would be a kind of "pre-style" indicating and pointing the direction of a change which will triumph in the end, a change which will truly change everything. This amounts to saying that the avant-garde cannot generally be recognized until after the event; when they have succeeded, when the avant-garde writers and artists have acquired a following, when they have founded a prevailing school, a cultural style which is recognized and will conquer an age. Consequently, one can only see that there has been an avant-garde when it no longer exists as such, when it has in fact become a rear guard; when it has been joined and even outstripped by the main army. But an army marching towards what?

I prefer to define the avant-garde in terms of opposition and rupture. While most writers, artists and thinkers believe they belong to their time, the revolutionary playwright feels he is running counter to his time. As a matter of fact, thinkers, artists and so on, after a certain time only make use of ossified forms; they feel they are becoming more and more firmly established in some ideological, artistic, or social order which to them seems up to date but which in fact is already tottering and yawning with unsuspected cracks. By the very force of circumstances any system, the moment it is established, is already outworn. As soon as a form of expression becomes recognized, it is already out of date. A thing once spoken is already dead, reality lies somewhere beyond it and the thought has become petrified, so to speak. A manner of speaking—and therefore a manner of being—once accepted is already unacceptable. An avant-garde man is like an enemy inside a city which he is bent on destroying, against which he rebels; for like any system of government, an established form of expression is also a form of oppression. The avant-garde man is the opponent of an existing system. He is a critic of, and not an apologist for, what exists now. It is easy to criticize the past particularly when the prevailing regime encourages you to do so; but this is only to sanctify ossification and kowtow to tyranny or convention. I am well aware that I have not thrown any light on the problem. The word avant-garde in fact is used with various meanings. It can quite simply be identified with the "art theatre," that is the theatre which is more literary, exacting and daring than the kind known in France as the "théâtre de boulevard." This, it seems, is what Georges Pillement meant when, in his theatre anthology published in 1946, he divided dramatists into two categories: the writers of the "comédie de boulevard" among whom Robert de Flers ranked with François de Curel; and those of the avant-garde which included Claude-André Puget as well as Passeur, Jean Anouilh, and Giraudoux. This seems rather strange today for the works of these writers are now practically classics. But Maurice Donnay, in his time, as well as Bataille were avant-garde writers since they expressed a rupture, a new departure and an opposing force. They finally merged into the theatrical tradition and that is what must happen to every good avant-gardist. In any case they represented a protest and the proof of this was that at the outset these authors were given a bad reception by the critics, who protested at their protestations. The protestation of an avant-garde dramatist can be a reaction against Realism when that is the most prevalent and abused form of expression in the theatre; it can be a protest against a certain Symbolism when that Symbolism has become abused, arbitrary, and no longer captures reality. In any case what we call the avant-garde theatre, which coexists with the conventional theatre, seems by its expression, its questing nature and difficulty to be of greater value. For the very reason that it is exacting and difficult to follow, it is obvious that before it becomes generally accepted it can only be the theatre of a minority. The avant-garde theatre, and indeed all new art and theatre must be unpopular.

It is certain that any attempt to introduce new ideas will be met on all sides by conformities and mental apathy. Obviously it is not essential that a dramatist should wish to be unpopular, but neither is it essential that he should wish to be popular. His efforts, his creative work are above such considerations. Either this theatre will always remain unpopular, will never be recognized and so will never exist as theatre or it will in time, naturally and by the force of circumstances, become popular and generally recognized.

Today everyone understands the elementary laws of physics or geometry which must certainly have been at first only understood by learned men who never thought of offering the public popular geometry or physics. They did not express the truth of a certain narrow caste but truths which were undeniably objective. The question of the similarities which may exist between science and art does not fall within any province. We all know that the differences between these two domains of the mind are far greater than the similarities. However, each new author seeks to fight in the name of the truth. Boileau wished to express truth. In his foreword to *Cromwell*, Victor Hugo considered that Romantic Art rather than Classical contained more truth and was more complex. The aim of Realism and Naturalism was also to extend the realms of reality or reveal new and still unknown aspects of it. Symbolism and later Surrealism were further attempts to reveal and express hidden realities.

The question then is simply for an author to discover truths and to state them. And the manner of stating them is naturally unfamiliar for this statement itself is the truth for him. He can only speak it for himself. It is by speaking it for himself that he speaks it for others. Not the other way round.

If I should consider the popular theatre, I run the risk of imparting truths which have not been discovered by myself, but which have already been imparted to me by others and which I would only be passing on at second hand. The artist is not a pedagogue, neither is he a demagogue. Dramatic creation satisfies a mental need, this need must be sufficient in itself. A tree is a tree, it does not need my permission to be a tree, the tree is not faced with the problem of being a certain kind of tree in order to be recognized as a tree. It does not make itself explicit. It exists and is made manifest by its very existence. It does not seek to make itself understood. It does not assume a more understandable form; otherwise it would no longer be a tree but only the explanation of a tree. In the same way, a work of art is sufficient in itself and I can easily imagine theatre without a public. The public will come by itself, and will recognize this theatre as it recognizes a tree as a tree.

The songs of Béranger were far more popular than the poems of Rimbaud, who was quite incomprehensible in his day. Should one for that reason exclude Rimbaud's poetry? Eugène Sue was extremely popular. Proust was not. He was not understood. He did not speak to everyone. He simply contributed his kind of truth towards the development of literature and the mind. Should one debar Proust and recommend Sue? Today it is Proust who offers a wealth of truth, it is

Eugène Sue who seems empty. How fortunate that the authorities did not forbid Proust to write in Proustian language!

A creative idea can only be expressed by a means of expression which is suited to it, so much so that idea and means of expression are one and the same.

There is popular theatre and popular theatre. We think, erroneously, that popular theatre must be theatre for those who are lacking in intellect: but there is the kind which is intended to instruct, a theatre for our edification, the tool of a political creed, of some ideology of which it is the duplicate—a useless and "conformist" repetition.

A work of art and a dramatic work too, therefore, must be a primary instinct, profound or vast according to the talent or genius of the artist, but a truly primary instinct which owes nothing to anything but itself. But in order that it may rise up and take shape, one must let the imagination run free above external and secondary considerations such as those of its future, its popularity or its need to express an ideology. In this flowering of the imagination, meanings emerge by themselves and they are eloquent for some and less so for others. For my part I cannot understand how anyone can have the ambition to speak for everybody, to possess the unanimous support of the public while, within one class of people for instance, some prefer strawberries, others cheese, some prefer aspirin for their headaches, others bismuth for their stomach-aches. In any case, I don't worry about the support of the public. Or perhaps I do, but only when the play has been written and I am considering the question of how to place it. Support comes or doesn't come, quite naturally. It is quite certain that one can never speak for everybody. At the most, one can speak on behalf of a large majority and in this case one can only produce demagogic or ready-made drama. If you wish to speak to everybody, you will really speak to no one: the things which interest everybody in general have very little interest for each man in particular. Besides which, a creative work of art is, by its very novelty, aggressive, spontaneously aggressive, it strikes out at the public, against the vast majority; it rouses indignation by its nonconformity which is, in itself, a form of indignation. This is inevitable for it does not keep to the beaten track but opens up a new one, cutting across country, alone. This is the sense in which a work of art is unpopular, as I have already said. But new art is only apparently unpopular; it is not so in essence, it is unpopular only because of its unfamiliarity. The so-called popular theatre is actually far more unpopular. It is a theatre which is arrogantly imposed throughout by a ruling aristocracy, a special class of initiates who know or think they know in advance what the public needs. They even say to the public: "You must only need what we want you to need and you must only think in the way we think." Paradoxically, the free work of art, by its individualistic character, despite its unusual appearance, alone springs from men's hearts, through a man's heart; it is the only thing which really expresses the people.

It is said that the theatre is in danger and in a critical state. This is due to many reasons. Very soon dramatists will be made apostles of all kinds of theologies, they will not be free, they will be told only to defend, attack or praise this or that. If they are not apostles then they are pawns. Elsewhere the theatre is the prisoner not of ideologies but conventions, taboos, hardened mental habits, fixations. When the theatre could be the place of the greatest freedom, of the wildest imaginings, it has become that of the greatest constraint, of a rigid and set system of conventions which may be called "realist" or otherwise. We are afraid of too much humor (and humor is freedom). We are afraid of freedom of thought, of a play which is too tragic or too despairing. Optimism and hope are compulsory under pain of death. And what is sometimes labeled the absurd is only the denunciation of the ridiculous nature of a language which is empty of substance, sterile, made up of clichés and slogans; of theatre-that-is-known-in-advance. I personally would like to bring a tortoise onto the stage, turn it into a racehorse, then into a hat, a song, a dragoon and a fountain of water. One can dare anything in the theatre and it is the place where one dares the least.

I want no other limits than the technical limits of the stage machinery. People will say that my plays are music-hall or circus. So much the better: let's bring in the circus! One can accuse the dramatist of being arbitrary, but the theatre is the place where one can be arbitrary. As a matter of fact, it is not arbitrary. The imagination is not arbitrary, it is revealing. Without the guarantee of total freedom, the dramatist will never be himself, he will say nothing except what has already been formulated: my own intention was not to recognize any laws except those of my imagination and since the imagination has laws that is a further proof that finally it is not arbitrary.

It has been said that what distinguishes man from the other animals is that he is the animal that laughs; he is above all else the animal that creates. He introduces into the world things which were not there before: temples and rabbit-hutches, wheelbarrows, locomotives, symphonies, poems, cathedrals and cigarettes. The usefulness of all these things is often only a pretext. What is the use of existing?—to exist. What is the use of a flower?—to be a flower. Of what use is a temple or a cathedral? To house the faithful? I doubt it, since the temples are no longer used and we still admire them. They serve to reveal to us the laws of architecture and perhaps of universal construction which are apparently reflected in our mind since the mind discovers these laws within itself. But the theatre is dying for lack of courage. We seem no longer to realize that a world we invent cannot be false. It can only be false if I want to fabricate a truth and imitate truth for in so doing I fabricate a false truth. I am conscious of being true when I invent and imagine. Nothing is more rational than the imagination. I could even go so far as to say that to me it is the world which seems irrational, which is growing irrational and which baffles my understanding. The laws to which I try continually to adapt and submit it, I find in my own mind. But this again lies outside our province.

When an author writes something, a play for instance, he has as I have said, the clear or confused impression that he is fighting a battle, that if he has something to say, it is because others have not said that thing properly, or that they no longer know how to say it. He wishes to say something new, otherwise why would he write? To say what he has to say, to impose his world is itself the battle. A tree in order to grow must overcome the resistance of matter. For an author, this matter is the already-done, the already-said. He writes not for or against something but in spite of something. In this sense, each artist is to varying degrees and according to his powers, a rebel. If he copies, if he reproduces, if he exemplifies, he is nothing. It therefore seems that a poet is fighting against a tradition, but in most cases involuntarily, by the very fact of his existence.

To the extent that a poet feels that the language no longer corresponds to reality, no longer expresses a truth, he must endeavor to capture reality, to express it better, in a way which is more pungent, more eloquent, clearer, more precise and adequate. By this means, he overtakes and modernizes a living tradition which had got lost. An avant-garde dramatist can feel, and in any case this is his wish, that he is making a better attempt than others around him. He is making a real attempt to return to the source. But what source? That of the theatre. A return to an inner ideal of the theatre; for it is in oneself that one discovers the deep and permanent foundations of theatre.

Pascal discovered within himself the principles of geometry, Mozart as a child discovered in himself the rudiments of his music. Very few artists of course can measure up to the stature of these two giants. Nevertheless, it seems certain to me that one hasn't got what is so aptly called "theatre in the blood" if one cannot reinvent a little oneself. I am also quite certain that if all libraries were swallowed up in some great cataclysm together with all museums, those who escaped would sooner or later rediscover for themselves painting, music, and theatre which, like bodily functions are as natural, necessary and instinctive as breathing. He who does not possess even to a slight degree the function of theatre, is not a man of the theatre. To discover it one must perhaps have a certain ignorance, a certain naïveté, a boldness which springs from this naïveté, but a naïveté which is not simplicity of mind, and an ignorance which does not rule out knowledge but which assimilates and rejuvenates it. A work of art is not devoid of ideas. Since it is life or the expression of life, ideas are emanated from it: the work of art does not emanate from an ideology. The new dramatist is one who, contradictorily, endeavors to overtake what is most ancient: new language and subject matter in a dramatic structure which aims at being clearer, more stripped of inessentials and more purely theatrical; the rejection of traditionalism to rediscover tradition; a synthesis of knowledge and invention, of the real and the imaginary, of the particular and the universal or as they say now, of the individual and the collective; the expression, over and above classes of that which transcends them. By expressing my deepest feelings, I express my deepest humanity. I become one with all others, spontaneously, over and above all the barriers of cast and different psychologies. I express my solitude and become one with all other solitudes; my joy at existing or my surprise at being are those of everyone even if, for the moment, everyone refuses to recognize it. A play such as *The Quare Fellow* by the Irish writer, Brendan Behan was the fruit of his own experience: prison. Nevertheless I feel concerned, for this prison becomes all prisons, it becomes the world and all its classes of people. Inside this English prison there are of course prisoners and there are warders. That is slaves and masters, the rulers and the ruled. They are all enclosed within the same walls. The prisoners hate their warders, the warders scorn their prisoners. But the prisoners also loathe each other, and neither do the warders agree amongst themselves. If there were just the simple conflict between the warders on the one hand and the prisoners on the other; if the play were limited to this obvious conflict, there would be nothing new, profound, or revealing, but a coarse and crudely sketched reality. But this play shows that reality is far more complex. A man in this prison is to be executed. The condemned man does not appear on the stage. He is, however, present in our consciousness and continually haunts us. He has the leading role. Or rather death has the leading role. Warders and prisoners feel together this presence of death. The play's deep humanity dwells in the terrible communion of this haunting thought, this agony which is that of all, above the category of warders or prisoners. It is a communion beyond differences, an almost unconscious feeling of fellowship of which the dramatist makes us conscious. The common identity of all men is revealed to us. This could help to draw the enemy camps together. Indeed the prisoners and warders suddenly appear to us as mortals, united and governed by the same problem which surpasses all others. Here is popular theatre indeed, one of communion in the same agony. It is an old play for it deals with a fundamental and age-old problem. It is a new and localized play for it deals with a prison at a certain moment in time in a particular country.

At the beginning of this century and in the 1920's in particular, a vast universal avant-garde movement was felt in all domains of the mind and human activity. An overthrowing of our mental habits. Modern painting from Klee to Picasso, from Matisse to Mondrian, from Cubism to Abstractionism expresses this overthrow, this revolution. It emerged in music and films and it affected architecture. Philosophy and psychology were transformed. Science (but I am not competent to speak on this subject) gave us a new vision of the world. A new style emerged and continues to emerge. An age is distinguished by its unity of style, a synthesis of various styles and so there are obvious similarities between architecture and poetry, mathematics and music. There is an essential unity between the Palace of Versailles and Cartesian thought, for instance. Literature and drama from André Breton to Maïakovski, from Marinetti to Tristan Tzara or Apollinaire, from the Expressionist drama to Surrealism, down to the most recent novels by Faulkner and Dos Passos and quite recently those of Nathalie Sarraute and Michel Butor, have all shared in this surge of new life. But all literature did not follow this movement and in the theatre it seems to have been arrested in 1930. The theatre is the most behindhand. The avant-garde were halted at the theatre if not in literature. Wars, revolutions, Nazism and other forms of tyranny, dogmatism, and in some countries bourgeois inertia too, have prevented it developing for the moment. But it must be resumed. I myself hope to be one of the modest artisans who may restart this movement. Indeed, this abandoned avant-garde movement has not been outstripped but buried by the reactionary return of old dramatic formulas which sometimes dare to pretend they are new ones. The theatre is not of our age: it manifests a limited psychology, the light comedy style, bourgeois prudence and a realism which refuses to be called conventional but which really is, a submission to dogmatism which is a menace to the artist.

The young generation of French film production is far more advanced than that of the theatre. Young film producers have been trained in film libraries, and film clubs. This is where they have received their instruction. There they have seen art films; the great classics of the cinema, avant-garde films, uncommercial and nonpopular, many of which have never been shown in big cinemas or have only been shown for a short time because of their uncommercial nature. Although it is far more difficult for the theatre, it also needs these places for experiment, these laboratories protected from the superficiality of the general public. A danger in some countries, and still a necessary evil unfortunately, is the manager. He is a tyrant in this domain. The theatre must show a profit; to do so all boldness and creativeness must be eliminated so as not to upset anyone. A manager who is also a friend of mine once asked me to change everything in my plays and make them comprehensible. I asked him by what right he interfered with matters of dramatic construction which should only concern myself and my director: for it seemed to me that to pay money to produce a play was not sufficient reason to dictate conditions and alter my work. He replied that he represented the public. I replied that we had to wage war against the public and upon him, the manager. To wage war against or else to ignore.

We need a liberal State, befriending thought and art, believing in their necessity and the necessity for laboratories. Before an invention or a scientific theory is made known, it has been long prepared, tested out and thought out in the laboratories. I demand that dramatists should have the same opportunities as scientists for making experiments. One cannot say that a scientific discovery is, for that reason, unpopular. I do not think that the realities of the mind, welling up from the deepest part of my being are unpopular. To have a following is not always to be popular. The aristocracy of a poet is not a false aristocracy as the aristocracy of a class is false. In France we have some exciting new dramatists: Jean Genet, Beckett, Vauthier, Pichette, Schéhadé, Audiberti, Ghelderode who carry on the tradition, while opposing it, of Giraudoux, Anouilh, Jean-Jacques Bernard and many others. They are only points of departure for a possible development of a free and living theatre.

For the avant-garde stands for freedom.

SAMUEL BECKETT

> But what can a decent man speak of with
> most pleasure?
> Answer: Of himself.
> Well, so I will talk about myself.
>
> —Dostoevski

Beckett's heroes are forever talking about themselves: characters of the abyss, on the ledge before dying, they probe themselves and their condition, recording their findings with a shortening pencil stub, telling themselves stories to distract themselves, or so they say, from their impossible surroundings; moving, as they move toward death, toward the only goal, toward the answers to the unanswerable questions. Beckett, the writer, has created a cast of comic heroes writing, recording, in the ultimate solitude, the mutations—those present, as they occur, those dimly remembered—enamored of the "I" not for itself but because, in the prison of the self lies the only path to revelation. From work to work the world grows dimmer, less precise, less meaningful, less important; the "I" moves from it, deeper into itself. The line from, or affinity with, Descartes, has been noted: the affirmation cannot come from the world without, but from within alone, from the thought and the knowledge of thought.

The motion has been imparted, the end is as obvious as absurd: what is there to do but search and register the "*comment c'est*"—rationally, analytically, perhaps even hopefully, as Vladimir and Estragon are hopeful? "The only problem for me was how to go on, since I could not do otherwise, to the best of my declining powers, in the motion that had been imparted to me," says one of his characters. And they do go on—on bicycles, on foot (with the help of crutches), even, when reduced to crawling, by inching forward through the (one suspects) primeval mud—with amazing tenacity, toward a goal at best dimly discernible, which gives the lie to those who, disturbed by the initial premises and implications of all of Beckett's work, see in it only darkness and unredeeming solipsism.

Besides this basic, and all-important, quality of affirmation, infinitely more profound than the affirmative mouthings of those afraid to face the world naked, or the naked world, Beckett's work reveals two (at least two) other qualities of greatness: a wonderful comic sense, in the tradition of Swift, and a command of language perhaps unrivaled in our time. It has been said Joyce's command of the language was second only to Shakespeare's in the history of English literature; it is not impossible that Beckett, once the helpmate of his elder compatriot, may well surpass the master even in this domain.

THE END

They clothed me and gave me money. I knew what the money was
for, it was to get me started. When it was gone I would have to get
more, if I wished to go on. The same for the shoes, when they were
worn out I would have to get them repaired, or get myself another
pair, or go on barefoot, if I wished to go on. The same for the coat
and trousers, needless to say, with this difference, that I could go on
in my shirtsleeves, if I wished. The clothes—shoes, socks, trousers,
shirt, coat, and hat—were not new, but the deceased must have been
about my size. That is to say, he must have been a little shorter, a little
thinner, for the clothes did not fit me so well in the beginning as they
did at the end, the shirt especially, and it was many a long day before
I could button it at the neck, or sport the collar that went with it, or
pin the skirts together between my legs in the way my mother had
taught me. He must have put on his Sunday best to go to the con-
sultation, perhaps for the first time, unable to bear it any longer. Be
that as it may the hat was a bowler, in good shape. I said, Keep
your hat and give me back mine. I added, Give me back my greatcoat.
They replied that they had burnt them, together with my other clothes.
I understood then that the end was near, at least fairly near. Later on
I tried to exchange this hat for a cap, or a slouch which could be pulled
down over my face, but without much success. And yet I could not go
about bare-headed, with my skull in the state it was. At first this hat
was too small, then it got used to me. They gave me a tie, after long

350

discussion. It seemed a pretty tie to me, but I didn't like it. When it came at last I was too tired to send it back. But in the end it came in useful. It was blue, with sort of little stars on it. I didn't feel very well, but they told me I was well enough. They didn't say in so many words that I was as well as I would ever be, but that was the implication. I lay inert on the bed and it took three women to put on my trousers. They didn't seem to take much interest in my private parts which to tell the truth were nothing to write home about. I didn't take much interest in them myself. But they might have passed some remark. When they had finished I got up and finished dressing unaided. They told me to sit on the bed and wait. All the bedding had disappeared. It made me angry that they had not let me wait in the familiar bed, instead of leaving me standing in the cold, in these clothes that smelt of sulphur. I said, You might have left me in bed till the last moment. Men all in white came in with mallets in their hands. They dismantled the bed and took away the pieces. One of the women followed them out and came back with a chair which she set before me. I had done well to pretend I was angry. But to make it quite clear to them how angry I was that they had not left me in my bed, I gave the chair a kick and sent it flying. A man came in and made a sign to me to follow him. In the hall he gave me a paper to sign. What's this, I said, a safe-conduct? It's a receipt, he said, for the clothes and money you have received. What money? I said. It was then I received the money. To think I had almost departed without a penny in my pocket. The sum was not large, compared to other sums, but to me it seemed large. I saw the familiar objects, companions of so many bearable hours. The stool, for example, dearest of all. The long afternoons together, waiting for it to be time for bed. At times I felt its wooden life invade me, till I myself became a piece of old wood. There was even a hole for my cyst. Then the window pane with the patch of frosting gone, where I used to press my eye in the hour of need, and rarely in vain. I am greatly obliged to you, I said, is there a law which prevents you from throwing me out naked and penniless? That would damage our reputation in the long run, he replied. Could they not possibly keep me a little longer, I said, I could make myself useful. Useful, he said, joking apart you would be willing to make yourself useful? A moment later he went on, If they believed you were really willing to make yourself useful they would keep you, I am sure. The number of times I had said that I was going to make myself useful, I wasn't going to start that again. How weak I felt! Perhaps, I said, they would consent to take back the money and keep me a little longer.

This is a charitable institution, he said, and the money is a gift you receive when you leave. When it is gone you will have to get more, if you wish to go on. Never come back here in any case, you would not be let in. Don't go to any of our branches either, they would turn you away too. Exelmans! I cried. Come, come, he said, and anyway no one understands a tenth of what you say. I'm so old, I said. You are not so old as all that, he said. May I stay here just a little longer, I said, till the rain is over. You may wait in the cloister, he said, the rain will go on all day. You may wait in the cloister till six o'clock, you will hear the bell. If anyone challenges you, you need only say you have permission to shelter in the cloister. Whose name will I give? I said. Weir, he said.

I had not been long in the cloister when the rain stopped and the sun came out. It was low and I reckoned it must be getting on for six, considering the season. I stayed there looking through the archway at the sun as it went down behind the cloister. A man appeared and asked me what I was doing. What do you want? were the words he used. Very friendly. I replied that I had Mr. Weir's permission to stay in the cloister till six o'clock. He went away, but came back immediately. He must have spoken to Mr. Weir in the interim, for he said, You must not loiter in the cloister now the rain is over.

Now I was making my way through the garden. There was that strange light which follows a day of persistent rain, when the sun comes out and the sky clears too late to be of any use. The earth makes a sound as of sighs and the last drops fall from the emptied, cloudless sky. A small boy, stretching out his hands and looking up at the blue sky, asked his mother how that was possible. Fuck off, she said. I suddenly remembered I had not thought of asking Mr. Weir for a piece of bread. He would surely have given it to me. I had as a matter of fact thought of it during our conversation in the hall. I had said to myself, Let us first finish our conversation, then I'll ask. I knew well they would not keep me. I would gladly have turned back, but I was afraid one of the guards would stop me and tell me I would never see Mr. Weir again. That might have added to my sorrow. And anyway I never turned back on such occasions.

In the street I was lost. I had not set foot in this part of the city for a long time and it seemed greatly changed. Whole buildings had disappeared, the palings had changed position and on all sides I saw, in hugh letters, the names of tradesmen I had never seen before and which I would have been at a loss to pronounce. Streets were there where I remembered none, some I did remember had vanished and others had completely changed their names. The general impression was the same as before. It is true I did not know the city very well. Perhaps it was quite a different one. I did not know where I was supposed to be going. I had the great good fortune, more than once, not to be run over. My appearance still made people laugh, with that hearty jovial laugh so good for the health. By keeping the red part of the sky as much as possible on my right hand, I came at last to the river. Here all seemed at first sight more or less as I had left it. But if I had looked more closely I would doubtless have discovered many changes. And indeed I subsequently did so. But the general appearance of the river, flowing between its quays and under its bridges, had not changed. Yes, the river still gave the impression it was flowing in the wrong direction. That's all a pack of lies I feel. My bench was still there. It was shaped to fit the curves of the seated body. It stood beside a watering trough, gift of a Mrs. Maxwell to the city horses, according to the inscription. During the short time I rested there several horses took advantage of this monument. The iron shoes approached and the jingle of the harness. Then silence. That was the horse looking at me. Then the noise of pebbles and mud that horses make when drinking. Then the silence again. That was the horse looking at me again. Then the pebbles again. Then the silence again. Till the horse had finished drinking or the driver deemed it had drunk its fill. The horses were uneasy. Once, when the noise stopped, I turned and saw the horse looking at me. The driver too was looking at me. Mrs. Maxwell would have been pleased if she could have seen her trough rendering such services to the city horses. When it was night, after a tedious twilight, I took off my hat which was hurting me. I longed to be under cover again, in an empty place, close and warm, with artificial light, an oil lamp for choice, with a pink shade for preference. From time to time someone would come to make sure I was all right and needed nothing. It was long since I had longed for anything and the effect on me was horrible.

In the days that followed I visited several lodgings, without much success. They usually slammed the door in my face, even when I showed my money and offered to pay a week in advance, or even two. It was in vain I put on my best manners, smiled and spoke distinctly, they slammed the door in my face before I could even finish my little speech. It was at this time I perfected a method of doffing my hat at once courteous and discreet, neither servile nor insolent. I slipped it smartly forward, held it a second placed in such a way that the person to whom I was speaking could not see my skull, then slipped it back. To do that naturally, without creating an unfavorable impression, is no easy matter. When I deemed that to tip my hat would suffice, I naturally did no more than tip it. But to tip one's hat is no easy matter either. I subsequently solved this problem, always fundamental in time of adversity, by wearing a British kepi and saluting in military fashion, no, that must be wrong, I don't know, I had my hat at the end. I never made the mistake of wearing medals. Some landladies were in such need of money that they let me in immediately and showed me the room. But I couldn't come to an agreement with any of them. Finally I found a basement. With this woman I came to an agreement at once. My oddities, that's the expression she used, did not alarm her. She nevertheless insisted on making the bed and cleaning the room once a week, instead of once a month as I requested. She told me that while she was cleaning, which would not take long, I could wait in the area. She added, with a great deal of feeling, that she would never put me out in bad weather. This woman was Greek, I think, or Turkish. She never spoke about herself. I somehow got the idea she was a widow or at least that her husband had left her. She had a strange accent. But so had I with my way of assimilating the vowels and omitting the consonants.

Now I didn't know where I was. I had a vague vision, not a real vision, I didn't see anything, of a big house five or six stories high, one of a block perhaps. It was dusk when I got there and I did not pay the same heed to my surroundings as I might have done if I had suspected they were to close about me. And by then I must have lost all hope. It is true that when I left this house it was a glorious day, but I never look back when leaving. I must have read somewhere, when I was small and still read, that it is better not to look back when leaving. And yet I sometimes did. But even without looking back it seems to me I should have seen something when leaving. But there it is. All I remember is my feet emerging from my shadow, one after the other. My shoes had stiffened and the sun brought out the cracks in the leather.

I was comfortable enough in this house, I must say. Apart from a few rats I was alone in the basement. The woman did her best to respect our agreement. About noon she brought me a big tray of food and took away the tray of the previous day. At the same time she brought me a clean chamber-pot. The chamber-pot had a large handle which she slipped over her hand, so that both her hands were free to carry the tray. The rest of the day I saw no more of her except sometimes when she peeped in to make sure nothing had happened to me.

Fortunately I did not need affection. From my bed I saw the feet coming and going on the sidewalk. Certain evenings, when the weather was fine and I felt equal to it, I fetched my chair into the area and sat looking up into the skirts of the women passing by. Once I sent for a crocus bulb and planted it in the dark area, in an old pot. It must have been coming up to spring, it was probably not the right time for it. I left the pot outside, attached to a string I passed through the window. In the evening, when the weather was fine, a little light crept up the wall. Then I sat down beside the window and pulled on the string to keep the pot in the light and warmth. That can't have been easy, I don't see how I managed it. It was probably not the right thing for it. I manured it as best I could and pissed on it when the weather was dry. It may not have been the right thing for it. It sprouted, but never any flowers, just a wilting stem and a few chlorotic leaves. I would have liked to have a yellow crocus, or a hyacinth, but there, it was not to be. She wanted to take it away, but I told her to leave it. She wanted to buy me another, but I told her I didn't want another. What lacerated me most was the din of the newspaper boys. They went pounding by every day at the same hours, their heels thudding on the sidewalk, crying the names of their papers and even the headlines. The house noises disturbed me less. A little girl, unless it was a little boy, sang every evening at the same hour, somewhere above me. For a long time I could not catch the words. But hearing them day after day I finally managed to catch a few. Strange words for a little girl, or a little boy. Was it a song in my head or did it merely come from without? It was a sort of lullaby, I believe. It often sent me to sleep, even me. Sometimes it was a little girl who came. She had long red hair hanging down in two braids. I didn't know who she was. She lingered awhile in the room, then went away without a word. One day I had a visit from a policeman. He said I had to be watched, without explaining why. Suspicious, that was it, he told me I was suspicious. I let him talk. He didn't dare arrest me. Or perhaps he had a kind heart. A priest too, one day I had a visit from a priest. I informed him I belonged to a branch of the reformed church. He asked me what kind of clergyman I would like to see. Yes, there's that about the reformed church, you're lost, it's unavoidable. Perhaps he had a good heart. He told me to let him know if I ever needed a helping hand. A helping hand! He gave me his name and explained where I could reach him. I should have made a note of it.

One day the woman made me an offer. She said she was in urgent need of cash and that if I could pay her six months in advance

she would reduce my rent by one fourth during that period, something of that kind. This had the advantage of saving six weeks' (?)
rent and the disadvantage of almost exhausting my small capital. But
could you call that a disadvantage? Wouldn't I stay on in any case till
my last penny was gone, and even longer, till she put me out? I gave
her the money and she gave me a receipt.

One morning, not long after this transaction, I was awakened by
a man shaking my shoulder. It could not have been much past eleven.
He requested me to get up and leave his house immediately. He was
most correct, I must say. His surprise, he said, was no less than mine.
It was his house. His property. The Turkish woman had left the day
before. But I saw her last night, I said. You must be mistaken, he said,
for she brought the keys to my office no later than yesterday afternoon. But I just paid her six months' rent in advance, I said. Get a
refund, he said. But I don't even know her name, I said, let alone her
address. You don't know her name? he said. He must have thought I
was lying. I'm sick, I said, I can't leave like this, without any notice.
You're not so sick as all that, he said. He offered to send for a taxi,
even an ambulance if I preferred. He said he needed the room immediately for his pig which even as he spoke was catching cold in a
cart before the door and no one to look after him but a stray urchin
whom he had never set eyes on before and who was probably busy
tormenting him. I asked if he couldn't let me have another place, any
old corner where I could lie down long enough to recover from the
shock and decide what to do. He said he could not. Don't think I'm
being unkind, he added. I could live here with the pig, I said, I'd
look after him. The long months of peace, wiped out in an instant!
Come now, come now, he said, get a grip on yourself, be a man, get
up, that's enough. After all it was no concern of his. He had really
been most patient. He must have visited the basement while I was
sleeping.

I felt weak. Perhaps I was. I stumbled in the blinding light. A bus
took me into the country. I sat down in a field in the sun. But it seems
to me that was much later. I stuck leaves under my hat, all the way
round, to make a shade. The night was cold. I wandered for hours in
the fields. At last I found a heap of dung. The next day I started back
to the city. They made me get off three buses. I sat down by the roadside and dried my clothes in the sun. I enjoyed doing that. I said to
myself, There's nothing more to be done now, not a thing, till they
are dry. When they were dry I brushed them with a brush, I think it
was a kind of curry-comb, that I found in a stable. Stables have

always been my salvation. Then I went to the house and begged a glass of milk and a slice of bread and butter. They gave me everything except the butter. May I rest in the stable? I said. No, they said. I still stank, but with a stink that pleased me. I much preferred it to my own which moreover it prevented me from smelling, except a waft now and then. In the days that followed I took the necessary steps to recover my money. I don't know exactly what happened, whether I couldn't find the address, or whether there was no such address, or whether the Greek woman was unknown there. I ransacked my pockets for the receipt, to try and decipher the name. It wasn't there. Perhaps she had taken it back while I was sleeping. I don't know how long I wandered thus, resting now in one place, now in another, in the town and in the country. The town had suffered many changes. Nor was the country as I remembered it. The general effect was the same. One day I caught sight of my son. He was striding along with a satchel under his arm. He took off his hat and bowed and I saw he was as bald as a coot. I was almost certain it was he. I turned round to gaze after him. He went bustling along on his duck feet, bowing and scraping and flourishing his hat left and right. The insufferable son of a bitch. One day I met a man I had known in former times. He lived in a cave by the sea. He had an ass that grazed winter and summer, over the cliffs, or along the little tracks leading down to the sea. When the weather was very bad this ass came down to the cave of his own accord and sheltered there till the storm was past. So they had spent many a night huddled together, while the wind howled and the sea pounded on the shore. With the help of this ass he could deliver sand, seawrack, and shells to the townsfolk, for their gardens. He couldn't carry much at a time, for the ass was old and small and the town was far. But in this way he earned a little money, enough to keep him in tobacco and matches and to buy a piece of bread from time to time. It was during one of these excursions that he met me, in the suburbs. He was delighted to see me, poor man. He begged me to go home with him and spend the night. Stay as long as you like, he said. What's wrong with your ass? I said. Don't mind him, he said, he doesn't know you. I reminded him that I wasn't in the habit of staying more than two or three minutes with anyone and that the sea did not agree with me. He seemed deeply grieved to hear it. So you won't come, he said. But to my amazement I got up on the ass and off we went, in the shade of the red chestnuts springing from the sidewalk. I held the ass by the mane, one hand in front of the other. The little boys jeered and threw stones, but their aim was poor, for they only hit me once, on the hat. A policeman stopped us and accused us of disturbing the peace. My friend replied that we were as nature had made us, the boys too were as nature had made them. It was inevitable, under these conditions, that the peace should be disturbed from time to time. Let us continue on our way, he said, and order will soon be restored throughout your beat. We followed the quiet, dustwhite inland roads with their hedges of hawthorn and fuchsia and their footpaths fringed with wild grass and daisies. Night fell. The ass carried me right to the mouth of the cave, for in the dark I could not have found my way down the path winding steeply to the sea. Then he climbed back to his pasture.

I don't know how long I stayed there. The cave was nicely arranged, I must say. I treated my crablice with salt water and seaweed, but a lot of nits must have survived. I put compresses of seaweed on my skull, which gave me great relief, but not for long. I lay in the cave and sometimes looked out at the horizon. I saw above me a vast trembling expanse without islands or promontories. At night a light shone into the cave at regular intervals. It was here I found the phial in my pocket. It was not broken, for the glass was not real glass. I thought Mr. Weir had confiscated all my belongings. My host was out most of the time. He fed me on fish. It is easy for a man, a proper man, to live in a cave, far from everybody. He invited me to stay as long as I liked. If I preferred to be alone he would gladly prepare another cave for me farther on. He would bring me food every day and drop in from time to time to make sure I was all right and needed nothing. He was kind. Unfortunately I did not need kindness. You wouldn't know of a lake dwelling? I said. I couldn't bear the sea, its splashing and heaving, its tides and general convulsiveness. The wind at least sometimes stops. My hands and feet felt as though they were full of ants. This kept me awake for hours on end. If I stayed here something awful would happen to me, I said, and a lot of good that would do me. You'd get drowned, he said. Yes, I said, or I'd jump off the cliff. And to think I couldn't live anywhere else, he said, in my cabin in the mountains I was very unhappy. Your cabin in the mountains? I said. He repeated the story of his cabin in the mountains, I had forgotten it, it was as though I were hearing it for the first time. I asked him if he still had it. He replied he had not seen it since the day he fled from it, but that he believed it was still there, a little dilapidated no doubt. But when he urged me to take the key I refused, saying I had made other arrangements. You will always find me here, he said, if you ever need me. Ah people. He gave me his knife.

What he called his cabin was a sort of wooden shed. The door had been removed, for firewood, or for some other purpose. The glass had disappeared from the window. The roof had fallen in at several places. The interior was divided, by the remains of a partition, into two unequal parts. If there had been any furniture it was gone. The vilest acts had been committed on the ground and against the walls. The floor was strewn with excrements, both human and animal, with condoms and vomit. In a cowpad a heart had been traced, pierced by an arrow. And yet there was nothing to attract tourists. I noticed the remains of abandoned nosegays. They had been greedily gathered, carried for miles, then thrown away, because they were cumbersome or already withered. This was the dwelling to which I had been offered the key.

The scene was the familiar one of grandeur and desolation.

Nevertheless it was a roof over my head. I rested on a bed of ferns, gathered at great labour with my own hands. One day I couldn't get up. The cow saved me. Goaded by the icy mist she came in search of shelter. It was probably not the first time. She can't have seen me. I tried to suck her, without much success. Her udder was covered with dung. I took off my hat and, summoning all my energy, began to milk her into it. The milk fell to the ground and was lost, but I said to myself, No matter, it's for nothing. She dragged me across the floor, stopping from time to time only to kick me. I didn't know our cows too could be so inhuman. She must have recently been milked. Clutching the dug with one hand I kept my hat under it with the other. But in the end she prevailed. For she dragged me across the threshold and out into the giant streaming ferns, where I was forced to let go.

As I drank the milk I reproached myself with what I had done. I could no longer count on this cow and she would warn the others. More master of myself I might have made a friend of her. She would have come every day, perhaps accompanied by other cows. I might have learnt to make butter, even cheese. But I said to myself, No, all is for the best.

Once on the road it was all downhill. Soon there were carts, but they all refused to take me up. In other clothes, with another face, they might have taken me up. I must have changed since my expulsion from the basement. The face notably seemed to have attained its climacteric. The humble, ingenuous smile would no longer come, nor the expression of candid misery, containing the stars and the distaff. I summoned them, but they would not come. A mask of dirty old hairy leather, with two holes and a slit, it was too far gone for the old turn of please your honour and God reward you and pity upon me. It was disastrous. What would I crawl with in future? I lay down on the side of the road and began to writhe each time I heard a cart approaching. That was so they would not think I was sleeping or resting. I tried to groan, Help! Help! But the tone that came out was that of polite conversation. My hour had not yet come and I could no longer groan. The last time I had cause to groan I had groaned as well as ever, and no heart within miles of me to melt. What was to become of me? I said to myself, I'll learn again. I lay down across the road at a narrow place, so that the carts could not pass without passing over my body, with one wheel at least, or two if there were four. The town planner with the red beard, they removed his gall-bladder, a gross mistake, and three days later he died, in the prime of life. But the day came when, looking round me, I was in the suburbs, and from there to the old haunts it was not far, beyond the stupid hope of rest or less pain.

So I covered the lower part of my face with a black rag and went and begged at a sunny corner. For it seemed to me my eyes were not completely spent, thanks perhaps to the dark glasses my tutor had given me. He had given me the *Ethics* of Geulincz. They were a man's glasses, I was a child. They found him dead, crumpled up in the water closet, his clothes in awful disorder, struck down by an infarctus. Ah what peace. The *Ethics* had his name (Ward) on the front page, the glasses had belonged to him. The bridge, at the time I am speaking of, was of brass wire, of the kind used to hang pictures and big mirrors, and two long black ribbons served as wings. I wound them round my ears and then down under my chin where I tied them together. The lenses had suffered, from rubbing in my pocket against each other and against the other objects there. I thought Mr. Weir had confiscated all my belongings. But I had no further need of these glasses and used them merely to soften the glare of the sun. I should never have mentioned them. The rag gave me a lot of trouble. I got it in the end from the lining of my greatcoat, no, I had no greatcoat now, of my coat then. The result was a grey rag rather than a black, perhaps even chequered, but I had to put up with it. Till afternoon I held my face raised towards the southern sky, then towards the western till night. The bowl gave me a lot of trouble. I couldn't use my hat because of my skull. As for holding out my hand, that was quite out of the question. So I got a tin and hung it from a button of my great-coat, what's the matter with me, of my coat, at pubis level. It did not hang plumb, it leaned respectfully towards the passer-by, he had only to drop his mite. But that obliged him to come up close to me, he risked touching me. In the end I got a bigger tin, a kind of big tin box, and I placed it on the sidewalk at my feet. But people who give alms don't much care to toss them, there's something contemptuous about this gesture which is repugnant to sensitive natures. To say nothing of their having to aim. They are prepared to give, but not for their gift to go rolling under the passing feet or under the passing wheels, to be picked up perhaps by some undeserving person. So they don't give. There are those, to be sure, who stoop, but generally speaking people who give alms don't much care to stoop. What they like above all is to sight the wretch from afar, get ready their penny, drop it in their stride and hear the God bless you dying away in the distance. Personally I never said that, nor anything like it, I wasn't much of a believer, but I did make a noise with my mouth. In the end I got a kind of board or tray and tied it to my neck and waist. It jutted out just at the right height, pocket height, and its edge was far enough from my person for the coin to be bestowed without danger. Some days I strewed it with flowers, petals, buds and that herb which men call fleabane, I believe, in a word whatever I could find. I didn't go out of my way to look for them, but all the pretty things of this description that came my way were for the board. They must have thought I loved nature. Most of the time I looked up at the sky, but without focussing it. Most of the time it was a mixture of white, blue and grey, and then at evening all the evening colours. I felt it weighing softly on my face, I rubbed my face against it, one cheek after the other, turning my head from side to side. Now and then to rest my neck I dropped my head on my chest. Then I could see the board in the distance, a haze of many colours. I leaned against the wall, but without nonchalance, I shifted my weight from one foot to the other and my hands clutched the lapels of my coat. To beg with your hands in your pockets makes a bad impression, it irritates the workers, especially in winter. You should never wear gloves either. There were guttersnipes who swept away all I had earned, under cover of giving me a coin. It was to buy sweets. I unbuttoned my trousers discreetly to scratch myself. I scratched myself in an upward direction, with four nails. I pulled on the hairs, to get relief. It passed the time, time flew when I scratched myself. Real scratching is superior to masturbation, in my opinion. One can masturbate up to the age of seventy, and even beyond, but in the end it becomes a mere habit. Whereas to scratch myself properly I would have needed a dozen hands. I itched all over, on the privates, in the bush up to the navel, under the arms, in the arse, and then patches of eczema and psoriasis that I could set raging merely by thinking of them. It was in the arse I had the most pleasure. I stuck in my fore-finger up to the knuckle. Later, if I had to shit, the pain was atrocious. But I hardly shat any more. Now and then a flying machine flew by, sluggishly it seemed to me. Often at the end of the day I discovered the leg of my trousers all wet. That must have been the dogs. I person-ally pissed very little. If by chance the need came on me a little squirt in my fly was enough to relieve it. Once at my post I did not leave it till nightfall. I had no appetite, God tempered the wind to me. After work I bought a bottle of milk and drank it in the evening in the shed. Better still, I got a little boy to buy it for me, always the same, they wouldn't serve me, I don't know why. I gave him a penny for his pains. One day I witnessed a strange scene. Normally I didn't see a great deal. I didn't hear a great deal either. I didn't pay attention. Strictly speaking I wasn't there. Strictly speaking I believe I've never been anywhere. But that day I must have come back. For some time past a sound had been scarifying me. I did not investigate the cause, for I said to myself, It's going to stop. But as it did not stop I had no choice but to find out the cause. It was a man perched on the roof of a car and haranguing the passers-by. That at least was my interpretation. He was bellowing so loud that snatches of his discourse reached my ears. Union . . . brothers . . . Marx . . . capital . . . bread and butter . . . love. It was all Greek to me. The car was drawn up against the kerb, just in front of me, I saw the orator from behind. All of a sudden he turned and pointed at me, as at an exhibit. Look at this down and out, he vociferated, this leftover. If he doesn't go down on all fours, it's for fear of being impounded. Old, lousy, rotten, ripe for the muckheap. And there are a thousand like him, worse than him, ten thousand, twenty thousand—. A voice, thirty thousand. Every day you pass them by, resumed the orator, and when you have backed a winner you fling them a farthing. Do you ever think? The voice, Certainly not. A penny, resumed the orator, tuppence—. The voice, Thruppence. It never enters your head, resumed the orator, that your charity is a crime, an incentive to slavery, stultification and organized murder. Take a good look at this living corpse. You may say it's his own fault. Ask him if it's his own fault. The voice, Ask him yourself. Then be bent forward and took me to task. I had perfected my board. It now con-sisted of two boards hinged together, which enabled me, when my

work was done, to fold it and carry it under my arm. I liked doing
little odd jobs. So I took off the rag, pocketed the few coins I had
earned, untied the board, folded it and put it under my arm. Do you
hear me, you crucified bastard! cried the orator. Then I went away,
although it was still light. But generally speaking it was a quiet corner,
busy but not overcrowded, thriving and well-frequented. He must have
been a religious fanatic, I could find no other explanation. Perhaps he
was an escaped lunatic. He had a nice face, a little on the red side.

I did not work every day. I had practically no expenses. I even
managed to put a little aside, for my very last days. The days I did not
work I spent lying in the shed. The shed was on a private estate, or
what had once been a private estate, on the riverside. This estate, the
main entrance to which opened on a narrow, dark and silent street, was
enclosed with a wall, except of course on the river front, which marked
its northern boundary for a distance of about thirty yards. From the
last quays beyond the water the eyes rose to a confusion of low
houses, wasteland, hoardings, chimneys, steeples and towers. A kind of
parade ground was also to be seen, where soldiers played football all
the year round. Only the ground-floor windows—no, I can't. The
estate seemed abandoned. The gates were locked and the paths were
overgrown with grass. Only the ground-floor windows had shutters.
The others were sometimes lit at night, faintly, now one, now another.
At least that was my impression. Perhaps it was reflected light. In this
shed, the day I adopted it, I found a boat, upside down. I righted it,
chocked it up with stones and pieces of wood, took out the thwarts and
made my bed inside. The rats had difficulty in getting at me, because
of the bulge of the hull. And yet they longed to. Just think of it, living
flesh, for in spite of everything I was still living flesh. I had lived too
long among rats, in my chance dwellings, to share the dread they inspire in the vulgar. I even had a soft place in my heart for them. They
came with such confidence towards me, it seemed without the least
repugnance. They made their toilet with catlike gestures. Toads at
evening, motionless for hours, lap flies from the air. They like to squat
where cover ends and open air begins, they favour thresholds. But I
had to contend now with water rats, exceptionally lean and ferocious.
So I made a kind of lid with stray boards. It's incredible the number
of boards I've come across in my lifetime, I never needed a board but
there it was, I had only to stoop and pick it up. I liked doing little
odd jobs, no, not particularly, I didn't mind. It completely covered the
boat, I'm referring again to the lid. I pushed it a little towards the
stern, climbed into the boat by the bow, crawled to the stern, raised

my feet and pushed the lid back towards the bow till it covered me completely. But what did my feet push against? They pushed against a cross bar I had nailed to the lid for that purpose, I liked these little odd jobs. But it was better to climb into the boat by the stern and pull back the lid with my hands till it completely covered me, then push it forward in the same way when I wanted to get out. As holds for my hands I planted two spikes just where I needed them. These little odds and ends of carpentry, if I may so describe it, carried out with whatever tools and material I chanced to find, gave me a certain pleasure. I knew that it would soon be the end, so I played the part, you know, the part of—how shall I say, I don't know. I was comfortable enough in this boat, I must say. The lid fitted so well I had to pierce a hole. It's no good closing your eyes, you must leave them open in the dark, that is my opinion. I am not speaking of sleep, I am speaking of what I believe is called waking. In any case, I slept very little at this period, I wasn't sleepy, or I was too sleepy, I don't know, or I was afraid, I don't know. Flat then on my back I saw nothing except, dimly, just above my head, through the tiny chinks, the grey light of the shed. To see nothing at all, no, that's too much. I heard faintly the cries of the gulls ravening about the mouth of the sewer near by. In a spew of yellow foam, if my memory serves me right, the filth gushed into the river and above the slush of birds screaming with hunger and fury. I heard the lapping of water against the slip and against the bank and the other sound, so different, of open wave, I heard it too. I too, when I moved, felt less boat than wave, or so it seemed to me, and my stillness was the stillness of eddies. That may seem impossible. The rain too, I often heard it, for it often rained. Sometimes a drop, falling through the roof of the shed, exploded on me. All that composed a rather liquid world. And then of course there was the voice of the wind or rather those, so various, of its playthings. But what does it amount to? Howling, soughing, moaning, sighing. What I would have liked was hammer strokes, bang bang bang, clanging in the desert. I let farts to be sure, but hardly ever a real crack, they oozed out with a sucking noise, melted in the mighty never. I don't know how long I stayed there. I was very snug in my box, I must say. It seemed to me I had grown more independent in recent years. That no one came any more, that no one could come any more to ask me if I was all right and needed nothing, distressed me then but little. I was all right, yes, precisely, and the fear of getting worse was less with me. As for my needs, they had dwindled as it were to my dimensions and become, if I may say so, of so exquisite a quality as to exclude all thought of succour. To know I had a being, however faint and false, outside of me, had once had the power to stir my heart. You become unsociable, it's inevitable. It's enough to make you wonder sometimes if you are on the right planet. Even the words desert you, it's as bad as that. Perhaps it's the moment when the vessels stop communicating, you know, the vessels. There you are still between the two murmurs, it must be the same old song as ever, but Christ you wouldn't think so. There were times when I wanted to push away the lid and get out of the boat and couldn't, I was so indolent and weak, so content deep down where I was. I felt them hard upon me, the icy, tumultuous streets, the terrifying faces, the noises that slash, pierce, claw, bruise. So I waited till the desire to shit, or even to piss, lent me wings. I did not want to dirty my nest! And yet it sometimes happened, and even more and more often. Arched and rigid I edged down my trousers and turned a little on my side, just enough to free the hole. To contrive a little kingdom, in the midst of the universal muck, then shit on it, ah that was me all over. The excrements were me too, I know, I know, but all the same. Enough, enough, the next thing I was seeing visions, I who never did, except sometimes in my sleep, who never had, real visions, I'd remember, except perhaps as a child, my myth will have it so. I knew they were visions because it was night and I was alone in my boat. What else could they have been? So I was in my boat and gliding on the waters. I didn't have to row, the ebb was carrying me out. Anyway I saw no oars, they must have taken them away. I had a board, the remains of a thwart perhaps, which I used when I came too close to the bank, or when a pier came bearing down on me or a barge at its moorings. There were stars in the sky, quite a few. I didn't know what the weather was doing, I was neither cold nor warm and all seemed calm. The banks receded more and more, it was inevitable, soon I saw them no more. The lights grew fainter and fewer as the river widened. There on the land men were sleeping, bodies were gathering strength for the toil and joys of the morrow. The boat was not gliding now, it was tossing, buffeted by the choppy waters of the bay. All seemed calm and yet foam was washing aboard. Now the sea air was all about me, I had no other shelter than the land, and what does it amount to, the shelter of the land, at such a time. I saw the beacons, four in all, including a lightship. I knew them well, even as a child I had known them well. It was evening, I was with my father on a height, he held my hand. I would have liked him to draw me close with a gesture of protective love, but his mind was on other things. He also taught me the names of the mountains. But to have done with these visions I also saw the lights of the buoys, the sea seemed full of them, red and green and to my surprise even yellow. And on the slopes of the mountain, now rearing its unbroken bulk behind the town, the fires turned from gold to red, from red to gold. I knew what it was, it was the gorse burning. How often I had set a match to it myself as a child. And hours later, back in my home, before I climbed into bed, I watched from my high window the fires I had lit. That night then, all aglow with distant fires, on sea, on land and in the sky, I drifted with the currents and the tides. I noticed that my hat was tied, with a string I suppose, to my buttonhole. I got up from my seat in the stern and a great clanking was heard. That was the chain. One end was fastened to the bow and the other round my waist. I must have pierced a hole beforehand in the floor-boards, for there I was down on my knees prying out the plug with my knife. The hole was small and the water rose slowly. It would take a good half hour, everything included, barring accidents. Back now in the stern-sheets, my legs stretched out, my back well propped against the sack stuffed with grass I used as a cushion, I swallowed my sedative. The sea, the sky, the mountains and the islands closed in and crushed me in a mighty systole, then scattered to the uttermost confines of space. The memory came faint and cold of the story I might have told, a story in the likeness of my life, I mean without the courage to end or the strength to go on.

—Translated from the French by RICHARD SEAVER
in collaboration with the author